CATCH THE WIND

Senior Authors
Carl B. Smith
Virginia A. Arnold

Linguistics Consultant
Ronald Wardhaugh

Macmillan Publishing Company
New York

Collier Macmillan Publishers
London

ACKNOWLEDGMENTS

The publisher gratefully acknowledges permission to reprint the following copyrighted material:

"Because It Is There," adapted from pages 33-34 of *All About Mountains and Mountaineering* by Anne Terry White. Copyright © 1962 by Anne Terry White. By permission of Random House, Inc.

"Cameras and Courage," adapted from *Cameras and Courage: The Story of Margaret Bourke-White* by Iris Noble. Copyright © 1973 by Iris Noble. By permission of the author and Julian Messner, a Simon & Schuster division of Gulf + Western Corporation.

"Can You Explain It?" from *It's Still a Mystery* by Lee Gebhart and Walter Wagner. Copyright © 1970 by Scholastic Magazines, Inc. By permission of Scholastic Magazines, Inc.

"The Champion" by Peg Roberts from *Child Life Mystery and Science-Fiction Magazine.* Copyright © 1977 by The Saturday Evening Post Company. By permission of The Saturday Evening Post Company.

"The Cheetah Remembers," from *True Stories from the Moscow Zoo* by Vera Chaplina translated by Estelle Titiev and Lila Pargment. Copyright © 1970 by Lila Pargment and Estelle Titiev. Published by Prentice-Hall, Inc., Englewood Cliffs, New Jersey 07632.

"Communicating," from *When the Pie Was Opened* by Jean Little. Copyright © 1968 by Jean Little. By permission of Little, Brown and Co.

"A Debt to Dickens" by Pearl S. Buck was originally published in *The Saturday Review* in April 1936. Copyright 1936 by Pearl S. Buck. Copyright renewed. By permission of Harold Ober Associates Incorporated.

"Dreams" contains an excerpt from *I Have a Dream* by Martin Luther King, Jr. Copyright © 1963 by Martin Luther King, Jr. By permission of Joan Daves.

"The Easter Island Mystery," from *Mysteries From The Past* by Carrol Alice Stout, edited by Thomas G. Aylesworth. Copyright © 1964, 1965, 1968 by The American Museum of Natural History. By permission of Doubleday & Company, Inc.

"Excuse Us, Animals in the Zoo," from *All Through the Year: Three Hundred and Sixty-five New Poems for Holidays and Every Day* by Annette Wynne. Copyright 1932, 1960 by Annette Wynne. By permission of J. B. Lippincott, Publishers, and Society for the Propagation of the Faith, Brooklyn, New York.

"An Extra Brave" by Marion Holland, adapted from the American Red Cross *Youth News,* November 1955. By permission of Marion Holland.

"Ezra Meeker: Marker of the Oregon Trail," from *Frontier Leaders and Pioneers* by Dorothy Heiderstadt. Published by David McKay Co., Inc. By permission of Dorothy Heiderstadt.

This work is also published in individual volumes under the titles: *Awakening, Journeys, Dialogues, Inroads, Expressions,* and *A Horse Came Running,* copyright © 1983 Macmillan Publishing Co., Inc. Parts of this work were published in earlier editions of SERIES r.

Macmillan Publishing Company
866 Third Avenue, New York, New York 10022
Collier Macmillan Canada, Inc.

Printed in the United States of America
ISBN 0-02-136750-7
9 8 7 6 5 4 3

Contents

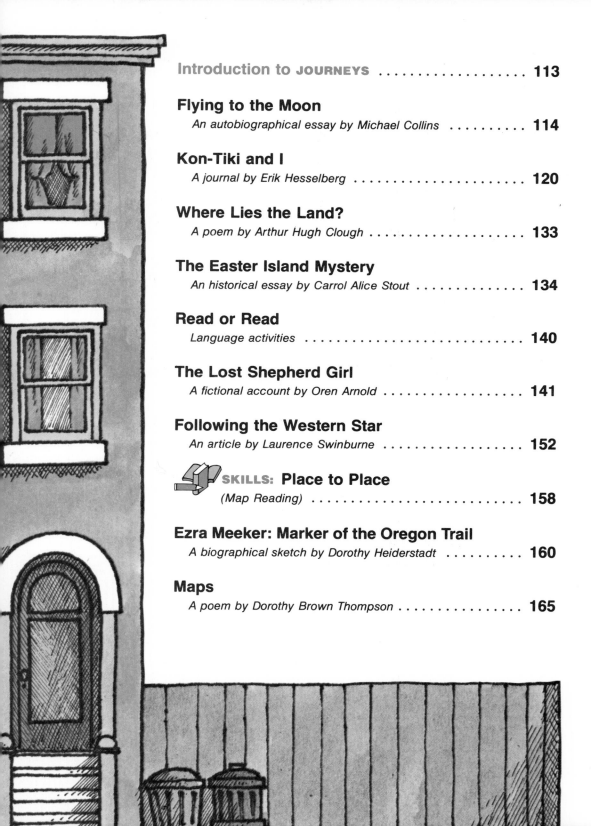

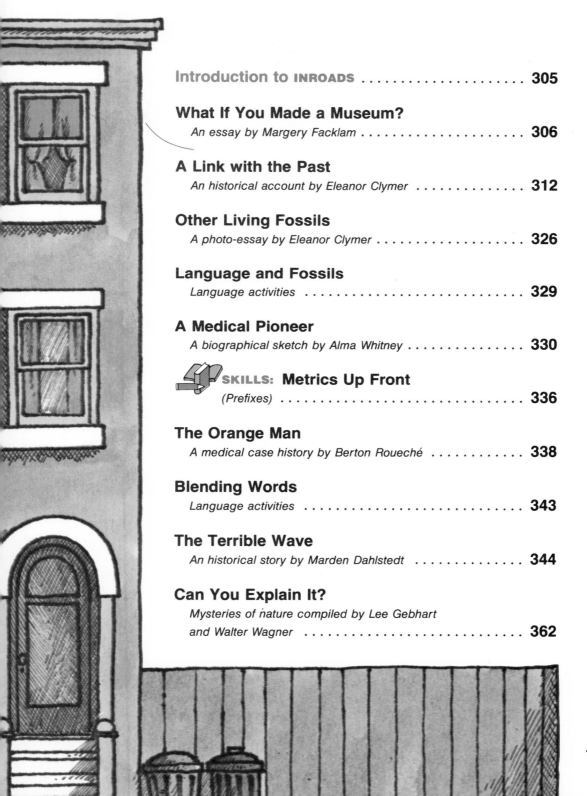

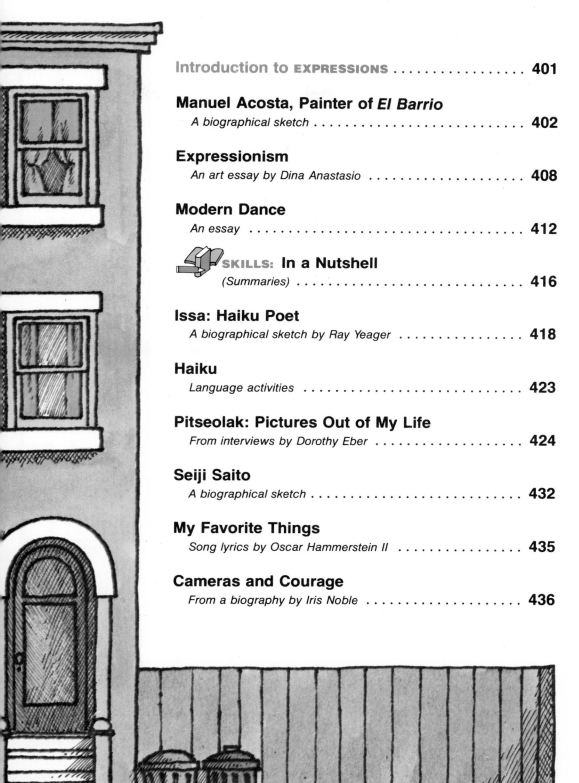

AWAKENING

All your life, new experiences awaken you to yourself and to the world around you. Sometimes an awakening is sudden—a new idea dawns on you. Other times an awakening is gradual—you form a new friendship. Awakenings help you realize what makes you the same as other people, and what sets you apart and makes you special.

The selections in "Awakening" are about learning or understanding something for the first time. From their experiences, the characters make discoveries about animals, about other people, and most of all, about themselves. A zookeeper learns that friendship can survive a long period of separation. A lonely girl discovers the world of books and makes a lasting group of friends. A young baseball player finds that with practice and determination, he can develop his skills and become a star. A new classmate helps a group of children reach a new understanding of the first Thanksgiving feast.

As you read, think about experiences that have awakened you to yourself and to the world around you.

Little by Little

Frances Cavanah

Young Abe Lincoln and his sister Sally lived with their father in a rough, dirt-floored cabin. Their mother had died, and their father had remarried. His new wife, Sarah, had joined the Lincoln family with three children of her own. Sarah was shocked at her first view of the Lincoln home and the two children, with their poor, soiled clothing, matted hair, and thin faces smudged with soot. But Sarah was a kind woman, and she had a sense of humor.

As this story opens, Sarah has just succeeded in getting Abe to take a bath. Now she is going to give him a haircut.

"I'm just going to cut away some of that brush heap on top of your head," she told him. She took another look at his mop of unruly black hair.

"Then how will folks know I'm me?" he asked sadly.

"What do you mean, Abe?"

"When we came to Indiana, Pappy marked off our claim by brush along the boundary lines. He said he wanted everyone to know this was our farm. I figured that brush heap atop of me is my boundary line. How will folks know I'm Abe Lincoln if you clear it away?"

It was the first time Sarah had heard him say more than "yes'm" or "no'm," and such a long speech took her by surprise. Was he joking? It was hard to tell, he was such a serious-looking boy. Or was he frightened? He sat quietly as she snipped at his unruly black hair.

"There!" she said at last. "It's all over."

The boy gazed in the mirror, a pleased expression in his eyes. "It's Abe, I reckon. I'm still not the purtiest boy in Pigeon Creek. On the other hand, there isn't quite so much of me to be ugly now."

Suddenly he grinned, and Sarah laughed. "You're a caution, Abe. Smart, too. Had much school?"

Abe shook his head, serious again. "I've just been to school by littles."

"Have you a mind to go again?"

"There isn't any school since Master Crawford left. Anyhow, Pappy doesn't set much store by education."

Sarah looked at him sharply. "Can you read?"

"Yes'm, but I haven't any books."

"Now, that's odd," said Sarah. "You can read and you haven't any books. I have books and can't read."

Abe stared at her, amazed. "You have books?"

She walked over to the bureau and came back carrying four worn-looking little volumes. "Books are good things to have, so I brought them along. You sit yourself down there at the table, and I'll show you."

Abe, his brown cheeks flushed with pleasure, spelled out the titles: "*Rob-in-son Cru-soe, Pil-grims Prog-ress, Sin-bad the Sail-or, Ae-sop's Fa-bles.* Oh, Ma'am this book, *Aesop's Fables,* is one Master Crawford told us about."

Sarah sat down beside him and turned the pages. "The stories look like little bitty ones. Could you read one of them to me, Abe?"

The book was open to the story of "The Crow and the Pitcher." Abe began to read. " 'A crow was almost dead of th-thirst, when he found a p-pit-cher with a little water in the bottom.' "

It had been so long since Abe had seen a book that he stumbled over a few words, but he gained more confidence as he went along. " 'The crow reached in his bill to take a drink. He tried and tried, but he could not reach the water. He was al-most ready to give up, when he had an i-dea. He picked up a peb-ble in his bill and dropped it into the pitcher. He picked up an-other pebble and an-other.

" 'With every pebble that he dropped, the water in the pitcher rose a little high-er. At last the water rose so high that the crow could reach it with his bill. He took a long drink, and so was a-ble to qu-qu-quench his thirst and save his life.' "

"You read right well," said Sarah.

Abe laughed delightedly, "It says something else here. 'Moral,'" he read. "'Little by little does the trick.'"

Abe took the book closer to the fireplace where it was easier to see the words. He read story after story, pausing only now and then to throw another log on the fire. As Sarah went about her household tasks, she watched him closely. Abe was different from what her John would ever be. He was different from any boy she had ever seen.

"Which story do you like best?" she asked.

Abe looked up. "The one about the smart crow."

"That story reminds me of you," she told him. "Mr. Aesop said, 'Little by little does the trick.' Well, you go to school by littles. Each time you learn something. I figure those little bits of learning are like pebbles. Keep piling them up higher, and you'll make something of yourself."

Abe shook his head. "I reckon I won't ever get to go to school again. Pappy says I already have more education than he ever had. I—I can't help it, Ma'am. I want to know more than Pappy knows."

"Your pappy's a good man," said Sarah, "and the next time a school keeps in these parts, I'm going to ask him to let you and the other kids go. That's a promise, Abe."

Again Abe could only stare.

"Meanwhile, you can learn by reading these books."

"I can read 'em—any time I like?"

"I'm giving them to you to keep."

"Oh, Mama," said Abe. The name slipped out as though he had always been used to saying it.

Only the fire crackling softly on the hearth broke the long silence. "You're my boy now, Abe," said Sarah softly, "and I'm going to help you all I can."

A Lesson in Reading

Robert C. O'Brien

This story is taken from the book Mrs. Frisby
and the Rats of NIMH. *NIMH was a research laboratory run
by a group of scientists. In the laboratory, the scientists
hoped to develop the most intelligent rats that ever existed.
But the rats became smarter than the scientists suspected.*

The most important phase of our training began
after weeks of really hard work at shape recognition. For the
first time they used sounds along with the shapes, and pictures, real pictures we could recognize. One of the first and
simplest of these exercises was a picture, a clear photograph, of a rat. I suppose they felt sure we would know what
that was. This picture was shown on a screen. Then, after I
had looked at the picture and recognized it, a shape
flashed under it on the screen. It was a sort of half-circle and
two straight lines, not like anything I had seen before. Then
the voice began:
    "Are."
    "Are."
    "Are."
The voice had a tinny sound—it was a record.
After repeating "are" a dozen times or so, that shape disappeared. Another one came on the screen, still under the
picture of the rat. It was a triangle with legs on it. The voice
began again:
    "Aiee."
    "Aiee."
    "Aiee."

When that shape disappeared, a third one came
on the screen. This one was a cross. The voice said:

"Tea."

"Tea."

"Tea."

Then all three shapes appeared at once, and the
record said:

"Are."

"Aiee."

"Tea."

"Rat."

You will already have recognized what was going
on: They were teaching us to read. The symbols under the
picture were the letters R-A-T. But the idea did not become
clear to me or to any of us for quite a long time. Because,
of course, we didn't know what reading <u>was</u>.

Oh, we learned to recognize the shapes easily enough. And when I saw the rat picture, I knew straight away what symbols would appear beneath it. In the same way, when the picture showed a cat, I knew the same shapes would appear, except the first one would be a half-circle. And the voice would repeat "see-see-see." I even learned that when the photograph showed not one but several rats, a fourth shape would appear under it—a snaky line—and the sound with that one was "ess-ess-ess." But as to what all that was <u>for</u>, none of us had any inkling.

It was Jenner who finally figured it out. By this time we had developed a sort of system of communication, a simple enough thing. We just passed spoken messages from one cage to the next. It was like passing notes in school. Justin, who was next to me, called to me one day:

"Message for Nicodemus from Jenner. He says it's important."

"All right," I said, "what's the message?"

"Look at the shapes on the wall next to the door. He says to look carefully."

My cage, like Jenner's and those of the rest of our group, was close enough to the door so I could see what he meant. Near the doorway there was a large, square piece of white cardboard fastened to the wall—a sign. It was covered with many black markings to which I had never paid any attention (though it had been there ever since I had arrived at the laboratory).

Now for the first time I looked at them carefully. And I understood what Jenner had discovered.

The top line of black marks on the wall were instantly familiar: R-A-T-S. As soon as I saw them, I thought of the picture that went with them. And as soon as I did that,

I was reading for the first time. Because, of course, that's what reading is: interpreting symbols that suggest a picture or an idea. From that time on, it gradually became clear to me what all these lessons were for. And once I understood the idea, I was eager to learn more. I could hardly wait for the next lesson, and the next. The whole concept of reading was, to me at least, fascinating. I remember how proud I was when, months later, I was able to read and understand that whole sign. I read it hundreds of times, and I'll never forget it:

RATS MAY NOT BE REMOVED FROM THE LABORA-TORY WITHOUT WRITTEN PERMISSION. And at the bottom, in smaller letters, the word NIMH.

Our training continued with new words and pictures every day. But the fact is, once we understood the idea and learned the different sounds each letter stood for, we leaped way ahead of our teachers. I remember well, during one of the lessons, looking at a picture of a tree. Under it the letters flashed on: T-R-E-E. But in the photograph, though the tree was in the foreground, there was a building in the background and a sign near it. I hardly looked at T-R-E-E, but concentrated instead on reading the sign near the building. The sign said:

NIMH. PRIVATE PARKING BY PERMIT ONLY. RESERVED FOR DOCTORS AND STAFF. NO VISITOR PARKING.

The building behind it, tall and white, looked very much like the building we were in. I was sure there were plans for testing our reading ability. I could even guess, from the words we were being taught, what the tests were going to be like. For example, we were taught "left," "right," "door," "food," "open," and so on. It was not hard to imagine the test; I would be placed in one chamber, my food in another. There would be two doors and a sign saying: "For food,

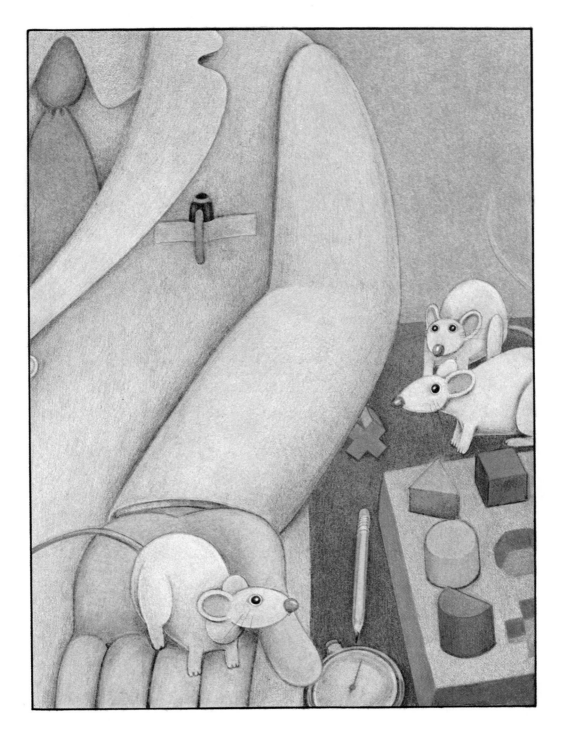

open door at right." Or something like that. Then if I—if all of us—always moved toward the proper door, it would be known that we understood the sign.

As I said, I was sure there were plans to do this, but apparently they did not think we were ready for it yet. I think maybe they were even a little afraid to try it. Because if they did it too soon, or if for any other reason it did not work, the experiment would be a failure. They wanted to be sure.

Around the partition one evening Justin announced: "I'm going to get out of my cage tonight and wander around a bit."

"How can you? It's locked."

"Yes. But did you notice that along the bottom edge there's a printed strip?"

I had not noticed it. I should perhaps explain that, when the people at the laboratory opened our cages, we could never quite see how they did it; they moved something under the plastic floor, something we couldn't see.

"What does it say?"

"I've been trying to read it the last three times they brought me back from training. It's very small print. But I think I've finally made it out. It says: 'To release door, pull knob forward and slide right.'"

"Knob?"

"Under the floor about an inch back there's a metal thing just in front of the shelf. I think that's the knob. And I think I can reach it through the wire. Anyway, I'm going to give it a try."

"Now?"

"Not until they close up."

Closing up was a ritual the people in the laboratory went through each night. For about an hour they sat at their desks, wrote notes in books, filed papers in cabinets, and finally locked the cabinets. Then they checked all the cages, dimmed the lights, locked the doors, and went home, leaving us alone.

About half an hour after they left that night, Justin said: "I'm going to try now." I heard a scuffling noise, a click and scrape of metal, and in a matter of seconds I saw his door swing open. It was as simple as that—when you could read.

"Wait," I said.

"What's the matter?"

"If you jump down, you won't be able to get back in. Then they'll know."

"I thought of that. I'm not going to jump down. I'm going to climb up the outside of the cage. It's easy. I've climbed up the inside a thousand times. Above these cages there's another shelf, and it's empty. I'm going to walk along there and see what I can see. I think there's a way to climb to the floor and up again."

"Why don't I go with you?" My door would open the same way as his.

"Better not this time. If something goes wrong and I can't get back, they'll say it's just A-9 again. But if two of us are found outside, they'll take it seriously. They might put new locks on the cages."

He was right, and you can see that already we both had the same idea in mind: that this might be the first step toward escape for all of us.

New Expressions Using Verbs

In the story "A Lesson in Reading," Jenner, the rat, waited for the scientists to "close up" before he tried to escape from his cage. In the expression *close up,* the verb *close* has been combined with the adverb *up.*

There are many expressions in English that have been formed by combining verbs with other words. Some of the most popular ones are listed below. How many others can you remember?

set up	give away	tie up	sit in
hold over	count down	clean up	make up
show off	lay off	mix up	run around

Many of these word combinations have also become nouns. When they become nouns, the words are usually joined together as one word or as a hyphenated word.

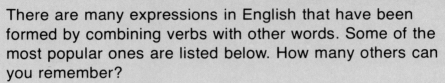

$$\text{run + around} \Rightarrow \text{runaround}$$
$$\text{count + down} \Rightarrow \text{countdown}$$
$$\text{mix + up} \Rightarrow \text{mix-up}$$

Can you form other nouns using words in the list above?

Now read each pair of sentences below. Use a noun formed from the underlined words to complete the second sentence in each pair.

1. The spacecraft will <u>splash down</u> in the Pacific Ocean.
   We plan to watch the _____ on TV.

2. The plane will <u>take off</u> in two minutes.
   Fasten your seat belt for the _____.

3. Let's both help <u>clean up</u> the kitchen.
   If we help, the _____ will take only a few minutes.

Sometimes the people we meet in books become as real to us as our friends. Pearl Buck, the author of the next story you will read, learned this when she was very young. The daughter of American missionary parents, Pearl grew up in China. Although she loved the land and the people of China, she always felt different and alone. It was not until Pearl read the book Oliver Twist *that she made her first real friend.*

Pearl learned more than just friendship from Charles Dickens, the creator of the character Oliver Twist. She learned to understand people and to fight injustice. Pearl Buck grew up to be a writer, too. Most of her books are about her life in China. This story is Pearl's thank you note to Charles Dickens, who gave her many friends and many happy days.

PEARL S. BUCK

A Debt to Dickens

I have long looked for an opportunity to pay a certain debt which I have owed since I was seven years old. My debt is to an Englishman. Long ago in China he did a great service to a small American child. That child was myself. And that Englishman was Charles Dickens. I know no better way to pay my debt than to write down what Charles Dickens did for an American child in China.

First you must picture that child. She was living quite alone in a mission bungalow upon a hill in a remote Chinese countryside. Below were rice fields. In the near distance wound that deep, golden river, the Yangtse. Some of the most terrifying and sinister, as well as the most delightful and exciting, moments of that child's life were spent beside the river. She loved to crawl along its banks and linger among the villages of boat folk. She

wandered small and strange among the farm folk who lived in houses among the fields. Often at mealtime she accepted a bowl of rice and cabbage and sat among the people. Usually she sat in silence, listening to their kindly, teasing laughter at her yellow curls and unfortunate blue eyes, which they thought so ugly. She was, she knew, very different.

She grew from a very tiny child into a bigger child, still knowing she was different. However kindly the people around her might be, and they were much more often kind than not, she knew that she was foreign to them. And she wondered very much about her own folk and where they were and how they looked and at what they played. But she did not know. In the bungalow were her parents, very busy, very busy. And after she had learned her lessons in the morning, they were too busy to pay much attention to her. So she wandered about a great deal, seeing and learning all sorts of things. She had fun. But very often she used to wonder, "Where are the other children like me? What is it like in the country where they live?" She longed very much, I can remember, to have some of them to play with. But she never had them.

To this small, lonely creature
there came an amazing accident. She was
a great reader. She would like to have
had children's books, but there were none.
Then one day she looked at a long row
of blue books on a very high shelf. They
were quite beyond her reach. But being
desperate, she put a three-cornered stool on
top of a small table and climbed up.
Among the faded black titles she read
"*Oliver Twist* by Charles Dickens." She
was then a little past seven years old. It
was a very hot August afternoon when the
household was asleep—all except her
parents, and they were very, very busy.
She took *Oliver Twist* out of his place and
carefully descended. After stopping for a
pocketful of peanuts, she made off to a
secret corner of the porch into which only
a small child could squeeze. There she
opened the closely printed pages of an old
edition and discovered her playmates.

How can I make you know what
that discovery was to that small, lonely
child? There in that corner above the
country road in China, I entered into my
own heritage. I cannot tell you about those
hours. I know I was roused at six o'clock
by the call to supper. I looked about dazed
to discover the long rays of the late afternoon sun streaming across the valleys. I

remember twice I closed the book and burst into tears, unable to bear the tragedy of *Oliver Twist*. And then I opened it quickly again, burning to know more. I remember, most important of all, that I forgot to touch a peanut. My pocket was still quite full when I was called. I went to my supper in a dream and read as late as I dared in my bed afterward. And I slept with the book under my pillow and woke in the very early morning and took it up again. When *Oliver Twist* was finished, I felt I must read it all straight over again, and yet I was hungry for that long row of blue books. What was in them? I climbed up again finally and put *Oliver Twist* at the beginning and began on the next one, which was *David Copperfield*. I decided to read straight through the row and then begin at the beginning once more and read straight through again.

This is just what I did, over and over, for about ten years. And after that I still kept a Dickens book nearby to read and feel myself at home again. Today I have for him a feeling which I have for no other human soul. He opened my eyes to people. He taught me to love all sorts of people, high and low, rich and poor, the old and the young. He taught me that beneath gruffness there may be kindness and that kindness is the sweetest thing in the world. If he saw everything black and white, it was because life rushed out of him strong and clear, full of love and hate. He gave me that immense joy in life and in people and in their variety.

I went to his parties over and over again, for I had no others. I remember one dreadful hungry winter the thing that kept me laughing and still a child was *Pickwick Papers.* I read it over and over and laughed, as I still laugh, at Mr. Pickwick and all his merry company. They were as real to me as the sad folk outside my walls. And they saved me.

This is what Charles Dickens did for me. His influence I cannot lose. He has made himself a part of me forever.

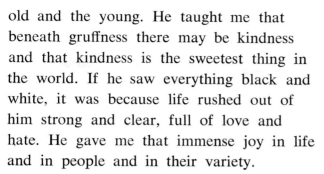

Frank B. Gilbreth, Jr.
and Ernestine Gilbreth Carey

Nantucket

Dad had promised before we came to Nantucket for summer vacation that there would be no formal studying—no language records and no school books. He kept his promise. But we found he was always teaching us things when our backs were turned.

For instance there was the Morse code matter.

"I have a way to teach you the code without any studying," he said one day at lunch.

We said we didn't want to learn the code. We didn't want to learn anything until school in the fall.

"There's no studying," said Dad. "And the ones who learn it first will get rewards. The ones who don't learn it are going to wish they had."

After lunch he got a small paint brush and a can of black paint. He locked himself in the bathroom, where he painted the alphabet in code on the wall.

For the next three days Dad was busy with his paint brush. He wrote code over the walls in every room. On the ceiling in the bedrooms, he wrote the alphabet together with key words, whose accents were a reminder of the code for the various letters. It went like this: A, dot-dash, A-pron; B, dash-dot-dot-dot, BOIS-ter-ous-ly; C, dash-dot-dash-dot, CARE-less CHIL-dren; D, dash-dot-dot, DAN-ger-ous; and so on.

When you lay on your back, dozing, the words kept going through your head, and you'd find yourself saying, "DAN-ger-ous, dash-dot-dot, DAN-ger-ous."

He painted secret messages in code on the walls of the front porch and dining room.

"What do they say, Daddy?" we asked him.

"Many things," he replied mysteriously. "Many secret things and many things of great humor."

We went into the bedrooms and copied the code alphabet on pieces of paper. Then looking at the paper we started translating Dad's messages. He went right on painting as if he were paying no attention to us. But he didn't miss a word.

"What awful puns," said Anne. "And this, I guess, is one of the 'things of great humor.' Listen to this one: 'Bee it ever so bumble, there's no place like comb.' "

"And we're stung," Ern moaned. "We're not going to be satisfied until we translate them all. I see dash-dot-dash-dot, and I hear myself repeating CARE-less CHILD-ren. What's this one say?"

We figured it out: "Eat, drink, and be merry. Tomorrow you may diet." And still another, "Two maggots were fighting in dead Ernest."

Every day or so after that, Dad would leave a piece of paper containing a Morse code message on the dining-room table. Translated, it might read something like this: "The first one who figures out this secret message should look in the right-hand pocket of my linen knickers. They are hanging on a hook in my room. Daddy." Or: "Hurry up before someone beats you to it. Look in the bottom, left drawer of the sewing machine."

In the knickers' pocket and in the drawer would be some sort of reward—a bar of candy, a quarter, a receipt entitling the bearer to one chocolate ice cream soda, payable by Dad on demand.

Some of the Morse code notes were false alarms. "Hello. This one is on the house. No reward, but there may be a reward next time. When you finish reading this, dash off like mad so the others will think you are on some hot clue. Then they'll read it, too, and you won't be the only one who got fooled. Daddy."

As Dad had planned, we all knew the Morse code fairly well within a few weeks. Well enough, in fact, so that we could tap out messages to each other by bouncing the tip of a fork on a plate. When a dozen or so persons all attempt to broadcast in this manner, and all of us preferred sending to receiving, the accumulation of noise is very loud.

The wall writing worked so well in teaching us the code that Dad decided to use the same system to teach us astronomy. His first step was to capture our interest. He did this by building a telescope. He'd carry it out into the yard on clear nights and look at the stars while apparently ignoring us.

We'd gather around and nudge him and pull at his clothes, demanding that he let us look through the telescope.

"Don't bother me," he'd say with his nose stuck into the glasses. "Oh, my golly, I believe those two stars are going to collide! No. Awfully close, though."

"Daddy, give us a turn," we'd insist. "Don't be such a pig."

Finally with pretended reluctance he agreed to let us look through the glasses. We could see the ring around Saturn, three moons of Jupiter, and the craters on our own moon.

When he finally was convinced he had interested us in astronomy, Dad started a new series of wall paintings dealing with stars. On one wall he made a scale drawing of the major planets. They ranged from little Mercury, represented by a circle about as big as a marble, to Jupiter, as big as a basketball. On another wall he showed the planets in relation to their distances from the sun. Mercury was the closest and Neptune the farthest away—almost in the kitchen. Pluto still hadn't been discovered, which was just as well because there really wasn't room for it.

There was still some wall space left. And Dad had more than enough ideas to fill it. He put up a piece of graph paper which was a thousand lines long and a thousand lines wide and thus contained exactly a million little squares.

"You hear people talk a lot about a million," he said, "but not many people have ever seen exactly a million things at the same time. If a man has a million dollars, he has exactly as many dollars as there are little squares on that chart."

"Do you have a million dollars?" Bill asked.

"No," said Dad. "I have a million children, instead. Somewhere along the line a man has to choose between the two."

AN EXTRA BRAVE

MARION HOLLAND

If the new boy had come into Ms. Gowdy's room at any other time, Ms. Gowdy might have paid more attention to him. The other children might have paid more attention to him, too. But it was the week before the Thanksgiving pageant, and they were all very busy.

Ms. Gowdy had the janitor bring in an extra desk and chair and set them at the back of the room. Then she asked the new boy if he could see the blackboard all right from there, and he said yes.

And that was all he did say for a long time. His name was Jed Black, and he just sat quietly. With his dark, watchful eyes, he took in everything that was going on.

Plenty was going on, but not the usual things, like reading, spelling, and arithmetic. Ms. Gowdy's room had had plenty of reading, looking up everything in the library about the first Thanksgiving; and plenty of spelling, writing a play about that event and copying out all the parts. And plenty of arithmetic, too, figuring out how many yards of material had to be sent home for the costumes the

Pilgrims would make. The braves of the Wampanoag tribe were just going to wear khaki pants and blankets and a few feathers, which was a break for them.

Now they were all busy finishing up a life-sized deer upside down. That is, the deer was upside down. It was hung by the feet from a long stick, which two braves were to carry onto the stage as their contribution to the feast. Of course, there had really been five deer at the first Thanksgiving. But then there had really been ninety American Indians, too. As there were only fourteen of them in the play, they figured that one deer would do.

They had a wire framework of a deer, which they were padding out with paper and paste and paint. The new boy stayed in his seat and watched. When they were finished, everybody admitted that one side looked more like a cow; but the other side was a pretty fair deer. So they stuck the arrow in that side and warned the two braves who were to carry it to keep that side toward the audience.

Then they got on with their rehearsing. Everybody had a part. All the girls were Pilgrims; they had to be, because all the American Indians at the first Thanksgiving were braves. Three of the boys were Pilgrims. Ms. Gowdy didn't want the audience to get the idea that all the Pilgrim Fathers had been Pilgrim Mothers.

Finally, Ms. Gowdy remembered the new boy. She said that he had better be a Pilgrim, too, and they could write a few lines for him to say.

Diana Carr, who had the most important Pilgrim part, next to Governor Bradford, said quickly: "Oh, but we all know our parts, and it would mix us up. Besides, there isn't time for him to get a costume fixed."

"Let him be a Wampanoag," said Johnny Schmidt, who played Massasoit, the leader of the tribe. "We can always use an extra brave."

So for the last few rehearsals Jed was a Wampanoag. He was the brave who came on the stage last, behind all the others, and he didn't say anything. But that didn't matter, because quite a few of the others didn't say anything either, which was one of the

reasons so many kids wanted to be Wampanoags.

"It's a good thing we didn't have to write in a part for him," said Diana to Joan, her best friend. "He'd never have learned it. Why, I don't think he can even talk."

"Maybe he's a foreigner," suggested Joan kindly. "He sort of looks like one."

"Well, if he is, of course he can't help it," admitted Diana. "But naturally the Pilgrims ought to be Americans."

"But they weren't. Anyway, not yet. They were English," Joan pointed out.

At the dress rehearsal, everybody was in costume except the new boy. He just wore the same T-shirt and faded blue jeans that he wore to school. He stood so far in the back that Ms. Gowdy didn't notice; but Johnny did, and he was worried about it. After all, he was Massasoit. He was responsible for these braves.

He stopped Jed after school. "Look, I can lend you some things to wear for the play tomorrow," he said, speaking very slowly and distinctly. "If you don't have any."

"I'll have something," replied Jed. "Anyway, I hope so. My brother sent away for some things. They probably came in the mail today."

Why, he talked just like anybody! Imagine that dumb Diana, going around and telling everybody that the new boy was some kind of a foreigner and didn't know a word of English!

"Why don't I go home with you and see if the things came?" suggested Johnny. "Then if they didn't, we'll go over to my house and I'll fix you up with some feathers. We'll go over to my house, anyway, and shoot a few baskets if you like basketball. OK?"

"OK," said Jed.

By 9:30 the next morning all the seats in the school auditorium were filled, and people were standing up in the back. Behind the drawn curtains on the stage the Pilgrims were all in their places. But the Wampanoags were still in the dressing room, rubbing grease paint on their arms and faces.

Just as the audience finished singing "America the Beautiful,"

Johnny stuck his head out of the dressing room and said, "Ready!" to Ms. Gowdy. She hurried to one side of the stage and pulled the curtain.

There were the Pilgrims, seated at a long table piled high with corn and pumpkins and fish. They talked about what a hard year they had had, their first year in the new country. They talked about how they had finished building houses and had gathered a good harvest and how thankful they were for these blessings.

Then Governor Bradford stood up and reminded them all about how helpful the natives had been

and how the Pilgrims might not have survived the terrible winter if it hadn't been for the American Indians. He said he had invited Massasoit to bring some of his braves to share the Thanksgiving feast.

This was the Wampanoags' cue to enter. First came Johnny Schmidt, then after a little pushing at the entrance, the two braves with the deer. Then came the others, and last of all Jed.

But Jed didn't stay at the back as usual. The others parted left and right, and Jed walked forward to stand beside Governor Bradford at the head of the table.

A noisy gasp of surprise went up behind the Pilgrims, but the audience didn't hear it, because the audience was gasping, too. There was a confused rustling sound from the auditorium as everyone leaned forward to get a better view.

Jed was dressed in fringed deerskin embroidered at the neck and sleeves with porcupine quills. On his feet were beaded moccasins; on his head a sweeping war bonnet with silver ornaments that glittered beside his thin cheeks. No dyed turkey feathers, these, but proud white-and-gray eagle feathers.

He raised his right hand, palm outward, and spoke. He spoke Johnny's lines, Massasoit's lines; he spoke them quietly, but so clearly that everyone in the audience could hear every word.

He said that his people, too, always give thanks for a good harvest. He said that now the white people and the red people were friends and they would remain friends, as long as they kept their word when it was given. He said all the things that Ms. Gowdy's class had written down for Massasoit to say. But now they listened to them as if they had never heard them before.

He ended: "This country to which you have come is a beautiful country full of good things. If we share the good things fairly, there is room for all."

Governor Bradford was supposed to reply. But his words were drowned out in a thunder of clapping from the audience. So the Pilgrims and the Wampanoags just bowed their head in grateful thanks, and Ms. Gowdy pulled the curtain.

Backstage everything was confusion. The deer was dropped, and several people stepped on it, but

nobody needed it anymore, anyway. Everyone crowded around Jed and Johnny, asking questions, and Johnny answered them as fast as he could talk.

"Jed's a full-blooded American Indian, and his whole name is Jed Black Horse Running. So when I went to his house yesterday and saw his clothes, I knew he ought to be Massasoit instead of me. He learned the lines in a flash. Knew most of 'em already, just from listening."

"Do you wear these all the time at home?" asked someone, fingering the deerskin fringes.

Jed just shook his head, but Johnny said: "Of course not. These are extra special, just for the most important ceremonies. When Jed told his brother about the play, they decided it was an important ceremony and sent for 'em back on the reservation. That's where Jed used to live. But now he's living with his brother so he can finish school here and be an engineer like his brother."

Diana said to Joan as they went into the dressing room: "So that's what he is, a Wampanoag. I knew he was some kind of foreigner."

"Listen, you!" Joan said to Diana, "if you went somewhere else you'd be a foreigner, did you ever think of that? Besides, compared to Jed, everybody in this whole school is a foreigner. And hurry up and change, because all of us Pilgrims have an important date to play basketball with the braves."

57

Two by Two

An *analogy* is a way of comparing things. Some analogies compare two pairs of words. The words in the first pair are related in some way. The words in the second pair are related in the same way.

Here is an example of an analogy:

Car is to street as boat is to river.

The first two words are *car* and *street*. These words are related: A car travels on a street. Similarly, a boat travels on a river. Another way to write this analogy is:

car : street :: boat : river

An analogy may relate pairs of opposites, or antonyms.

up : down :: heavy : light

The two words in each pair are antonyms.

Some analogies relate words that have similar meanings, or synonyms.

large : huge :: hard : difficult

The two words in each pair are synonyms.

Sometimes you must supply the last word of an analogy.

doctor : hospital :: teacher : ____

   a. store   **b.** factory   **c.** homework   **d.** school

A *doctor* works in a *hospital*. The missing word must tell where a teacher works. Teachers don't work in a store or a factory. Homework is not a place to work. The correct answer is *school*. A teacher works in a school.

Read each analogy. Decide how the first two words are related. Then, on your paper, write the word that correctly completes the analogy.

1. snow : white :: sky : ____
   a. clouds   **b.** blue   **c.** cold   **d.** rain

2. pen : ink :: pencil : ____
   a. crayon   **b.** chalk   **c.** eraser   **d.** lead

3. tired : sleepy :: loud : ____
   a. noisy   **b.** headache   **c.** soft   **d.** speaker

4. fish : water :: worm : ____
   a. insect   **b.** wiggly   **c.** soil   **d.** speaker

5. dog : bark :: frog : ____
   a. voice   **b.** pond   **c.** green   **d.** croak

6. toes : ten :: eyes : ____
   a. see   **b.** two   **c.** nose   **d.** four

7. smart : wise :: unkind : ____
   a. silly   **b.** mean   **c.** dumb   **d.** polite

8. chair : furniture :: hammer : ____
   a. tool   **b.** nail   **c.** board   **d.** bang

9. glove : hand :: shoe : ____
   a. lace   **b.** polish   **c.** foot   **d.** ankle

10. magician : trick :: singer : ____
    a. dancer   **b.** song   **c.** actor   **d.** violin

11. sandals : summer :: boots : ____
    a. socks   **b.** bare feet   **c.** winter   **d.** snow

12. flock : geese :: herd : ____
    a. people   **b.** frogs   **c.** corn   **d.** cattle

13. dull : cloudy :: bright : ____
    a. sunny   **b.** yellow   **c.** warm   **d.** hard

The CHAMPION

Peg Roberts

Chuck whirled around as he heard a high whistling sound! Something bright and blue whizzed past him into the hydrangea bush. What could it be? It wasn't a bird, that was for sure. He carefully parted the top branches of the bush and almost fell over backward. Two enormous, black eyes set in a pale-blue face were clinging to the main branch and staring up at him.

"Hi," said the grinning face, "how about helping a guy out of this trap?"

Before Chuck could reply, two thin blue arms grabbed him, and the—whatever it was—leaped to the ground. "Thanks, pal. That bush isn't exactly my idea of a comfortable felooma."

In front of Chuck stood a little man not more than two feet tall, dressed all in blue. In fact, everything about him was blue except for his large black eyes. The eyes examined Chuck intently.

"F—felooma?" stammered Chuck. "What's that? Who are you?"

"You mean you don't know me? Why, I'm Orwick from the Planet Ganis. I've had the shuttle patrol in your galaxy for a long time."

"Aw, there isn't a planet named Ganis, is there?"

"Not in your galaxy, buddy boy."

Chuck stared. "How did you get here?"

"My rocket booster failed as I was revving up for the trip home, and I was pulled into your gravity. Next thing I knew, I was up to my neck in green mirkels. I've got a problem, too. I seem to have lost my magnesium watch. Without that, I can't signal my people to beam me back to Ganis. Will you help me hunt for it?"

While he was helping search, Chuck glanced at the little man out of the corner of one eye. He began wishing some of his friends would come along. Would they ever be impressed to see Chuck on speaking terms with someone from outer space.

A voice hailed him. "Hey, Chuck, it's almost time for Little League. Why are you crawling

around on the ground?" Without waiting for an answer, Paul flopped down beside Chuck and began talking about the Red Sox game he had seen on TV. He paid no attention to Orwick, who came to sit between the boys.

Chuck cleared his throat. "Paul, this is—er, that is—gosh, Paul, don't you want to know who he is? Aren't you curious?"

Paul craned his neck. "Know who? What is there to be curious about? Come on, let's get over to the ball park. I picked up your glove and bat for you."

Paul couldn't see Orwick!

"Am I the only person who can see him?" wondered Chuck, scooping up his bat and glove. "You want to come with us, Orwick?" he whispered.

Orwick nodded. "Might as well. We can look for my watch on the way. No telling where it fell."

"Why are you mumbling to yourself, Chuck?" Paul frowned.

Without answering, Chuck loped off in the direction of the ball park.

Both teams were warming up as they arrived. No one else could see Orwick.

The little blue man wandered away to sit in the bleachers during the game, but hopped down and trotted along beside Chuck as he went home. The big black eyes glittered in the twilight.

"No offense intended, but you're not very good at this baseball, are you?" remarked Orwick in a soft voice.

Chuck sighed. "You noticed that, did you?"

"How good would you like to be?" asked Orwick.

Chuck's eyes crinkled up. "I want to be the best hitter in the world. I'd like to be as terrific as Hank Aaron."

Orwick hopped around on one foot. "I can fix that easily. I like you, buddy boy. I want to help you. Beginning tomorrow, you'll hit a homer every time you come to bat."

"Oh, sure," Chuck snorted. "I have yet to hit my first home run. The whole team groans when it's my turn at bat."

"Not any more, they won't." As Chuck stared, Orwick began to shimmer and slowly melt into the night air.

Warming up at practice next evening, Chuck wondered if he would see the little blue man again. He hadn't appeared yet.

The game started. By the time Chuck came to bat, the other team was ahead by one run. Chuck heard one of his teammates scoff, "Here goes old 'sock the wind.' "

Chuck held the bat with an iron grip as the pitcher's ball sped toward him. There was a solid **crack**. Chuck looked up, unbelieving. The ball was soaring above the spectators, out toward the fence.

"Run, Chuck! Run!" yelled Paul.

Chuck ran. As he slid into home base, his eye caught something blue high up in the bleachers. It was Orwick, grinning and waving at him.

Chuck hit another homer later in the game, and walked home in a daze. He, Chuck Martin, who hardly ever connected with the ball, had hit two home runs!

Going up to his room, Chuck found Orwick sitting cross-legged on the bed, black eyes sparkling. "How's that, buddy boy?"

"Orwick, you did it! I was the star of the game. Can you make me play like this every game?"

"Certainly. Nothing to it."

Chuck tumbled into bed and dreamed Hank Aaron was shaking his hand.

He became the most valuable player on the team. The coach began grooming him for the division championship game. Each time Chuck came to bat, he looked up at Orwick in the bleachers, and blasted one over the fence. Most evenings Orwick was also waiting in Chuck's room, and they talked baseball until bedtime.

But one night Chuck sat stiffly on the bed with an empty feeling in his stomach. Orwick moved closer and placed one blue hand on Chuck's arm. "What's the matter, buddy boy? Are you losing your enthusiasm for this baseball? Are you tired of being a hero?"

"Oh, no, Orwick. But somehow it doesn't seem right. I'm not hitting all those homers; you are. Without you, I'm a lousy batter. It's not quite honest, you know?"

"Nonsense! Everyone thinks you're tremendous!"

"But I'm not. I don't feel good about it inside. I don't . . ." said Chuck, choosing his words carefully, "I don't want you to help me any more, Orwick. I'll just muddle through on my own."

"You'll disappoint your team. They're counting on your batting to win them the conference pennant."

"I understand that, but it wouldn't be fair," Chuck gulped. "I'll practice every extra minute until then. Maybe I can improve

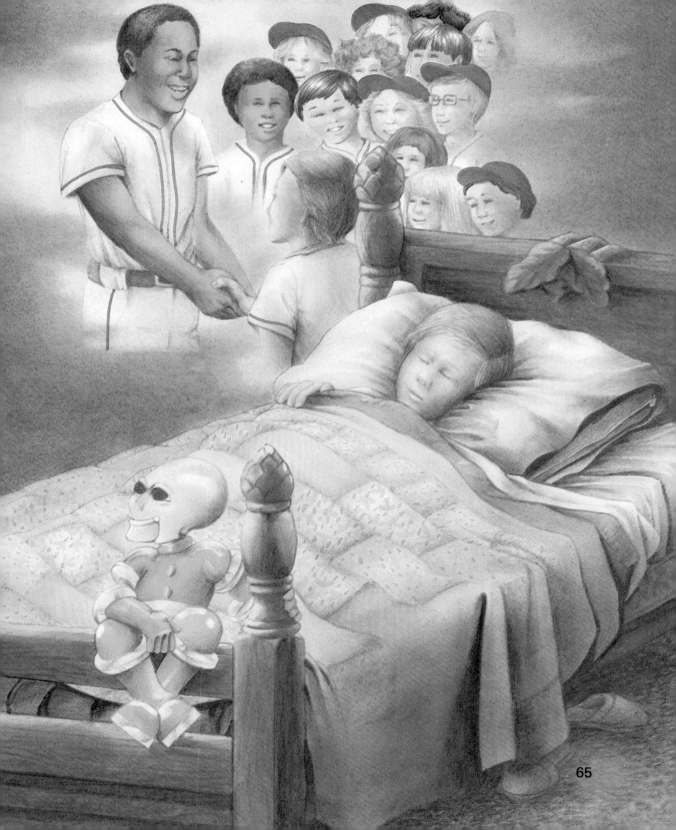

enough to hit a homer once in a while."

Orwick jumped down from the bed. "All right. I think you're making a mistake, but if that's the way you want it . . . I sure wish I could find my magnesium watch." With that, he faded into the darkness.

Swearing him to secrecy, Chuck got Paul to pitch balls to him every afternoon in the meadow on the other side of the woods, where no one would find them. As the championship game approached, Chuck was beginning to slam a few, but he knew in his heart it wasn't good enough. He could see the coach was worried about his sudden poor playing.

The night of the championship game, Chuck fingered his cap, dreading his turn at bat. When he found himself at the plate with the pitcher drawing back his arm to hurl the ball, Chuck gripped the bat hard. A feeling of failure swept over him, and he slumped, holding the bat loosely. He swung back slowly, expecting to hear the ball thud into the catcher's mitt.

Instead, there was an explosion and the ball shot high in the air, winging out of the ball park. Chuck hesitated a second, then flew. The crowd cheered as he rounded the bases, but anger was rising in him. Orwick had gone back on his word! As he touched home base, Chuck searched the bleachers for the little blue man, but couldn't see him.

After the game, Chuck and Paul walked home together. "I always knew you could do it, Chuck," Paul crowed. "All that extra practice didn't mean a thing until you relaxed. And that's exactly what you did tonight, for the first time. All of a sudden everything you've been trying to learn clicked. From now on I wouldn't be surprised if you're a top hitter. You've got the makings of a real champion."

Chuck's shoulders slumped. "Sure, Paul."

"For a guy who just led his team to the conference pennant, you don't seem too happy. Is anything wrong?"

"Guess I'm a little tired. See you tomorrow. Good night, Paul."

Chuck raced for his room. "Orwick!" he yelled, taking the steps two at a time. "You promised you wouldn't interfere. Why did you. . ." But there was no Orwick.

Instead, Chuck found a note on his pillow. It said, "Too bad I can't stick around for the important game. But I located my magnesium watch under the porch, and decided I'd better beam straight back to Ganis. Good luck." It was signed, "Orwick."

Chuck quickly sat down. "Orwick didn't help me after all. I hit that homer all by myself." A slow smile spread over his face. "Paul is right. I really can hit a ball if I remember to relax—the way I did tonight."

He ran to the window and looked up at the starry sky. "I'm sorry I doubted you, Orwick."

Just for a minute, it seemed to Chuck there was a white blur between two stars. "I wonder if Orwick heard me," he murmured.

One morning when the boy called Waukewa was off hunting along the mountainside, he found a young eagle with a broken wing. It was lying at the base of a cliff. The bird had fallen from a ledge and, being too young to fly, had fluttered down the cliff. It was hurt so severely that it was likely to die. When Waukewa saw it, he was about to drive one of his sharp arrows through its body. But then he saw that the young bird at his feet was quivering with pain and fright. Waukewa slowly stooped over the panting eaglet. For fully a minute the wild eyes of the wounded bird and the keen, dark eyes of the boy, growing gentler and softer as he gazed, looked into one another. Then the struggling of the young eagle stopped. The wild, frightened look passed out of its eyes. And the bird allowed Waukewa to pass his hand gently over its ruffled feathers. The desire to fight, to defend its life, gave way to the charm of the tenderness and pity expressed in the boy's eyes. From that moment Waukewa and the eagle were friends.

Waukewa went slowly home, the wounded eaglet in his arms. He carried it so gently that the broken wing gave no pain. The bird lay perfectly still, never trying to strike the hands of the boy with its sharp beak.

Waukewa warmed some water over the fire at the lodge. He bathed the broken wing of

JAMES BUCKHAM

WAUKEWA'S EAGLE

S. Dion

the eagle and bound it up with soft strips of skin. Then he made a nest of ferns and grass inside the lodge and laid the bird in it. The boy's mother looked on with shining eyes. Her heart was very tender. From girlhood she had loved all the creatures of the woods. It pleased her to see some of her own gentle spirit waking in the boy.

When Waukewa's father returned from hunting, he said, "Nurse it until it is well. But then you must let it go. We will not raise up an eagle in the lodges." So Waukewa promised that when the eagle's wing was healed and when the bird had grown so that it could fly, he would give it its freedom.

It was a month before the young eagle was strong enough to fly. In the meantime Waukewa cared for it and fed it daily. And the friendship between the boy and the bird grew very strong.

But at last the time came when the eagle had to be freed. So Waukewa carried it far away from the tribe's lodges. He took it to where none of the young braves might see it flying over and be tempted to shoot their arrows at it. At this faraway place, he let it go. The young eagle rose toward the sky in great circles. It rejoiced in its freedom and its strange new power of flight. But when Waukewa began to move away from the spot, it came swooping down again. All day it followed him through the woods as he hunted. At dusk, when Waukewa turned toward home, the eagle started to follow him. But the boy suddenly slipped into a hollow tree and hid. After a long time the eagle stopped sweeping about in search of him. It flew slowly and sadly away.

Summer passed and then winter. And spring came again with its flowers and birds and fish in the lakes and streams. Then it was that the tribe, old and young, braves and squaws, pushed their light canoes out from shore. With spear and hook they waged pleasant war against the salmon and the red trout. After winter's long imprisonment it was such joy to be in the sunshine and the

warm wind and catch fresh fish to take the place of dried meats and corn!

Above the great falls the salmon sported in the cool, swinging current. They were darting and leaping full length in the clear spring air. Nowhere else were such salmon to be caught as those which lay at the head of the rapids. But only the most daring would seek them there, for the current was strong. Should a light canoe once pass the danger point and get caught in the rush of the rapids, nothing could save it. It would go over the roaring falls.

Very early in the morning of a clear April day, just as the sun was rising splendidly over the mountains, Waukewa launched his canoe a half mile above the rapids. He floated downward, spear in hand, among the salmon. He was the only one of the tribe's lads who dared to fish above the falls. But he had been there often. Never yet had his watchful eye and his strong paddle allowed the current to carry his canoe beyond the danger point. This morning he was alone on the river, having risen long before daylight to be first at the sport.

Big salmon swam about the canoe on every side in an endless silver stream. Waukewa plunged his spear right and left. He tossed one fish after another into the canoe. He was so absorbed in the sport that he did not notice when the canoe began to move more swiftly among the rocks. But suddenly he looked up. He caught his paddle and dipped it wildly in the swirling water. The canoe swung sideways. At first it held its own against the torrent. And then slowly, inch by inch, it began to creep upstream toward the shore. But suddenly there was a loud, cruel snap. The paddle had broken just above the blade! Waukewa gave a cry of despair. Then with shattered blade he fought desperately against the current. But it was useless. The racing waters swept him downward. The hungry falls roared in his ears.

Then the young hunter knelt calmly upright in the canoe. He faced the mist of the falls and folded his arms. His young face

was solemn. So far he had lived like a brave. Now he would die like one.

Faster and faster sped the canoe toward the great waterfalls. The black rocks glided away on either side like ghosts. The roar of the terrible waters became like thunder in the boy's ears. But still he looked calmly and sternly ahead. At last he began to chant the death-song. He had learned it from the older braves. In a few minutes all would be over. But he would come before the Great Spirit with a fearless song upon his lips.

Suddenly a shadow fell across the canoe. Waukewa lifted his eyes. He saw a great eagle flying over. It had dangling legs and a spread of wings that blotted out the sun. Once more the eyes of the young hunter and his old friend the eagle met. But now the eagle was master!

With a glad cry the boy stood up in his canoe. The eagle flew lower. Now the canoe tossed up on the huge wave that climbed to the falls' edge. And the boy lifted his hands and caught the legs of the eagle. The next moment he looked down into the awful waters. The canoe was snatched from beneath him. It plunged down the black wall of the falls. But he and the struggling eagle were floating outward and downward through the cloud of mist. The falls roared like a wild animal robbed of its food. The spray of the water blinded them. And the air rushed upward as they fell. But the eagle struggled on with its burden. It fought its way out of the mist. Its great wings beat the air with a whistling sound. Down, down, they sank, the boy and the eagle, but ever farther from the falls and the rushing water below.

At length the eagle dropped on a sandbar below the falls. The eagle and the boy lay there a minute, breathless and exhausted. Then the eagle slowly lifted itself. It took the air under its free wings and flew away. The boy knelt on the sand and with shining eyes watched the great bird until it faded into the gray of the cliffs.

Words and Their History

Have you ever asked yourself, "How did we get that word?" Words have entered the English language in many ways. The history of a word is called its *etymology.* The English word *etymology* came from a French word *etymologie.* The French word came from a Latin word *etymologia.* The Latin word came from a Greek word *etymon,* which meant "true sense of a word according to its origin."

An English word, such as *etymology,* has a long history. Its spelling may have changed as it has become a part of several old languages. But its meaning in English and its original meaning in Greek may be very much the same.

Here are some other English words that are similar in meaning to the words from which they are derived.

teach: from the Old English word *taecan,* meaning "to show"

learn: from the Old English word *leornian,* meaning "to acquire knowledge"

message: from the Latin word *missus,* meaning "to send"

The English words below and the words from which they are derived are similar in both meaning *and* spelling.

communication: from the Latin word *communicare,* meaning "to impart, to share"

laboratory: from the Latin word *laboratorium,* meaning "a workshop"

experiment: from the Latin word *experimentum,* meaning "a proof, a test"

salary: from the Latin word *salarium,* meaning "pay or allowance"

If you are curious about the etymologies of other words, look them up in a dictionary. The etymology of a word is briefly described after the pronunciation of the word or at the end of the entry. It will usually look something like this:

e•ro•sion (i rō´zhən) *n.* gradual wearing or washing away of the soil and rock of the earth's surface by glaciers, running water, waves, or wind: *Soil conservation is intended to curb erosion.* [French *érosion,* from Latin *ērōsiō,* a gnawing away.]

SOME WHO FLEW

Wilbur and Orville Wright were the first
people to make controlled flights in airplanes.
They gathered much of their knowledge about
flying from studying the flying of birds.
In a speech given on September 18, 1901, Wilbur
made the following comments about birds and flying.

"The person who only watches the flight of a bird gathers the impression that the bird has nothing to think of but the flapping of its wings. As a matter of fact, this is a very small part of its mental labor. To even mention all the things the bird must keep in mind in order to fly safely through the air would take much of the evening. . . . The bird has learned its art . . . so thoroughly that its skill is not apparent to our sight. We only learn to appreciate it when we try to imitate it.

"Now, there are two ways of learning how to ride a horse. One is to get on it and learn by actual practice. The other is to sit on a fence and watch the animal awhile and then return to the house and figure out the best way of overcoming its jumps and kicks. The second system is the safest. But the first, on the whole, turns out more good riders. It is very much the same in learning to ride a flying machine. If you are looking for perfect safety, you will do well to sit on a fence and watch the birds. But if you really wish to learn, you must get into a machine and get to know its tricks by actual trial."

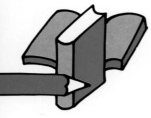

It's All in the Cards

Often, people who travel use a road map. The map helps them find the right roads to the place they are going. People in libraries use a card catalog. The card catalog helps them find the books they want to read or use.

A *card catalog* is a case of drawers filled with small cards. Each card gives information about a book in the library. The cards are arranged alphabetically. In the card catalog, there are three kinds of cards.

The *author card* shows the name of a book's author, last name first. The author's name is at the top of the card. Use this card if you know the name of an author whose book you want.

374.7	Kramer, Myron
K	The Blue and the Gray.

The *title card* shows the title of the book at the top of the card. If the first word in a title is *A, An,* or *The,* the title card will be filed alphabetically according to the second word in the title.

	The Blue and the Gray.
374.7	Kramer, Myron
K	The Blue and the Gray.

The *subject card* shows the general subject of the book at the top of the card. Use this card if you are looking for information on a subject and don't know the name of an author or a title.

	CIVIL WAR
374.7	Kramer, Myron
K	The Blue and the Gray.

Each card in the card catalog has a *call number* on the left side of the card. This number helps you locate the book on the library's shelves.

You should keep in mind that the card catalog at some libraries is a series of books instead of a case of drawers.

ACTIVITY A   Study the cards on the opposite page. Then read the questions below. Write the answer to each question on your paper.

1. What is the title of the book?
2. What is the call number of the book?
3. Who is the author of the book?
4. What is the general subject of the book?

ACTIVITY B   Decide whether you would use the author card, the title card, or the subject card to find the books listed below. Write the answers on your paper.

1. A book called *Land of Blue Waters*
2. A book by Robert Louis Stevenson
3. A book about the history of musical instruments
4. A book entitled *A Puzzle for Lucy*
5. A book about gardening
6. A book by P. L. Travers
7. A book called *The Lonesome Highway*
8. A book about racing cars
9. A book written by A. A. Milne
10. A book entitled *So Long, Gus!*
11. A book by Lewis Carroll
12. A book about meteorology

The Cheetah Remembers

VERA CHAPLINA

One day a cheetah was brought to the Moscow zoo. I was a section director there, and I had never seen a cheetah before. But I had read that they were graceful, handsome beasts that readily adapted themselves to people.

The crate in which the animal was brought was pulled up near a cage. When the door was opened, out stepped a spotted beast that looked very much like a leopard. A second look, however, and I saw thin legs and a body as graceful as a wolfhound's.

80

The cheetah came out slowly and went directly to the water trough. For a long time he lapped the water greedily. And then, without even touching the meat that had been put down for him, without sniffing around his new living quarters, he lay down in the furthermost corner of his cage. This seemed strange. Usually the first thing an animal does is to acquaint himself with his new surroundings.

I suspected that the cheetah was not well. And in the morning when the attendant came in, the animal was still lying in the same spot. His meat was untouched.

We called the veterinarian, who was an old, experienced man. It is no easy job to treat a wild beast. But he had cured quite a few of them.

The doctor watched the cheetah for a time and listened to his breathing. All the while the animal lay there, making no effort at all to get up. The vet came to the conclusion that the cheetah had caught a cold, which by now had probably turned into pneumonia.

It was important that the animal be given medicine at once. But this was difficult. The cheetah refused all food, and when the medicine was placed in his water, he stopped drinking. Day by day he grew weaker. His eyes looked sunken. And when he stood up, we could see his legs tremble.

During the night an electric heater was brought in to give him warmth. We watched him around the clock. He continued to refuse food. Finally the doctor declared that he must be made to eat, or else he would die.

Made to eat! Easier said than done. When meat was placed right in front of his nose, he would simply turn his head aside. Then an idea suddenly came to me. If I went into his cage, he might take the food from my hands. I suggested this to the vet. But he dismissed the idea with a wave of his hands.

"What's the matter with you? Why take such risks?" I tried to tell him that there would be no risk. The cheetah was so weak he could hardly stand up on his legs. And furthermore, one could see from his behavior that he was not a fierce animal. Besides, I had no intention of going into his cage without taking precautions. The vet did not agree, but I decided to go ahead anyway. After all, I was the head of the department. I could take whatever action I felt was right. But that didn't mean that I went ahead foolishly.

First of all I called the zoo from which the cheetah had come. I discovered that the animal would remain with us only for awhile. Then he would be sent on to a circus. This confirmed my feeling that the cheetah was tame.

When everyone had gone, I made my preparations for entering the cage. As a precautionary measure I pushed a hose in through the bars and placed it so that I could put my hands on it at any time if I should need it. Then I turned on a small stream of water. Now I was ready to enter the cage.

The cheetah turned his head in my direction but didn't try to get up. He didn't even raise himself when I came close.

Squatting down, I took a small piece of meat out of the bowl. With an even movement I put it right up to his mouth. He bared his teeth slightly and turned away. However, from the way in which he did it, I could tell he wasn't angry. He just wanted to be left alone. But that I couldn't do. Once again I offered him some meat, first mixed with egg, then egg alone, then meat dipped in milk. The cheetah refused all of this. He only licked my hand which had some drops of milk on it.

When I noticed this, I quickly dipped my hand in the milk and held it out to him. But he only sniffed at it and turned away. Then I realized that he was thirsty and wanted water, not milk. I put a very small piece of meat into some water. I held it

out, and he began to lick the water from my hand. And somehow, almost without noticing it, he swallowed the little bit of meat. I dipped another piece in water, and the cheetah ate that one, too. In this way, he swallowed several pieces. And then with a deep sigh he lowered his head to his paws and closed his eyes.

I carefully put my hand on his head. A tremor ran through his body. He opened his eyes slightly and then closed them again. That meant that he trusted me. For now it was enough.

Even though I felt very happy over this small victory, I walked out of the cage as calm as when I had entered. No animals, even if they are tame, like abrupt movements, particularly if they are made by a stranger.

As soon as I was out of the cage, I ran straight to the vet's office. I hoped to find him in, even though it was late. There he was, our dear, old Dr. O'Ache with his medicine case which was just as old as he was. How many hours of work and how many sleepless nights this man had spent at the zoo! Here it was almost midnight, and he was still at work. And he would stay, if necessary, until morning.

"He ate! He ate!" I called out as I ran into the office.

"Who ate? What did he eat?" the doctor asked. When he learned that I was talking about the cheetah, he jumped up from his chair and hurried along with me to the animal.

As we stood before the cage, I told him every detail of what had happened. Dr. O'Ache listened carefully without interrupting. He needed every bit of information in order to know how best to prescribe for his four-legged patient. When I had finished, he opened his bag. He took out some medicine in powdered form and handed it to me.

"Try to give him this no less than three times a day. No water beforehand. Do you know how to give it to him?"

Of course I did. First I had to remove some of the membrane from a piece of meat. Then I had to sprinkle the powder in it. This made a kind of capsule which was then placed in the meat and given to the animal.

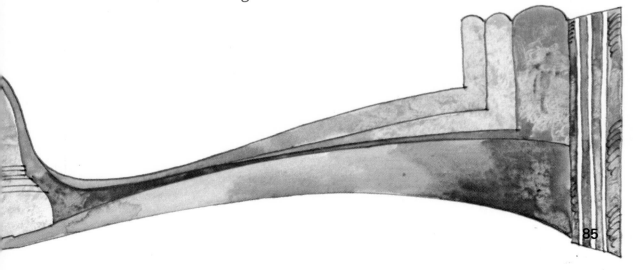

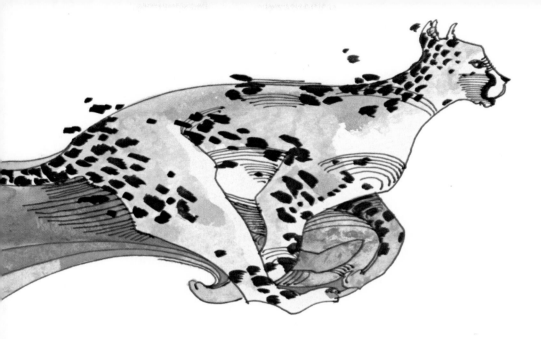

In the morning when I went to his cage, the cheetah accepted me as if we were old friends. He didn't jerk back when I put my hand on his head. Instead he took several pieces of meat—among them the one that had the medicine in it.

Now that he had started eating, his eyes started to shine again. And once when I arrived with his portion of meat, he even got up from his corner and came to meet me. I offered him some meat. He took it from my hand. He then reached out for more. Eating almost all that I had brought, he licked his lips. And purring loudly like a cat, he rubbed himself against my feet.

I stayed with him for a long time. Even after he lay down, I continued to sit next to him, stroking his thin and bony sides.

From then on I went into his cage without any fear. This friendly, warm animal soon became quite used to me. Whenever he saw me or heard my voice, he would run and press his head against the bars and watch to see if I were coming in.

The attendants had named him Lux, and he would respond when called. By this time Lux was much stronger. We decided to transfer him to another place. The doctor was particularly anxious to move him because every time the door opened, cold drafts of wind would blow in. The doctor was afraid that Lux would get sick again.

A room that had been occupied by parrots was now empty. It was not very large, but it was warm and bright. This was the room we chose for Lux. And I was assigned the job of caring for him. Here he stayed throughout the winter and spring. Summer came. And just when I was beginning to hope that Lux would remain with us, the circus people came to take him.

The director of the zoo, the doctor, and I all pleaded that Lux be allowed to stay on at the zoo. But our words fell on deaf ears.

It was hard to give up my pet. But I had no choice. I placed Lux in a cage. He seemed to sense that we were about to be separated. He pressed his head close against my hands, and he licked them for some time. Then he jumped away and nervously walked up and down.

Several men lifted the cage onto a truck. Long after they had gone out of sight, I stood there looking after them. It was hard to believe that Lux was gone. Somehow I had the feeling that we would meet again.

Four years passed. During that time I attended many circus performances—always with the thought that I might see Lux. Then one day I learned that some circus animals had been brought to the zoo in order to have films made of them. I went over at once.

Some of the beasts were still in the cages in which they had been moved. Others had already been placed in an unused building. A woman was standing near one of the cages.

"Are you interested in our animals?" she asked.

I told her that I worked at the zoo.

"We have a cheetah," she added, "but he is blind, the result of an illness. So we keep him apart from the others. Do you want to see him? He's in that building."

A cheetah! Could it be Lux? I went over as quickly as I could. There in one of the cages lay a cheetah eating some meat. Until then, I had always thought that I would have no trouble recognizing Lux. But here I stood, uncertain. Was it he? After four years his face had become a vague memory. As much as I stared at him, I could not be sure.

"Tell me," I asked the attendant. "Is he called Lux?"

"His name is Kai."

I was about to go away when I noticed that the cheetah had stopped eating and was straining to listen to us. He uttered a sharp, nervous meow. Then he lifted his head as if he were staring hard at something beyond me. I turned around. There was no one behind me.

"Why does he stare like that?" I asked.

"Who knows?"

"Lux, Lux," I called.

The cheetah jumped up and ran to the grill.

"Not Lux—Kai," corrected the attendant.

But I knew it was Lux. I opened the cage door.

"What are you doing! Be careful! He'll bite!" screamed the attendant.

I didn't listen. I had barely stepped into the cage when the cheetah was already pushing against me, seeking my hands. He found them, pressed his head against them and stood still.

The attendant was silent. I, too, said nothing. What was there to say?

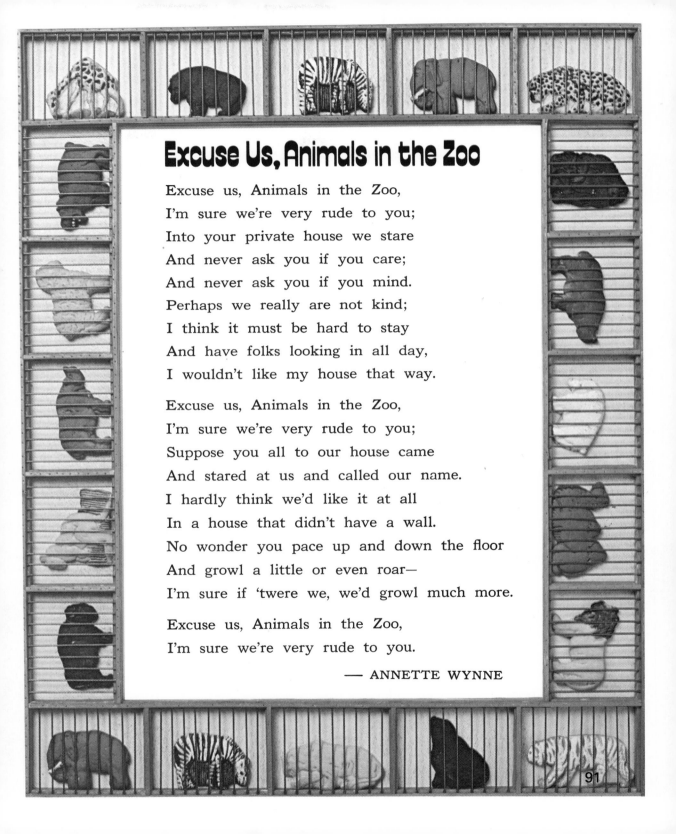

Excuse Us, Animals in the Zoo

Excuse us, Animals in the Zoo,
I'm sure we're very rude to you;
Into your private house we stare
And never ask you if you care;
And never ask you if you mind.
Perhaps we really are not kind;
I think it must be hard to stay
And have folks looking in all day,
I wouldn't like my house that way.

Excuse us, Animals in the Zoo,
I'm sure we're very rude to you;
Suppose you all to our house came
And stared at us and called our name.
I hardly think we'd like it at all
In a house that didn't have a wall.
No wonder you pace up and down the floor
And growl a little or even roar—
I'm sure if 'twere we, we'd growl much more.

Excuse us, Animals in the Zoo,
I'm sure we're very rude to you.

— ANNETTE WYNNE

The whole winter I kept to myself.
All the neighbors' boys of my own age
drifted away from me, and our friendships
were broken off. But when the cold began
to lose its hold and the darkness gave way
to light, my school books alone were no
longer enough to interest me. Now and
then I had to go to the park to see what
the others were doing. I didn't join them.
But I watched them from the side.

my childhood

TOIVO PEKKANEN

Later in the spring, when school was over, my restlessness became stronger. But I still could not associate with the other boys. Having gone my own secret ways the whole winter, I could not find the path back to the other boys.

One Sunday I asked Father for some money so that I could treat myself to something nice. But Father had no money at all. He looked at me for a moment thoughtfully. Then he got up from his rocking chair and went over to the chest of drawers in which he kept the little belongings that he valued. After looking through it, he found a piece of fishing line complete with float and hook.

"What about going fishing?" he asked. "I'll lend you my knife and you can make a rod. You'll probably find worms in the bog over there."

I was eager to go at once. I took the line and the knife, got a rusty old tin can from the cellar, and set off for the nearby bog. At the bog there were not only worms but also long, straight saplings of birch and willow. These made excellent rods. I picked out a young birch, cut off all the branches and the top, which was too thin, and took off the bark until the stem was smooth and clean. Onto this I fastened the line that Father had given me. And then I went to the dampest part of the dried-up bog to look for worms. When I had a dozen or two in my tin, I ran off down to the water's edge.

The people on this side of our island usually fished at the tip of the point. This was the same one where I had once gone swimming with Father when I was tiny. I rushed straight there with my rod and went right to the small rock from which the old people said they got the best catch. There were two men fishing when I arrived. They were sitting silently on the rocks by the water's edge. The day was warm and sunny. A few people could be seen splashing about in the water along the point. A warm, gentle breeze was blowing from the south, where the widest part of the Gulf of Finland could be seen between the islands and the far-off line where sea and sky met. The water was glistening in the bright sunlight. I stuck a

worm onto the hook, climbed on the nearest rock, and threw my line into the water.

I could not sit still like the old men. When I glanced at them, it seemed as if they didn't bother very much about their floats bobbing in the water. They either dozed or gazed at the horizon, the outline of the islands, or the sky. They let their rods rest. But I kept my eyes glued to my float. I had to stand up, to be ready every second to snatch my fish as soon as it took the bait. Excitement had seized me when Father gave me his knife and old fishing line, and now it grew stronger and stronger.

But on this day I learned the dying art of fishing. My excitement lasted perhaps a couple of hours, and the whole time I kept changing my rod from one spot to the next. All I caught was a couple of very small fish. Then all at once I felt tired. On top of a rock I sat down as quiet as the old men. I was sitting at exactly the same spot where I had once dipped my body in the sea for the first time. By now I was not thinking of anything. My mind was a blank, and my brain seemed to have stopped working and to be resting. Nevertheless I was aware of what was going on, though not in the same way as before. I knew that I was by the sea, under a bright, warm sky with the quiet water and the murmur of the breeze in my ears. And at

the same time I felt that I had stopped
being me. I was only a tiny speck of the
universe, like the rock on which I was
sitting, like the tree that was growing not
far away, like the fish swimming near my
feet. We specks might constantly change
and move about, grow and disappear. But
it would make no difference to the whole.

This mood of mine seemed to raise me
up, lift me away from myself and my small
needs, and make me part of eternity. All
my small actions, even my fishing, were
the same as the ripple of the water on the
shore. And I was filled with a peace that
nothing could threaten.

I have no idea how long I sat there—
perhaps an hour, perhaps two. The sun's
position in the sky moved slowly. The
shapes of the clouds kept changing behind
the nearby trees and bushes. And behind
me a shadow appeared.

Not until a faint chill came did my
float suddenly bob down out of sight. I
had been gazing into the distance. But I
saw the movement at once and began to
pull in my catch. My prisoner struggled
hard. I had to pull with all my strength
before I saw an unusually large perch rise
from the depths. I was so startled that I
didn't dare to take hold of the fish as the
old men did, but flung it onto the ground
between the rocks. There it was easy to
remove the hook and to thread the perch

onto the same forked twig where I had already put the smaller fish.

For a perch caught with an ordinary hook and line, this one was unusually big. It weighed about a pound. Even after I had stuck it on the twig, it fought desperately, flapping and twisting its body. I felt no pity for it, only the pride of a winner. I hurried back to my rock, put another worm on the hook, and threw the bait into the water.

But I caught no more fish that day. As evening drew on, other people came down to the water to fish. When they started throwing their lines into the water, the men who had been there for so long put their things together and went away. I was feeling hungry, so I went too. When I got home my big perch was the cause of delight. Everyone crowded round to admire the monster.

Early next morning, the minute I'd had my coffee and sandwiches, I set off fishing. First I went to the bog to look for worms, then down to the water. As on the day before, two old men were there, but only one of them was the same. The other I could not remember ever having seen. I sat down again on the rock from which I had caught the big perch. I threw my bait into the water and lowered the rod into my lap. And I gave myself up to the slow passing of time.

Outwardly this day was different from the day before, but inwardly it was the same. I caught no big fish, but the smaller ones were a little bigger than those of the day before, and there were more of them. Now and then I changed my place. But I continued to sit as silent as the old men and, like them, to gaze at the distant shapes of the earth and sky. I lived in a kind of timelessness in which the coming and going of people meant no more than the changing waves and clouds.

I had suddenly stepped into the middle of a completely new summer. I had become a different person from the one I had been before. Every morning I wandered down to the water with the rod on my shoulder, even when it was raining or clouds covered the sun. At home I spoke in the same way as before; when the weather grew still warmer and boys came down to swim, I would sometimes join them in the water. Nevertheless, I was not the same as I had been.

General and Specific Words

Compare the words in each of the pairs below. How are the two words in each pair alike? How are they different?

fruit — apple   picture — portrait
drinking — gulping   looking — staring

The first word in each pair is a *general word.* It names a group of items or describes an action. The second word in each pair is a *specific word.* For example, an apple is a particular kind of fruit, and gulping is a particular way of drinking. Authors often use specific words when they want to make their stories or essays interesting and accurate.

Look at the sets of words below. Can you find a specific word from the set on the right that goes with each of the general words on the left?

General Words		Specific Words	
vegetable	talking	typewriter	chatting
bird	machine	cabbage	wren

Read the paragraph below. Notice the underlined words. Then think of a specific word to use in place of each underlined general word. How do the specific words change the story? Do they make it more interesting and accurate?

Two people sat on the riverbank. They looked at their fishing poles. The poles did not move for a long time. Then suddenly, both poles moved at once. The people held their poles tightly and started to reel in their lines. They looked into the water, trying to see what they had hooked. They smiled when they saw two large fish.

MAWKOOM

HELEN CHETIN

This is a story about Mawkoom, a great chief, and how he tricked a man into being brave—almost as brave as Mawkoom, who was the bravest man of all the tribes.

In a land of thick woods, rolling hills, and green meadows live many tribes of people. The men are tall and black and handsome. They are swift and strong and proud of being good hunters and fighters.

While the men hunt for game, the women stay in the villages to care for the little ones, tend the gardens, and watch over the cooking fires. The women and girls are very beautiful. They put ribbons, combs, and bits of bright metal in their hair and dress in gay, hot colors.

The men like their families very much, but sometimes they grow tired of farming and fishing. Then they make long excursions into lands where other tribes live. When they come home, they have many tales to tell.

One day a stranger came to Mawkoom's tribe. His name was Bundar, and he carried three drums—a red, a

and BUNDAR

green, and a blue drum. Bundar was tall and good-looking and always ready with a story or a quick joke.

"Take food with us in the long house," Mawkoom said to Bundar. "Fish and track with us, and when we fight, carry one of our daggers and fight by our side."

Bundar smiled but said nothing. He wasn't a man to say what he thought of another man's ideas. What he liked best to do was spin long tales of brave deeds that made people drop what they were doing to come and listen.

People in the village soon learned that each of Bundar's drums meant a different thing. The sound of the deep red drum meant tales of war and danger. The sound of the blue drum meant love songs for young women and men. And the sound of the green drum—which could chirp like a bird, bark like a dog, and meow like a cat—announced to all the children that Bundar had a story or a song for them. It might be a fable about talking animals or a story of wicked witches, or it might be a simple song like this one:

Black is the sky of a jungle night,
Leopard spot and zebra stripe,
Black is the color of a storm at sea,
Eye of a friend, belly of a bee.

And you are beautiful, too, my son,
And you are beautiful, too!

Black is the color of the crow's wing,
Thundercloud and the song of wind,
Black is the sound of the big bass drum,
Sound of your heartbeat, thum, thum, thum.

And you are beautiful, too, my girl,
And you are beautiful, too!

One day when all the people of the tribe were fishing at the seashore, a band of bad men called Uckwars rushed into Mawkoom's village. They waved clubs, and hollered bad words. The frightened women and children ran into the woods and hid in the vines.

The Uckwars trampled the gardens, smashed the cooking pottery, and killed many pigs and chickens.

When Mawkoom and the men returned, they shook their fists in the air and shouted, "We will fight! We will fight the Uckwars!"

The men got their weapons—tall spears with red tassels waving from the top, daggers, and beautiful bronze and leather shields they carried before them when they went into battle.

They set off together. When they saw the Uckwars, they rushed at them with daggers and spears, and the battle started. How shocked Mawkoom was to see Bundar run into a thicket to hide!

The battle lasted all day, but when the sun set, the men stopped fighting. Each side returned to its own village. Mawkoom's men went to their long house, where they ate and talked of the day's events. No one mentioned Bundar. No one had seen him since he had run away.

Suddenly Bundar appeared at the door of the long house. He was carrying his drums. He was smiling as if nothing had happened. Mawkoom went to Bundar and led him to the front where he himself always sat.

"You are a brave man, Bundar," Mawkoom said in a loud voice as he thumped Bundar on the back. "You must have the best pieces of meat and a long drink from the jug. Come and sit beside me, brave Bundar."

The men were dumbstruck! Was Mawkoom crazy? They shook their heads and said nothing, but they all thought Bundar looked very foolish sitting beside the great Mawkoom.

The next day Mawkoom again led his braves into battle. For a while Bundar stayed by Mawkoom's side, but when the battle raged and the men fought hand to hand with fists and daggers, Bundar again ran away and hid.

That night Bundar came late to join the men at their meal in the long house. Mawkoom stepped up to Bundar and called loudly, "Sit and take food. Play the drums and tell us tales of big battles in the past."

The men remained silent, but they were not happy about the way Mawkoom was treating that cowardly Bundar, who got all the praise and took none of the risks. What was Mawkoom doing? Maybe it was a trick. They decided to wait and see.

They ate their food and passed the jug that was for brave men. Bundar took the jug, too. He looked foolish, but he took it and sipped from it. Mawkoom smiled and nodded. The men glanced at each other, but said nothing.

The next day Mawkoom again led the fighting with Bundar at his side. When Bundar saw how brave Mawkoom was, how handsome and shining black under the high, hot sun, Bundar, too, was filled with courage.

All that day Bundar stayed on the field with Mawkoom and other brave men. Daggers and spears clashed in the fighting. Mawkoom's men advanced steadily until the Uckwars threw down their arms and ran away. The battle was over! Mawkoom's braves were the winners!

That night when the men were all together in the long house, Mawkoom clapped his hands. He waited for silence and then announced:

"You have all seen that Bundar is a master of fighting. Tonight he will not sit with me. He will sit with you. He will sit beside the men who are better fighters than I— he will sit with the bravest men in all the land. Bundar is now as brave as they."

When the people heard this, they clapped. And they shook rattles made of elephant tusks and lions' teeth. They called for Bundar to pound the drums for chants and dances. The people were proud of Bundar, proud of their wise leader Mawkoom, and proud of the group to which they belonged!

Dreams

Now, I say to you today, my friends, even though we face the difficulties of today and tomorrow, I still have a dream. It is a dream deeply rooted in the American dream. I have a dream that one day this nation will rise up and live out the true meaning of its creed: "We hold these truths to be self-evident, that all men are created equal."

I have a dream that my four little children will one day live in a nation where they will not be judged by the color of their skin, but by the content of their character.

MARTIN LUTHER KING, JR.
August 28, 1963

And so, my fellow Americans: Ask not what your country can do for you—ask what you can do for your country.

My fellow citizens of the world: Ask not what America can do for you, but what together we can do for the freedom of man.

JOHN FITZGERALD KENNEDY
January 20, 1961

Can we, from now on—all of us—turn over a new leaf, and, instead of fighting with each other, can we all, united, fight poverty and disease and illiteracy?

Is it possible for us to put all our efforts and all our energy into one single purpose, the betterment and progress and development of all our lands and all our people?

GOLDA MEIR
March 1, 1957

I Dream a World

—Langston Hughes

I dream a world where man
No other will scorn,
Where love will bless the earth
And peace its paths adorn.
I dream a world where all
Will know sweet freedom's way,
Where greed no longer saps the soul
Nor avarice blights our day.
A world I dream where black or white,
Whatever race you be,
Will share the bounties of the earth
And every man is free,
Where wretchedness will hang its head,
And joy, like a pearl,
Attend the needs of all mankind.
Of such I dream—
Our world!

Hold Fast Your Dreams

Hold fast your dreams!
Within your heart
Keep one still, secret spot
Where dreams may go,
And sheltered so,
May thrive and grow—
Where doubt and fear are not.
Oh, keep a place apart
Within your heart,
For little dreams to go.

—LOUISE DRISCOLL

Who Says?

You have probably heard the expression, "There are two sides to every story." It means that two people may tell the same story from different points of view. Suppose two people make a mistake. Each might try to blame the other. The two descriptions of what happened will be very different.

When you read a story, it is important to know who is telling, or narrating, the events. Most stories are narrated in the *third person*. In a third-person narrative, the author acts as the storyteller. The author reports how all the characters speak, act, and feel. The author is an "outsider" who knows everything about everyone.

Some stories are narrated in the *first person*. In a first-person narrative, a character in the story describes the events. The storyteller is personally involved in the action. You hear the story only from that character's point of view. If another character told the story, you might form a different opinion of the people and events.

It is easy to tell if a story is narrated in the first person. The storyteller uses words like *I, me, my,* and *we*. "A Lesson in Reading" is narrated in the first person. The story is told by Nicodemus, a rat in the research laboratory. Nicodemus is personally involved in the action. Here is a passage from the story:

> I was sure there were plans for testing our reading ability. I could even guess, from the words we were being taught, what the tests were going to be like.

ACTIVITY A Read each passage. On your paper, write whether it is narrated in the first person or the third person.

1. The children and I ran along the shore. We found a bottle with a note inside. I couldn't believe my eyes. The note had been written thirty years ago.

2. The plane roared down the runway. Soon, it was well out of sight. The captain reported all was normal as she turned the plane east over the Atlantic Ocean.

3. The group began to argue as the storm grew. Some people wanted to continue the journey over the mountain. Others said they should return home.

4. It was evening, and I dressed in my best clothes. The President arrived on schedule. He shook my hand, and I almost fainted.

5. The tiger roared loudly. I wondered why it was so angry. "Maybe it isn't angry after all," I thought. "Perhaps it is just trying to speak to me."

6. Paul looked everywhere for his wallet. He couldn't find it anywhere. His friends joined the search for an hour. Paul was disappointed.

7. When the thunderstorm occurred, I was working out-side in the garden. The flowers were crushed by the rain. They needed two days to recover. I regained my dry condition by sitting by the stove.

ACTIVITY B Look back through "Awakening." Find each selection listed below. Decide if it was narrated in the first person or the third person. Write your answer on your paper.

1. "Mawkoom and Bundar"   2. "An Extra Brave"

3. "My Childhood"   4. "Nantucket"

5. "Waukewa's Eagle"   6. "A Debt to Dickens"

AWAKENING

Throughout your life, experiences will help you learn about yourself and your world. Your experiences will awaken you to new feelings and thoughts, to new opportunities, and to new accomplishments. Awakenings will expand your world.

Thinking About "Awakening"

1. In "Little by Little," what did Sarah see in Abe that made him different and somehow very special?
2. How did the characters in Dickens's books change Pearl Buck's feelings about herself and about other people?
3. In "An Extra Brave," how were Diana's feelings about Jed different from Joan's feelings about him?
4. Why would Chuck rather accept help from Paul than from Orwick?
5. In "The Cheetah Remembers" and "Waukewa's Eagle," you read about two unusual friendships between people and animals. What is similar about the way both friendships began and the way they both proved to be lasting?
6. What experiences in your life have helped you to understand something about yourself or someone else?
7. At the end of the story "A Lesson in Reading," the rats take their first step toward escape from the laboratory. Write an account of how learning to read helps them to escape.

JOURNEYS

At some time in our lives, we all take journeys. Some people take journeys to find new information about the geography of an area. Some journeys, such as a child's first trip to school, cover only a short distance. Other journeys, such as an astronaut's flight to the moon, carry one to a faraway place. Often, it takes courage to leave familiar surroundings and travel to a new place. But journeys can lead to discoveries of new friends, new places, and new ideas.

All the selections in "Journeys" tell about people who make discoveries. Three astronauts journey to the moon and back, gathering new information about space and about objects in space. A group of men cross the ocean on a raft to learn about something that happened hundreds of years ago. A girl lost in a windstorm makes an unexpected discovery.

As you read, think of the reasons for each journey. Ask yourself what other people have learned or might learn from these journeys.

Flying To The Moon

Michael Collins

July, 1969, was the month of one of the most historic journeys ever made. This trip was the Apollo II flight to the moon. The Apollo II spacecraft was boosted into space by a rocket. Three astronauts traveled to the moon in the spacecraft's command module. Then one astronaut remained in the command module while the other two landed on the moon in the lunar module.

Michael Collins was the astronaut who remained in the command module while Neil Armstrong and Edwin "Buzz" Aldrin landed on the moon. This selection is Collins's account of the first days of the Apollo II journey. The story begins on July 16, 1969, as the astronauts approach the launch pad at Cape Kennedy. It ends four days later, as the astronauts marvel at their first closeup look at the moon.

As we approached the rocket, I got my usual feeling of awe as I looked up at it. It was a monster— taller than a football field set on end, as tall as the largest redwood tree. Its sides were coated with ice where the moist Florida air touched the freezing-cold fuel tanks. This steaming ice somehow made the rocket seem alive.

Our elevator made its brief journey up past the rocket to our command module. I realized that our trip to the moon had, in a way, already begun; for we had left the actual surface of the Earth. Once inside the spacecraft, the three of us had some last-minute checks to make, and then it was time to go.

Now the voice on the radio was counting down to lift-off. At nine seconds before lift-off, the five engines of the rocket started up. When everything looked O.K., the clamps holding the rocket to the launch pad were released. We were on our way.

Right away the rocket engines began jerking back and forth. They were moving around to keep us in balance as we climbed. We felt this as little sideways jerks. What was happening to us was a little bit like what sometimes happens when you start off on a bicycle. You have to jerk the wheel back and forth to prevent tipping over. Once you pick up some speed, on a bicycle or in a

Michael Collins

Neil Armstrong

Edwin "Buzz" Aldrin

115

rocket, you can steer more smoothly. But the first few seconds were jerky and very noisy. I was glad when they were over.

As we climbed out over the Atlantic, I was glad to see that all my dials and instruments were normal. I could see that Neil and Buzz were pleased with what they saw. Buzz was checking with our computer, which showed we were on the right path. After two and a half minutes, the first stage of the rocket shut down and fell off into the sea. Then the rocket's second stage took over. It, too, finished its job after a few minutes and fell off. We were left with the engine of the third stage to see us safely into orbit. Finally, at

eleven minutes and forty-two seconds after lift-off, we began to orbit the Earth.

Clouds and sea glided silently by my window in the pure sunlight. We were upside down, our heads pointing toward the Earth and our feet toward the black sky. But since we were weightless, it didn't really matter which way we were pointed.

Exactly one hour after lift-off, we were over Australia. All our machinery seemed to be working perfectly. We had one more Earth orbit to make. Then we would be on our way to the moon.

We spent the time checking as much equipment as we could. On our second pass over Australia, we

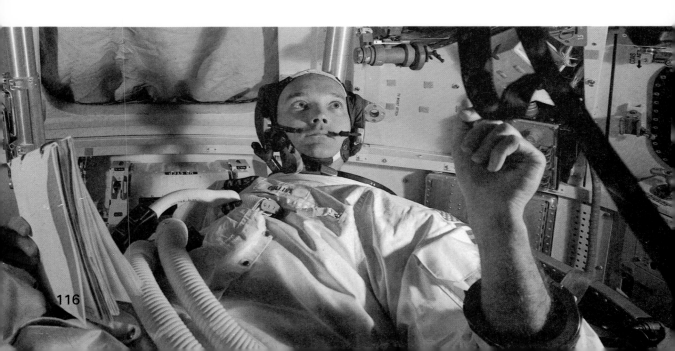

would start the rocket's third-stage engine for the second and last time. It would increase our speed from 18,000 to 25,000 miles (28,800 to 40,000 kilometers) per hour. We would be breaking the bonds of Earth's gravity.

The moment came. The engine's power pushed us back into our couches gently. For almost six minutes, we enjoyed this ride. Then the engine shut down. Our computer told us we were headed toward that empty point in the sky where the moon would appear in three days. I bet that many of the one million people who were at Cape Kennedy to watch our launch were still caught in the post-launch traffic jam.

We had several tasks to perform before our day was over. One task was to separate the command module from the lunar module, and then to reconnect them nose-to-nose. To do this, I had to fly the command module. My first chance to fly the command module felt good.

The next step was to throw the switch that separated the spacecraft from the rocket. The poor old rocket was finished now. It was an empty shell that would go into orbit around the sun.

Once our duties were finished, we could relax and watch the Earth and the moon slowly parade past our windows. By the end of our first

117

day in space, the Earth was so far off that it barely filled one small window. It was really bright, with the blue of the ocean and the white of the clouds most noticeable. We usually think of the moon as being quite bright, especially when it is full. But the moon is dull compared to Earth. The sunshine really bounces off the Earth, especially off the surface of the ocean. If your eyes and the sun are in just the right position, the ocean will sparkle and flash like a diamond held up to a bright light.

Our second day in space was a very quiet one. There was no feeling of speed. We seemed to be just hanging there as we went about our chores. Neil and Buzz were studying details in the lunar module while I checked the machinery inside the command module.

We had plenty of time to prowl around inside the command module. I found that weightlessness made it seem like a completely different place than it had been on the ground. Corners and tunnels were good places. You could wedge yourself in and did not need a lap belt to hold you in place. In weightlessness, you have to be wedged in or tied down. Otherwise your body will float around, banging into other people or equipment. At first, just floating around is great fun. But after a while it becomes

annoying, and you want to stay in one place.

Day number three was even quieter than day number two. But day number four had a very different feeling to it. We got our first look at the moon in nearly a day. The change in how it looked was spectacular! The moon I had known all my life was a small, flat, yellow disk in the sky. This had been replaced by the most awesome sphere I had ever seen. It was huge, completely filling our largest window. We could see its belly bulging out toward us. I felt that I could almost reach out and touch it. It was between us and the sun, putting us in its shadow. The sun created a halo around it. Its surface was lighted by earthshine, which was sunshine that had bounced off the surface of the Earth onto the surface of the moon. Earthshine cast a strange, bluish glow. In this blue light we could see large craters and the darker flat areas known as *maria,* or seas. It didn't look like a very friendly place, but Neil summed it up: "It's worth the price of the trip."

The climax of the trip is well-known. Neil Armstrong put the first human footprints on the surface of the moon on July 20, 1969. His words at that moment are often quoted: "That's one small step for a man, one giant leap for mankind."

In 1947, six men set out to cross the Pacific Ocean from Peru to Polynesia — 4,300 miles of open ocean — on a raft! This was the famous Kon-Tiki expedition, led by Thor Heyerdahl, a Norwegian archaeologist.

These men were attempting to prove that the people of Polynesia had originally come from Peru by crossing the ocean on a raft and that they had been led by a man called Kon-Tiki. Since no one would believe that it was possible to make such a voyage, these six decided to show that it was. They built a raft similar to the ancient Peruvian ones. They took no modern equipment except for a small radio. Nothing steered their craft besides the wind and current. And they succeeded in making the crossing!

Erik Hesselberg, the only licensed sailor on board, was the navigator of the raft, which was named Kon-Tiki. He was also an accomplished artist. He brought along a bottle of ink. He sketched a little every day on the raft in order to have a record for his friends and family.

Kon-Tiki and I is Erik Hesselberg's own story and drawings of this incredible voyage.

KON-TIKI AND I

Erik Hesselberg

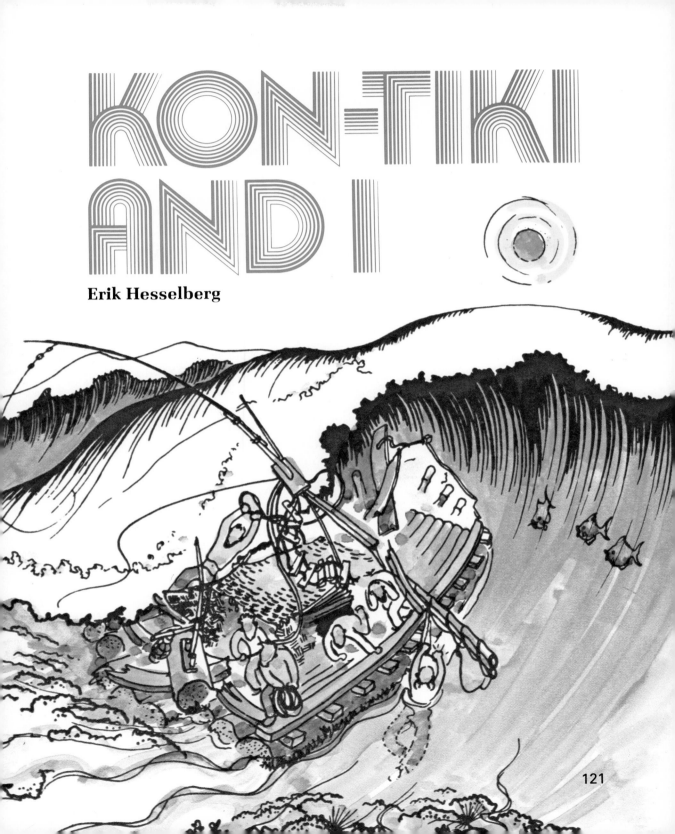

The Beginning

Fifteen-hundred years ago there were many people in Peru who knew of Kon-Tiki. According to Peruvian legend he was the leader of a people who worshiped the sun. In fact Kon-Tiki himself was thought to be the son of the sun. But the city near Lake Titicaca in which Kon-Tiki and his people lived was attacked by other Peruvians, and it was destroyed. Kon-Tiki and some followers managed to escape to the coast, where they embarked on balsa-wood rafts and disappeared across the Pacific—to go home to the sun, the legend says.

No one gave another thought to this lost race for 1,500 years. Then Thor Heyerdahl began to think about Kon-Tiki.

Thor had lived for a time on some small islands in the Pacific Ocean. While he was there, he heard talk about Tiki—one of the gods in Polynesian legend.

On some of the islands, Tiki was the most important god. It was said that he was the son of the sun and that he had led the people out into the Pacific Ocean.

At last Thor Heyerdahl became so interested in the Polynesians that he devoted himself wholly to the

KNUT   HERMAN   THOR

study of where they came from. He worked at it for many years and came to the conclusion that the Polynesians had originated in South America and that Kon-Tiki of Peru and Tiki in Polynesia were the same person.

To prove this idea, we went to Lima, Peru. We were to build a raft of balsa wood like the ones in old Spanish drawings and try to cross the sea as we believed Kon-Tiki had done. The Humboldt Current, the South Equatorial Current, and the Southeast Trade Wind would help us to cross just as they had helped Kon-Tiki.

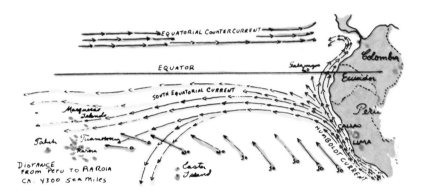

Shortly after I landed in Lima, the other members of the Kon-Tiki crew gathered. Pictured on the left are the six men who were going to take this voyage halfway across the Pacific on a raft:

Knut Haugland
Herman Watzinger
Thor Heyerdahl
Erik Hesselberg
Bengt Emmerick Danielsson
Torstein Raaby

Since I stand six feet four inches above sea level, I am easily recognizable.

After a few weeks, our raft was ready and we set out to sea.

JEG   BENGT   TORSTEIN

At Sea

One day the world's biggest fish came and sniffed at the Kon-Tiki. That was a sight we shall never forget.

If we had not seen the beast ourselves, we would not have believed my drawing.

Knut was sitting washing his pants when the monster slowly bore down on him. Then Knut gave such a loud and hideous roar that the rest of us rushed up to see what was the matter with him. Then we roared just as loud, shrieking and laughing at the same time, the creature was so unbelievably huge and strange. The tension was unbearable—would the monster start chewing at the balsa or not? We realized that the monster was really a whale shark, a very rare fish which can be 60 feet long and weigh 15 tons and has 3,000 teeth in its jaws. But this one was not quite so large. With a crowd of pilot fish ahead, he prowled around the raft, and he did this for so long that we got brave. When he lay under the steering oar to scratch his back

a bit, we thumped him in return, in a friendly way, to see how he took it. He liked it and came back to let himself be thumped three or four times. Then we gave him a bit of a jab with a harpoon, but we ought not to have done that, for he didn't like it and cleared off.

A day or two later we had a still bigger fright, for we came near to being capsized by whales, the giants of the sea. A large school of them bore straight down on our logs, blowing as they came. We lay there in the middle of the traffic and felt like a pushcart in New York City. And they didn't know anything about keeping to the right, either. Just as the blowhole of the first was on a level with our port mast, it dived under the raft with a gurgle, and the others did the same—luckily. We distinctly felt the backwash they made.

One remained lying under the raft for awhile and looked like a great black submerged rock.

It is curious to think that gigantic whales weighing up to 120 tons live on microscopic creatures. We caught these, too. They are called plankton and are found in great quantities in all the seas. With the help of a small, bag-shaped, finely-meshed net we could get more than three pounds of plankton per hour in some places.

The mass of plankton looked like porridge—sometimes violet porridge and sometimes red porridge. Now and then we could make out the shape of individual

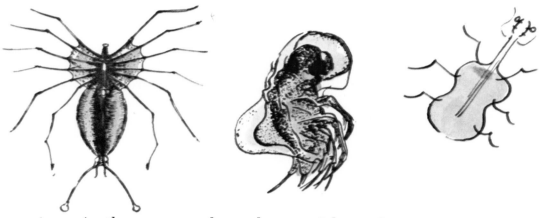

creatures in the mass, such as the two I have drawn here. One is a tiny little crab; the other is I don't know what—but it looked like an x-ray of itself.

Then there was one which looked like a guitar with legs.

We tried to eat the plankton. It tasted like a mixture of stewed crab and wet paper, I thought.

We examined and collected in glass jars everything of zoological interest that we found. In order to be able to look at submarine life without interference from sharks, we rigged up a diving basket of bamboo and ropes. We wore goggles and sat in this as long as our breath lasted. With the goggles we could see as well underwater as above.

We had now been at sea nearly two months and were more than halfway across. The wind was becoming more easterly. Each day carried us farther south, exactly as the current flowed.

All hands were in good shape; no one had even had as much as a fishbone caught in his throat.

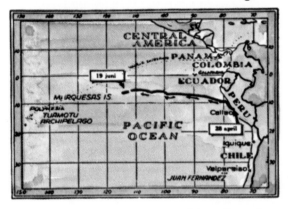

We never saw a ship, for there was no shipping in this area. We might have been on another globe, utterly remote from the world we knew.

Nor did we get bored with each other—on the contrary, we became like six brothers. If we felt an urge to be alone, we launched a small rubber boat which was attached by rope to the stern of the raft and floated in it until we wanted company again.

We had food enough—canned food and fish, coconuts, and groats. But some little black insects were living in the groats; they had been eating groats all the way from Peru. Steward Bengt separated them from the food, making two piles, and we took over for the insects.

We had brought drinking water from Peru in tins, and we collected rainwater. Now and then it rained so violently that the air was as wet as the water. Then things would grow moldy, and I got rheumatism in my right leg.

Otherwise the sun rose and set, and nothing changed except our position on the globe.

On June 28, the sea washed over the logs and carried away Lorita, the parrot. We could do nothing to save her. She must have been drowned at once, poor thing. It was terribly sad, for we were all so fond of her.

A little later the same thing almost happened to one of our crew. A breeze caught Torstein's sleeping bag and blew it overboard. Herman tried to catch the bag but made a false step, and he too tumbled into the sea. Since we were making good speed, the raft had passed before he could catch hold of it, and the steering oar was so covered with seaweed and so slippery that he did not get a grip on that either. The whole thing happened so quickly that none of us could help.

There he lay astern in the middle of the Pacific, thousands of miles from the nearest land. It was the worst thing that could have happened, for the raft could not turn back—that was absolutely impossible! We had to act quickly before the sharks came. And Knut was the quickest. He flung out a lifebelt with a line, jumped into the sea, and swam back to Herman with the lifebelt. He was just in time, for Herman was already exhausted and a shark's fin was approaching....

After this we realized that to fall overboard was the most dangerous thing that could happen—that the Kon-Tiki could face storms and great beasts, but she could not pick up a man who lay in her wake. Henceforward the man on watch was more carefully tethered to the vessel with a rope around his waist.

The weather was no longer as dependable. For a week the sail hung down slack, and the heat troubled us quite a bit. Then came a small black cloud which grew bigger and bigger—and soon we were racing ahead into a storm.

Suddenly a wall of rain burst upon us and pressed the sea flat. Only the Kon-Tiki stood up against it like an old sodden barn in a meadow. No sooner was the tap turned off than the wind rose.

So it went on for many days. I only remember that my rheumatism was very active and that Herman crawled out with the anemometer from time to time and measured the speed of the wind at forty-five miles an hour.

But the Polynesian islands were drawing steadily nearer. We were becoming anxious as to whether the Kon-Tiki would strike these small islands or simply float by them. But the current took us as we had calculated—straight down to the densest part of the Tuamotu group of islands.

First we saw a solitary bird, and I am sure we never looked at a bird with greater interest. Then for a long time nothing happened, and we were getting tired of arguing as to who had seen the bird first, when a whole flock appeared.

And then one morning, after ninety-three days, we saw the easternmost of the Coral Islands, Puka Puka.

A low island lay to port, there was no doubt of that, and our reckoning said it was Puka Puka, so there was no doubt either that we had reached Polynesia.

But the Kon-Tiki just tumbled on westward with the wind and current and did not seem to care if there were ever so many Puka Pukas in the neighborhood. She could not be maneuvered to the island, and Puka Puka disappeared astern of us. But three days later we sighted another little coral island, which was called Angatau.

We came so close to the island that we saw every coconut ashore and got ready for stranding. But when there was only another fifty yards to go, the current carried us past the westernmost point and out to sea.

But on the morning of August 7, 101 days from Peru, the lookout shouted, "Land ahead!" A look at the chart convinced us that it was Raroia, one of the larger islands. Soon we saw palms all along the horizon to the west, and we moved swiftly inshore toward them. Well, there was nothing else to do but to make ready for a landing in the midst of the breakers and coral reefs.

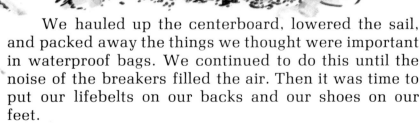

We hauled up the centerboard, lowered the sail, and packed away the things we thought were important in waterproof bags. We continued to do this until the noise of the breakers filled the air. Then it was time to put our lifebelts on our backs and our shoes on our feet.

The only chance we had was to be able to cling to the logs as long as our strength lasted and to hope that the Kon-Tiki would be flung upon the reef.

So we stood by.

It was a frightening sight, those breakers and reefs, and we were almost afraid we wouldn't make it. Before we had time to think any more about it, a wave came and heaved us right into the witch's cauldron. The raft gave a bump and a crack or two. Then we were drawn out again, as if to take off for the next jump. A green wall of water, as clear as glass, with foam on the top, rose behind us and the next minute rushed down and buried the Kon-Tiki and all on board. Finally the mast snapped, the cabin collapsed, and there was a smashing and twisting and crashing. But we were all alive, squeezed under the bamboos or clinging tight to ropes. Several seas of the same kind came until what was left of the raft was halfway up the reef.

Then one by one we jumped down onto the red corals and ran in across the reef to safety. And after us came the raft, like a good-natured horse, with Thor and Torstein on its back. I can tell you that we were pleased with our raft. It had brought us to Polynesia with our lives and most of our equipment safe.

That Kon-Tiki could have come to Polynesia in the same way was quite certain.

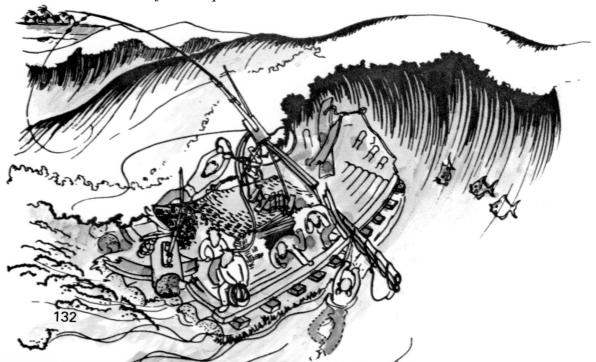

WHERE LIES THE LAND?

Arthur Hugh Clough

Where lies the land to which the ship would go?
Far, far ahead, is all her sailors know.
And where the land she travels from? Away,
Far, far behind, is all that they can say.

On sunny noons upon the deck's smooth face,
Linked arm and arm, how pleasant here to pace;
Or, o'er the stern reclining, watch below
The foaming wake far-widening as we go.

On stormy nights when wild north-westers rave,
How proud a thing to fight with wind and wave!
The dripping sailor on the reeling mast
Exults to bear, and scorns to wish it past.

Where lies the land to which the ship would go?
Far, far ahead, is all her sailors know.
And where the land she sails from? Away,
Far, far behind, is all that they can say.

133

The Easter Island Mystery

Carrol Alice Stout

Easter Island is a volcanic island in the Pacific Ocean. In 1955, Thor Heyerdahl (the same Thor Heyerdahl who led the Kon-Tiki expedition) led an expedition to Easter Island to investigate a 200-year-old mystery: How did the huge stone statues found on the island get there?

When Easter Island was first discovered in 1722, there were many stone statues standing on platforms of stone. Some of the statues weighed as much as twenty-five tons. But by the time Heyerdahl's expedition got there, the statues were no longer standing. Instead they lay on the ground.

For months the scientists and helpers in Heyerdahl's expedition examined the statues and looked for clues to the past. Wood from a statue platform was dated by the carbon-14 method. The test showed that the platform had been built sometime between 900 and 1,300 years ago.

Almost 300 years before now, according to legends and to clues Heyerdahl's men found, a war took place on the island. One of the two groups of people who lived on the island was wiped out except for one man. This group was known as the *long ears* because of their custom of lengthening their ear lobes by making holes in them and putting in weights.

When Heyerdahl arrived, he made friends with the island's mayor, Pedro Atan. Atan said that he was descended from the only long ear to survive the war. Heyerdahl asked Atan if he knew how the statues were carved.

"Yes," he said. "I will carve you a statue. My relatives and I. Only a real long ear can carve a statue."

The next day Atan and five of his relatives took a few expedition members to the quarry atop the crater of a dead volcano. There, hundreds of partly finished statues had remained for centuries, since an unknown day when the stonecutters had laid down their stone picks and never returned.

The long ears began collecting some of the hundreds of stone picks scattered over the quarry. The picks looked like flat front teeth of some giant animal. The mayor's men went right to work. They spread out their picks along the base of the rocky wall. Each man set a gourd of water near him. The mayor, still wearing his fern-leaf crown, measured the rock face using his outstretched arms and outspread fingers as a ruler. With a pick he marked the stone.

The mayor gave a signal, and the men lined up in front of the wall and suddenly began singing. They began hitting the wall in rhythm with the song. Slowly the marks grew deeper under the men's picks. Without breaking the rhythm, a worker would grab his gourd and splash water on

the rock to soften it and to keep rock splinters from flying into his eyes.

*A*fter they had worked three days, you could see the outlines of the statue. Whenever one of the men threw aside a dull pick, the mayor grabbed it and struck it against another pick on the ground to sharpen it again.

At the end of the third day the stonecutters stopped. They were wood-carvers and not trained to carve stone for long periods of time. Atan said that it probably would have taken twelve months, with two teams working all day, to finish a statue. An archaeologist with the expedition agreed. But Atan had shown how a huge statue could be carved from hard stone, using only tools the islanders had used centuries ago.

Heyerdahl asked the mayor if he also knew how the statues were lifted to the platforms. "Of course," said Atan.

To raise a statue, Atan needed twelve men, three poles, and a huge pile of pebbles and boulders. To begin, three men put the ends of their poles under the statue and pushed down on the other ends, using the poles as levers to lift the statue. The figure did not stir. They kept prying. Finally a tiny space could be seen between the ground and the statue. The mayor, lying on his stomach beside the statue, quickly shoved tiny pebbles under it. Steadily the process

went on. Lift, push stones under the statue, rest, and lift again. Now everyone except the lifters was gathering rocks. Larger and larger ones were needed as the huge figure gradually rose.

When men could no longer reach the ends of the poles, they tied ropes to the poles and pulled on the ropes. Other men had to climb up the stone pile to place new stones beneath the statue. One false move and the statue and the stones would topple.

The mayor passed ropes around the stone head and fastened them to stakes driven into the ground, to hold the statue on the platform. After eighteen days of work, the statue was finally eased into an upright position.

Heyerdahl then asked the mayor whether he knew how they were moved from Rano Raraku crater, where they were carved, to different places around the island. The mayor told him that possibly a kind of sled made out of a forked tree trunk had been used. He knew sleds were used to move heavy stones into position on top of the platforms. He knew how to make one, but he did not have enough relatives to move a statue, and other Easter Islanders were not interested in helping.

At the camp two large oxen were killed and barbecued. Everyone on the island was invited. After the people had enjoyed the food and fun of a good picnic, it was not difficult

to get nearly 200 of them to help move the statue.

They put the sled in place under a twelve-foot statue that had been left long ago on a road. Carefully they lashed the statue to the sled with strong ropes and pulled the giant over the ground.

In this way, scientists got an idea of how the giant statues may have been carved, carried across the island, and raised to their platforms. Why they were made is another question. Present-day islanders believe that the statues represented ancestors of the people who made them and that those people thought the statues had supernatural powers.

The statues are not the only remains found on the island. There are many elevated tombs and hundreds of stone towers that must have marked land boundaries. There are caves lined with stones fitted together, rocks with pictures carved into their sides, and the remains of stone houses and farmyards. There are also wooden tablets carved with a writing like no other writing known today.

By studying the remains left by these people, scientists may learn more about how they lived, worked, played, and worshiped. But unless someone finds the "key" to the writing on the tablets and learns to read their messages, the mystery of Easter Island may remain at least partly unsolved.

READ or READ

Words that are spelled the same but have different pronunciations
and different meanings are *homographs*.
See how many you can find in the story below.

THE LOST SHEPHERD GIRL

Oren Arnold

Young Dazbah, a Navaho Indian girl, could never have guessed that an exciting adventure awaited her on this new day in July. Dawn had given no hint of what the weather might do. It was cool and clear, with spears of sunlight streaking at her from the rim of a distant cliff, striking the door of her family's hogan. All Navaho hogan homes faced east—a part of the tribal religion—and Dazbah called the sun her Morning Friend. She had slept on sheepskins, woolly and soft, on the hogan's dirt floor. But now she was up and dressed in her crimson blouse and purple velvet skirt with its two petticoats.

Soon Dazbah turned her eyes to the left. Her sheep were 200 yards away, sounding their gentle bleating calls to her because they were eager to start for their feeding grounds.

"You must take them farther away each day," her father had reminded her only last week, "because they have thinned out the grass close to home."

At thirteen, Dazbah was the family shepherd, as most Navaho children around that age were likely to be. For sheep raising is a main industry with these proud folk. Dazbah had eaten a hearty breakfast of mutton that had been boiled until it was delicious and tender; thin sheetbread, with crisp and flaky bubbles, that had been baked on a flat rock near the fire; and fresh peaches.

Nearby her mother was sitting cross-legged on the ground in front of the outdoor loom, weaving a rug. Father also sat on the ground, with a sheepskin under him. Before him was a small anvil on which there were little hand tools with which he was making a silver bracelet. Dazbah smiled at her parents, glanced at her little brothers and sisters who were playing with a pet goat, then half-ran and half-skipped toward the waiting sheep.

She had understood her father about the grass. She had tended the family's sheep since she was nine. Now she herded 140 of them, assisted by her wise dog, Chee, who was already waiting for her, sitting on his haunches. He trotted over to her for his morning petting, then walked at her side, showing his affection for the girl.

Except for the sheep, Dazbah and Chee would be alone all day out in the vast wilderness of New Mexico. Yet she would know no real loneliness. For she loved the great dome of the turquoise sky, the high red-rock mountains, the sweeps of semidesert sands with their tints of vermillion, yellow, gray, and brown, the bright green junipers, and piñon trees from which came delicious, sweet nuts, brown and crackly like coffee beans. It was a beautiful wild region, and this was her life, her world. Probably nothing unusual would happen today, but Dazbah didn't mind, for she had a song in her heart.

With Chee gently driving the sheep, Dazbah followed the herd over a distant rise in the ground, then down a long slope, across a mile-wide flatland, around a series of boulders, then two or three more miles to a grassy area. She wasn't sure exactly how far from home she was, but it didn't matter, since the Navahos were at home anywhere and were never afraid of nature. With the sheep now eagerly grazing, Dazbah sat down to rest. Chee would stand guard.

She may have dozed a little at times. She found shade beside a rock cliff and enjoyed its soothing coolness. At noon, she ate cold food that had been prepared by her mother, and which she carried in a little leather bag. She had no water; she was trained to go all day —longer if need be—without it. She would drink when she drove the sheep back to their water hole at sundown.

After eating, Dazbah rested contentedly on the sand. She knew that probably no other human being was within several miles of her, yet she was happy. She still had no hint that anything unusual might happen. Nor did she consider it unusual when an afternoon storm blew up.

Storms often come snorting across the New Mexican plain. This one was heralded by great black tumbling clouds, then a crackling of lightning. The clouds grew blacker, looming like gigantic ghosts. Urgent bleatings told her that the sheep were frightened, but Chee was doing what he could to keep them assembled. He barked at them now and then, nipping at their legs.

Dazbah ran over to help Chee, and together they moved the sheep against a rock wall where they huddled closely, like a mass of gray-tan wool.

By now the wind was blowing. It blew harder and harder until finally it roared in gusts and swirls, blowing pebbles and sand about. Before Dazbah quite realized it, visibility had been so reduced that she could barely see ahead. She heard her flock of sheep start to run in a stampede, then Chee's frantic barking. She leaped to her feet to help him, but found that she couldn't. She had to feel her way with her toes, run a few yards during a lull in the storm, then wait and feel and run again.

No rain fell, but the sand was blasting Dazbah's face, arms, hands, and legs. It fell into her soft deerskin boots, and her feet began to hurt. The sandstorm was much worse than rain, even worse than hail, for not even the cliffs gave her any protection.

The bleatings of the sheep soon faded, and Dazbah could no longer see them, between the gusts of wind and sand. All she could hear now was the whine and moan of the storm. But she kept on running when she could, squinting and keeping her head ducked low. There was no sign of her sheep or dog anymore. Minutes passed and she hurried on, not knowing where she was going. But she had to keep trying to find her sheep, for they were her responsibility.

Finally the driving sand was so painful that Dazbah crouched on a rocky slope near a cliff, pulled her skirt over her head for protection, and waited. An hour or more passed before the wind began to quiet down. When Dazbah dared to look out, all she could see was an eerie world of dust and dryness. The slope on which she had crouched had been swept clean by the wind. But when she looked down, her eyes caught a glow of golden rocks and pebbles!

She stooped and picked up a few of them. They were strange—oddly shaped, yet beautiful. They seemed like bits of the sun itself, Dazbah thought. And they seemed to hold a light of their own. They had a rich, yellowish sheen and a metallic loveliness. The rocky slope seemed to be covered with them, as if they had been strewn there by the storms. Dazbah bent low, sitting on her heels, to examine them more closely. No, they had not been strewn there, for the streaks of yellow were in the bigger rocks there, too. There were slabs of gold as big as her hand, some the size and shape of her fingers and many bits the size of birds' eggs or peas.

"Such beautiful stones!" she murmured. "Perhaps they aren't stones. Perhaps they are yellow silver or something. Father works with silver. He might like to make jewelry of these pretty stones."

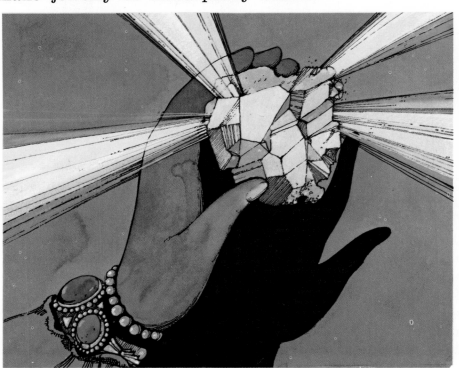

Dazbah was more curious than excited. She cupped up the front of her skirt and gathered the pretty pieces in it. She put more of them in the bag that had held her lunch and was now empty, humming happily as she worked. But she moved quickly. For she knew that she must hurry on and find her lost sheep and her good dog, Chee.

By walking in a wide circle, she hoped to find her animals. But she could not see them anywhere. Any trail they might have left had been erased by the driving sand. Moreover, the wind had begun to blow and snatch at her again, this time from the opposite direction it had first held. It was blowing gustily now, and she had to crouch again, head low in her arms to protect her face and eyes.

Another hour passed, during which Dazbah had tried several times to start walking again. But usually she was only able to go a hundred yards or so before she slipped and fell in the windstorm. She lost many of her golden nuggets but did not mind. Her leather bag was still full of them, and the slope she had left was almost solid gold, it seemed:

Twilight had begun to fall when Dazbah finally located Chee and the sheep. It was long after dark by the time she got them first to the water hole, then to their sleeping ground near the family hogan.

The storm had died now. Indeed, the world seemed as though no such thing as a storm had ever struck it. Dazbah's anxious parents welcomed her, although they had not been unduly worried. They knew that she could take care of herself during a storm.

She held out what remained of the yellow pebbles and rocks to her father. "Perhaps you can make me a yellow bracelet with some of them," she suggested, smiling up at him.

Her father grew excited as he studied the golden nuggets. "These are very valuable. Where did you get them?" he asked.

Dazbah pointed to the direction from which she had come and told of her adventure.

"Is there more?"

"Oh, yes, much more. A place wider than our hogan is covered with it. You say they are worth something? They are good stones to have, Father?"

"They are worth very much," her father answered. "Now I have things to do."

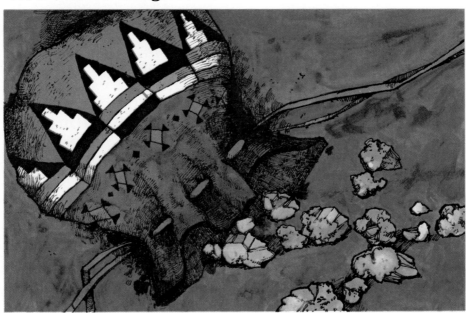

The next morning, he saddled a horse, took Dazbah's leather bag of nuggets, and rode away. After three days, he returned with two men. He asked Dazbah to show them where she had found the nuggets.

She was quiet for a long moment, thinking and trying to remember directions and distances. Finally she pointed vaguely and said, "That way."

But—exactly where? The wind had roared, the world had darkened, the stinging sand had blinded her as she walked, ran, and stumbled along. She had hunted in wide circles for her sheep, walking miles and trying bravely to do her duty in spite of the storm. But exactly where had she crouched in that vast wilderness of slopes and hills, crags and cliffs, valleys and plains? Had the freakish storm, reversing itself, brought sand back and deposited it again on that slope, covering the treasury of gold? Storms in New Mexico often did just such strange things. This was truly a wilderness—miles and miles of nothing but boulders, sparse vegetation, and sand.

The three men searched together for days. Soon other people came and searched, too. As the weeks passed, then months and years, hundreds of people hunted for the golden slope that had been found—then lost—by Dazbah, the little shepherd girl.

One day, six years after Dazbah's adventure, a rancher traveling across that same barren region also got caught in a sandstorm, and he, too, found the outcropping of gold. He brought back about $4,000 worth in his saddlebag, and said there were millions of dollars more in gold there. Only . . . the sand had also blinded him, so that he had wandered aimlessly on his horse. And just as Dazbah had done, he became lost—confused as to direction and distance—and was never able to find the golden treasure again. There had been no special rock formation that he could use as a landmark. There was just a limitless world, a wild and windy world, in which the whimsical gods of summer might uncover, then recover, that golden ore at any hour.

Thus it remains today. Dazbah grew into adulthood, married, became a mother, then a grandmother, and now is gone. But her heirs still seek the golden bonanza. So do people who have heard of the wandering rancher. No doubt New Mexicans will search for the Lost Shepherd Girl treasure for years to come.

FOLLOWING THE WESTERN ★ STAR ★

Laurence Swinburne

Americans have moved westward ever since they first reached America. The western star always seemed to gleam a little brighter, and the early pioneers wanted to see what lay under it. Farmers wanted new land, and others saw a future in cattle-raising. Many were just explorers at heart. And Daniel Boone crashed through the Wilderness Trail because he wanted "elbow room."

A good portion of the territory beyond the Mississippi was owned by the French, and President Jefferson had been trying to buy a small part of it. Finally France agreed to sell all of its mid-America-holdings—almost a million square miles—for only $16,000,000! The United States bought the land, and the territory became known as the Louisiana Purchase.

The first Americans to travel to this new land to make a living were called *mountain men.* In the early years of the nineteenth century, men's hats were made of beaver fur. Good money could be made by a skilled beaver trapper. So the mountain men went off in small groups, usually on swift ponies, but sometimes on foot, and now and then on mule-back.

Together, they blazed trails through the western wilderness. Once a year, the trappers met in one place to trade their furs with eastern agents for cash. It was more like a big party, though, than a business meeting.

The West has seen many robust, hardy people, but none of them were stronger or tougher than the mountain men. There was Jim Beckwourth, born a slave. He lived with the Crow Indians and became a war chief. He also found a way through the mountains to California, which is still called Beckwourth Pass.

There was Mike Fink, who ran boats, then became a trapper. Songs were written about him that are still sung today. There was Pegleg Smith, whose leg became so infected he had to cut it off himself. He stamped on

mountain trails with a wooden leg for many years after. There was Jim Bridger, who claimed he could outtalk, outshoot, and outride anyone in the West— and he could, too. There was Kit Carson. And many more.

Yet their time was not long. In the 1830s, due to one of the quirks of fashion, beaver hats disappeared from stores; then men wore silk hats. And the mountain men were out of jobs.

But as always seemed to happen in the West, something else came along to change bad luck into good. On January 24, 1848, James Marshall, who was building a sawmill on the American River in California, noticed a shining stone in the water. He picked it up...and began the California Gold Rush!

Gold! The news flashed around the world. Gold almost for the asking. Gold to be picked up in the rivers with hardly any work. Anyone could easily make $500 a day or more.

Well, these reports weren't quite true. But there was gold in California and plenty of it. By 1849 people were pouring into the state. Ships came into San Francisco Bay and anchored—and nearly 700 ships were left there to rot. Their passengers, crews, and captains dashed off for the American River and the gold fields. At the beginning of 1848, there were 20,000 people in California. By the end of 1849, there were 100,000!

Nearly half the newcomers came by sea. They sailed around South America. Mountaineers who knew how to handle horses and cattle came overland. They started at Independence, Missouri, where all western trails began. Usually they traveled by wagon train in the famous Conestoga wagons.

These vehicles had been invented many years before, in the Conestoga Valley of Pennsylvania, by German immigrants. They were the kind of wagon you see in western films today. The front wheels were smaller than the rear wheels. This made it easier to go up hills. The wagons were slightly higher in the front and back than in the center. This kept the loads from shifting around too much. The wagons were covered with canvas. From a distance, they looked almost like small ships. That's why they were nicknamed prairie schooners.

The average wagon train had thirty to thirty-five Conestogas. The wagon train started no later than seven o'clock each morning and traveled an average of fourteen miles each day. A car today travels this distance in fifteen or twenty minutes. Little wonder that it took five months to reach California from Independence. The wagon trains had to start for the West in the spring. Otherwise they would get caught in the early blizzards that came to the mountains.

When the trip began, the traveling was not difficult. In fact, it was almost fun, and everyone was happy and excited to be going to a new land. But after a few weeks, it wasn't much fun. There were rivers to cross. Oxen and horses became footsore. In dry areas, drinking water was often hard to find. Disease spread quickly through the trains, and many people died.

But these problems were just the beginning. After the wagon trains had passed through the Rocky Mountains, they entered the Humboldt Valley area. There was water there, all right—salt water. It was not fit for people or their animals to drink. Those animals who drank it died. Then furniture and other household items had to be thrown out of the wagons to make it easier for the remaining beasts to haul them. Some wagons had to be given up.

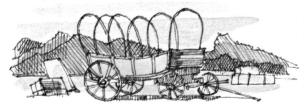

Once past this horrible region, the pioneers had to battle their way up the steep Sierra Nevadas. If they had not been delayed too much, they could probably get through these peaks before the snow fell. If not, they would be trapped in severe blizzards.

The Gold Rush did not last for too many years. A few people made their fortunes, but many did not. Most of the people who had come to California fell in love with the golden land, and they stayed.

Not all who went West were hungry for gold. Many wanted land to farm. They, too, started from Independence, but some went by a southern route (the Santa Fe Trail) to Santa Fe, and from there to the Los Angeles area by the Old Spanish Trail. Others struggled to the Northwest by the Oregon Trail.

The Old West has disappeared. Highways mark the old trails. All the pioneers are gone—the Forty-Niners, the mountain men, the wagon trains. But the remembrance is still there in the ruins of ghost towns, the white-topped mountains and wide plains, the forest lands. It is the memory of a time when human destiny lay to the West.

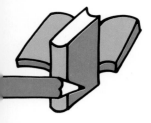

Place to Place

Maps give many different kinds of useful information. They may show the location of a place, the distance between places, and the position of a place in terms of compass directions.

Maps have several guides that help you use them easily:

1. The *scale* is a bar, or line, that represents distances. Each part of the bar stands for a certain number of miles or kilometers.

2. The *key* tells you what the colors and symbols on the map represent.

3. The *location symbols* are letters and numbers used to find a particular place on the map.

4. The compass *directions*—North, South, East, West— are usually shown by a compass symbol and the letters *N, S, E,* and *W.*

The map on the next page shows the route of Thor Heyerdahl's *Kon-Tiki* expedition. It also shows countries, states, and island groups that are bordered by the Pacific Ocean.

Find Easter Island. By using the scale and a ruler, you can see that Easter Island is about 2500 miles or 4000 kilometers from the coast of South America. The color blue on the key tells you that Easter Island is surrounded by water, the Pacific Ocean. The location symbols, or coordinates D3, will help you locate Easter Island. The direction symbol shows you that Easter Island is west of the South American coast.

Use the map of the Tiki expedition to answer the questions. Write the answers on your paper.

1. How many miles is it from Callao to Puka Puka? What is the distance in kilometers?

2. What are the location symbols, or coordinates, for Puka Puka? For Callao?

3. What symbol is used to show the direction of a current?

4. What symbol shows the route of the *Kon-Tiki*?

5. In what two directions does the Humboldt Current mainly flow?

6. Is Puka Puka located to the north, south, east, or west of Callao?

7. Did the *Kon-Tiki* travel the shortest route from Callao to Puka Puka? Why do you think it took the route it did?

The Route of the Kon-Tiki Expedition

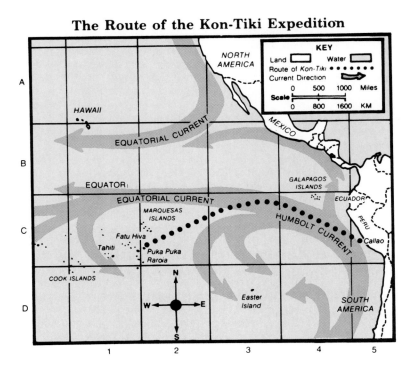

159

EZRA MEEKER:
Marker of the Oregon Trail

Dorothy Heiderstadt

When Ezra Meeker was nine years old, his family moved from Ohio to Indiana. Ezra and his eleven-year-old brother, Oliver, walked the 200 miles of the journey. Later Ezra's grandfather in Ohio offered to give the family $1,000 to buy a farm. Having no other way of getting the money, the family went back for it, bringing it—all in silver coins—to Indiana in their wagon.

Ezra and Oliver wondered what would happen if outlaws tried to rob them. They resolved to fight to the death for the box of money. Luckily they were not called upon to do so. The plainly dressed family—father, mother, and children—and the shabby covered wagon did not tempt any roving outlaws.

Ezra helped his father with the farm work. He loved working outdoors, loved the smell of newly plowed earth, the care of the farm animals, the sight of the green crops pushing up through the soil. But when the wind blew hard and the clouds scurried across the sky, he grew restless. Every day travelers went by in their wagons, westward bound. More and more the young farm boy longed to be one of them.

When Ezra was twenty years old, he married and decided to go west to Iowa. In October, 1851, he and his wife, Eliza Jane, and their small baby started westward in a covered wagon. They settled in Iowa, but after a winter there, they decided not to remain where the weather could get so cold. When spring came, they

left for the Oregon country. Their wagon was drawn by two oxen, animals well-suited for such a trip. Oxen could later be used on the farms; as work animals, they were much stronger than horses.

A friend, William Buck, went with the Meekers. He was twenty-seven years old and quite an experienced traveler. He told them what food to take and how to pack it: dried beef, dried pumpkins, fruit, and eggs packed in flour. Milk in cans could be churned into butter and buttermilk by the jolting of the wagons. Three cows traveled with the party to provide the milk. Ezra's older brother Oliver joined the party, along with some friends. There were now five wagons in the caravan.

As Ezra and his family and friends journeyed westward, they met wagonloads of travelers returning to the East. These travelers had given up and were going home.

Yet many continued to travel west. Once, when the Meeker party had to stop for a few days to look after Oliver, who had fallen ill, Ezra counted 1,600 wagons passing.

In Idaho, the wagon train divided. Some turned southwestward along the California Trail. Ezra's party went on toward Oregon. There were no boats to carry them across the Snake River. Those who wanted to go had to fill up all the cracks in the wagons with old clothes and tar. Then they floated the wagons across, driving the oxen and cattle ahead.

When Ezra and his party reached the Columbia River, the worst part of their journey was over. They went down the river in boats. They were 2,000 miles from home; many wept from homesickness, knowing that probably they would never go back. Still, they had come to the West hoping to make a better life for themselves and their children. Ezra looked a long time before he found a farm that suited him. He built a good house and established friendly relations with the neighboring American Indians. When enough other settlers came, a schoolhouse of logs was built, and the children went to school.

Ezra liked to write. He had kept a journal of his trip to Oregon. With this journal as a basis, he wrote a book, *Ox-Team Days on the Oregon Trail.* This was popular for many years. He was much interested in history and, as the years passed, he learned all he could about the country where he had settled.

In 1906, fifty-four years after he traveled to Oregon, Ezra decided to follow the old Oregon Trail back East. He felt that a trail which had meant so much to the United States should be marked in some way. He traveled in a covered wagon drawn by an ox team, and his destination was Washington, D.C. Along the way, he stopped frequently to paint inscriptions on landmarks. Whenever he came to a good-sized town,

he urged the people to place a marker on the Oregon Trail. Many markers were put up, but Ezra felt that there should be many more.

"The whole Oregon Trail should be plainly marked from beginning to end," he told everyone.

Traveling eastward by covered wagon, the little old gentleman with the snowy hair and beard attracted a lot of attention. Many people had never seen a covered wagon or an ox team before. Ezra left the Oregon Trail behind and drove straight across the country to New York City. There his covered wagon and oxen caused so many people to stop and stare that a big traffic jam was created.

When Ezra reached Washington, D. C., President Theodore Roosevelt promised to urge Congress to vote money for the project.

Mission accomplished, Ezra shipped his oxen home to Oregon and went home himself on the train. He traveled over the trail again, by automobile and by plane, to keep the public interested in the famous route. He was ninety-four years old when he flew 1,300 miles over the trail in a plane.

"Now, Mr. Meeker," said the young pilot anxiously, "you let me know when you feel tired, and we'll land so you can rest."

"Now, Mr. Pilot, you let me know when you're tired, and we'll rest," Ezra returned with spirit. "*I* don't tire easily!" He was proud of his good health and energy. He liked to boast that he had never spent a day in bed in all his long life.

Ezra died in 1928 at the age of ninety-eight. Two years before his death, he founded the Oregon Trail Memorial Association, which placed more markers along the old trail. All the way from Independence, Missouri, to Seaside, Oregon, the markers run, commemorating the great westward migration.

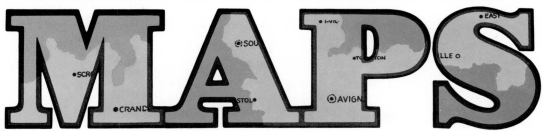

MAPS

High adventure
    And bright dream—
Maps are mightier
    Than they seem:

Ships that follow
    Leaning stars—
Red and gold of
    Strange bazaars—

Ice floes hid
    Beyond all knowing—
Planes that ride where
    Winds are blowing!

Train maps, maps of
    Wind and weather,
Road maps—taken
    Altogether

Maps are really
    Magic wands
For home-staying
    Vagabonds!

—Dorothy Brown Thompson

Sybil Ludington

Patricia Edwards Clyne

This story is historical fiction. It takes place in 1777 when the colonies of America were fighting for their independence from England. Sybil Ludington was a real person, and this story is based on a true event.

"Will Papa stay home this time?"

Sybil Ludington smiled as she tucked the covers around the boy. Each of her seven brothers and sisters had asked the same question at least twice since Colonel Ludington had come home from war.

"He'll be here for a while," Sybil told her youngest brother. "The troops have been given only enough time to do their spring planting."

"Then Papa will have to go back again?"

"Yes, the war is far from over," she replied with a sigh. "Now, close those eyes. I must get back downstairs, for I hear a horse coming into the mill yard."

The boy listened for a moment, then said, "Maybe it's General Washington!"

"Not likely," Sybil laughed. "He's probably gone home to Virginia to do his spring planting, too. Now, no more of your delaying tactics, young man. *Good night!*"

Her brother grinned in good-natured defeat. "Night, Syb," he called, for she was already on her way downstairs.

Before she reached the large kitchen, Sybil could hear the drumlike sound of a heavy fist on the front door.

"Colonel Ludington! Colonel Ludington!" a voice cried out urgently. "The British are raiding Danbury!"

Sybil raced into the room just as the exhausted messenger was being led to a chair by the fire.

"Why, Danbury's less than thirty miles to the east!" she exclaimed. But neither of the two men even noticed her presence.

Her grim-faced father was listening intently as the messenger related that Danbury, Connecticut, had been left virtually unprotected. When the American troops were dismissed to take care of the spring planting, only 150 soldiers had remained behind to guard the storehouses of the Continental Army. This small force could do little to stem the onrushing tide of the enemy. Even now, General William Tryon's 2,000 troops were looting and burning the town.

"We must immediately recall our troops from their farms!" Colonel Ludington declared. "Everyone must be

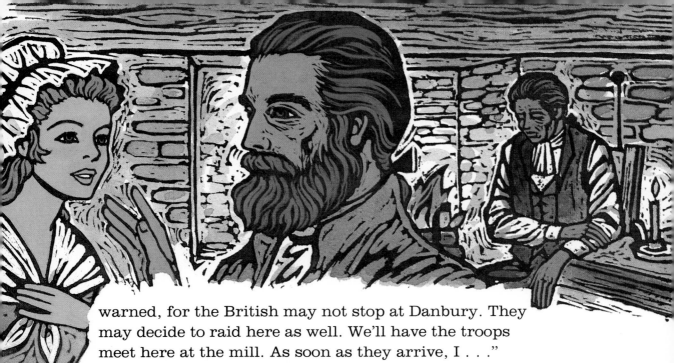

warned, for the British may not stop at Danbury. They may decide to raid here as well. We'll have the troops meet here at the mill. As soon as they arrive, I . . ."

Sybil's father stopped suddenly when he realized the spent condition of the man before him. With a worried frown, he went on, "But who will go to summon them? You're too exhausted to ride farther, and I must stay here to muster the troops as they arrive. There is no one else who . . ."

"I can!" Sybil's voice rang out. "I will sound the alarm."

"A sixteen-year-old girl?" Colonel Ludington almost gasped, then began shaking his head negatively. "The night is dark and the roads are unsafe. Tories and brigands infest every byway."

"I know all the farms. I can do it!" Sybil insisted.

"But daughter, it would be many miles — many dark and dangerous miles. I cannot permit . . ."

"Father," Sybil broke in, "the people must be warned — and there simply is no one else to do it."

Before Colonel Ludington could answer, Sybil had rushed outside to the shed where the horses were kept.

Within minutes, she had slipped a bridle over her favorite horse's head. After firmly cinching the saddle, she leaped on its back.

Colonel Ludington was standing outside as she rode up. There was worry—but also a touch of pride—in his voice when he told his daughter, "Remember, the troops are to muster here at the mill. Tell those who remain to gather their valuables and be ready to move out at a moment's notice should Tryon get this far."

Sybil nodded as she prodded her mount with the small stick she carried. The horse's hoofs sounded like

thunder on the frost-hardened ground. Soon the lights of the Ludington house were swallowed up by the dark trees that arched the road behind her.

Even though it was late April, the night was chilly and Sybil was shivering by the time she reached the first farmhouse. Without dismounting, she called, "The British are burning Danbury! Muster at Colonel Ludington's mill! Prepare for a British raid!"

The startled farmer who appeared at the door did not seem to comprehend, so Sybil shouted her message again, then galloped off.

She traveled south toward Carmel, crying out her warning at each farm. Then she went on to Lake Mahopac. There were no lights burning in the homes now, for the hour was late. Without these small and welcoming beacons, Sybil felt her courage faltering, and she fought back fear as she rode on.

All too well she remembered the stories of the notorious "cowboys" who roamed the area. Though they professed to be helping the British, the cowboys were really only lawless murderers who plundered outlying districts for their own selfish gain.

For one swift moment, Sybil felt like turning back. But the reality of the British at Danbury was much more frightening than the possibility of meeting any cowboys, so she rode on.

The coldness of the April night had numbed her hands and feet by the time she reached Tompkins Corners, and the horse's breath was rasping. She knew it would be impossible to reach each and every home in the area, but the ones she did notify could warn the others.

Farmer's Mills was a few minutes behind her when she felt her horse falter. The horse was tiring now, she

realized, and well it might, for they had already covered nearly thirty miles.

"Only a little while longer," she consoled the laboring animal, as well as herself.

Over and over her cry was heard, so that by the time Sybil left Pecksville on her way home, her voice was no more than a hoarse croak. But she had done it. She had warned her neighbors of the British threat!

The Ludington mill yard was full of troops when Sybil guided the weary horse through the front gate. In the flurry of preparing for the march to Danbury, there was little more than a hurried "Well done, Sybil." But in quieter days, when the British had finally been driven from the land, the story of Sybil Ludington's heroic ride would be repeated with pride, and she would be remembered forever afterward.

Going the Distance

Sybil Ludington was not the first person in history to carry important news over a great distance. In ancient times, the Greeks won a very important battle at a place called Marathon. News of their victory was carried from the battlefield to Athens by a long-distance runner. Today, one of the events of the Olympic Games is called the *marathon.*

The **marathon** is a race of 26 miles, 385 yards (42.2 kilometers). At the Olympic Games, it is a part of the track and field competition. Track events consist of races over many different distances. Field events involve jumping and throwing. Here are the English names of some other track and field events that are derived from other languages:

The **discus throw** is a field event. It is a contest to see how far a person can throw a round plate made of metal and wood. The word *discus* comes from the Greek word *diskos,* which means "plate."

The **javelin throw** is also a field event. A javelin is a long, thin spear. Athletes compete to see who can throw the javelin the farthest distance. The word *javelin* comes from an old French word *javeline,* which describes a kind of dart.

The **decathlon** is a track and field competition which tests an athlete's ability in ten different events. There are four track events and six field events. Each athlete competes in all ten events. The contest takes two days, and the contestants win points for their performances in each event. The athlete with the most points wins the contest. The word *decathlon* comes from two Greek words: *deka,* which means "ten," and *athlon,* which means "contest."

The Big Idea

Newspaper vendors want to interest passersby in the articles contained in the newspapers they sell. They often tempt buyers by announcing the headline of the main article. For example, they might shout, "Extra! Extra! Read all about it! Flood breaks dam!" The last sentence gives the topic of the article.

The *topic* of an article sums up the entire article. An article has several paragraphs, and each paragraph may have a main idea. A *topic sentence* will summarize the main idea of several paragraphs or the main idea of the entire article.

A topic, or theme, may not be stated specifically in an article. To find a topic, first read the entire article carefully. Find all the important ideas. Pay particular attention to the ideas in the first and last paragraphs of the article. Then use your own words to write a sentence that sums up all the important ideas.

The selection "Following the Western Star" has many paragraphs. These paragraphs contain many important ideas. Some paragraphs describe the *mountain men* who trapped furs in the Old West. Other paragraphs tell about the pioneers who sought gold in California. Still another paragraph mentions those who went west to find land for farming.

Here is one way you could state the topic, or theme, of the entire article: *Mountain men in search of furs, pioneers in search of gold, and farmers in search of land all traveled to the Old West to make a living.*

Read each selection. On your paper, write the
main idea of each paragraph. Then write the topic,
or theme, of the entire selection.

1.   More than four hundred years ago, Spanish
explorers brought horses to America. Many of the
horses ran off and banded together in wild, free
herds. These horses were called *mustangs*. They
grazed on the grass in the American West.

When the pioneers began to settle in the West,
many things changed. Their cattle needed grass, so
the settlers killed many of the mustangs.

Today, some people worry that the wild mustangs
will become extinct. They have asked lawmakers to
protect these horses. When and if the laws are passed,
mustangs may once again roam freely in protected
areas of the United States.

2.   The Pony Express was a special mail service
that began in 1860. Mail was delivered between
Missouri and California by riders on horseback.
Before that time, mail had traveled by boat. Then, it
had taken much longer for mail to be delivered.

Each Pony Express delivery was well planned.
The riders changed horses every 25 miles (40 kilometers). New riders took over after 75 miles (120
kilometers).

The Pony Express was a thriving business. It
involved 80 riders and 400 horses. Mail delivery
cost $1.00 per half ounce. The riders earned from
$100 to $150 a month. Eventually, telegraph lines
were stretched across the United States, and the
Pony Express was put out of business.

The Finish Line and Beyond

Jesse Owens,
with Paul G. Neimark

On September 12, 1913, Jesse Owens was born in a small Alabama town. As a child, Owens was frail and weak, but he was determined to become a runner. He worked hard and did become a track star in high school.

Later, he went to Ohio State University, where he also became a track star. But just before he was to compete in the National Collegiate Track and Field Championships, Owens injured his back. After much persuasion, his coach agreed to let him participate anyway.

I lined up for the one-hundred-yard dash with the other runners—the finest athletes from every corner of the country. As I hunkered down and fitted my spiked shoes into the ground so as to get a good start, a sharp pain ran down my back. But I didn't give it any thought. I was only thinking of the race that would start in a second.

"Runners, take your marks," the starter said.

We all fidgeted nervously.

"Get set," said the starter.

I felt my body lifting slowly into the air as it had hundreds and hundreds of times before. All my weight was on the tips of my fingers now. My feet were waiting to push me out as hard as they could. Out of the corner of my eye, I saw the starter point his gun up toward the sky. Then he pulled the trigger. The sound shot through the stadium like a crash of thunder.

But even before that sound had died away, we were all up and out, our feet dance-pounding over the cinders. I was in

front—far out in front—and moving more into the lead with each stride.

That race seemed to be over as soon as it began. I didn't notice my back at all. I didn't think about it either when Larry Snyder, our coach, came up to me and said I'd run the hundred yards as fast as any person in the world had ever run it before: nine and four-tenths (9.4) seconds.

Everybody crowded around me. I didn't know what to say. I'd never dreamed of tying the world record when I'd been flat on my back the day before. "I guess I need a backache more often, Coach," I called over to Larry Snyder.

He laughed and took me aside. Then he asked me whether I wanted to try the broad jump, too. "You bet I do!" I told him. "I've got a good feeling about this day."

I didn't notice the pain any more as I placed a towel twenty-six feet, two inches from the board off which I was to jump. Twenty-six feet, two inches was the length of the world record

jump. I wanted something at that spot so I could see exactly what distance I had to cover.

I'd never jumped that far before, of course, but I hoped to come close. I'd learned that having something "impossible" to shoot for is what brings out your best.

Now I stood very still at the end of the long runway leading to the broad-jump pit. I was ready to take my first jump.

I waited for the wind to die down. It was at my back, but too much of a breeze behind a jumper would disqualify him or her. The wind continued blowing for a few seconds and then suddenly died away to a faint whisper.

I began to run slowly, then faster, gaining speed with each step. My legs were moving at top speed now. I came closer and closer to the takeoff board. At the last moment, I shortened my stride as Larry had taught me and hit the board with a pounding right foot. I felt my body rise in the air. I scissors-kicked at the peak of the jump, flying fifteen, then twenty, then twenty-five feet through the air—straining closer and closer to the towel.

Then I landed—past it!

Could I have equaled the world record? Maybe the wind had blown the towel. Maybe I had made a mistake and put it at the wrong place.

I waited while the officials measured. Then they measured again. Then they measured one more time. Finally, they made their announcement.

They said I hadn't tied the world record. I had *broken* it—by more than half a foot! I didn't know it then, but almost a quarter of a century would pass before anyone would jump farther than my twenty-six feet, eight and one-quarter inches.

I'd never had so many people crowding around me at once. I tried to answer their questions as best I could. But the biggest question was: Would I try for one more record?

You bet I was going to try for it. Fifteen minutes later, I lined up for the two-hundred-and-twenty-yard dash. Once again, I fitted my spiked shoes into the holes I made in the ground. Once again, the starter told us to take our marks and to get set. Just like before, we all poised in midair as the official raised the gun toward the sky for that eternity that was not even a couple of seconds.

Bam!

I streaked out of the blocks just as before. For the first thirty or forty yards, the race seemed like the hundred-yard dash. I'd gotten off to a good start and was an entire stride ahead of the next two runners.

But this time, one thing was different. It wasn't only my aching back. Now I just didn't have the fresh energy that I'd had in the shorter sprint or in the broad jump. As we passed the midpoint of the race, I started to lose my lead. Bobby Greaves, one of the country's finest sprinters, was closing the gap. Then, Bobby was almost even with me!

I knew it was now or never. I had to reach inside myself and find some final reserve of energy.

I strained. Greaves was still gaining.

I strained again. He pulled exactly even with me.

I strained one more time—and then another—and another. Now Bobby started falling back, farther and farther. I was moving out to a one-yard lead. I was pulling away!

Suddenly I felt the finish line against my chest. The race was over.

"Twenty and three-tenths seconds!" shouted one official, holding up his stopwatch.

Another official also held up his watch. "Twenty point three (20.3)," he agreed.

What a day! I had broken the world record in the two-hundred-and-twenty-yard dash, too.

But Jesse Owens was not finished yet. Before the day was over, he had broken still another world record—in the low hurdles. The following year, he raced his way to victory in the 1936 Olympic Games, winning four gold medals in the track and field events.

"BECAUSE IT IS THERE"

Once someone asked George Leigh Mallory, a famous British mountaineer who later lost his life on Mount Everest, "Why do you want to climb this mountain?"

Mallory answered: "Because it is there."

We can understand how he felt. He wanted to test himself, to pit his strength against the mountain's difficulties, to conquer it by standing on its highest peak. But this feeling is something modern. In earlier days, nobody thought of climbing mountains. Mountains were feared. They were a sort of unclaimed land between the earth and sky. The Greeks said the gods lived on Mount Olympus, but they didn't climb up to see.

Until approximately 200 years ago, nobody climbed mountains at all. A few people had risked their lives in the Alps to hunt chamois or to collect crystals to sell. But they didn't climb high. And the idea of standing on top of snowy Mount Everest, giant of the Himalayas, never crossed anybody's mind.

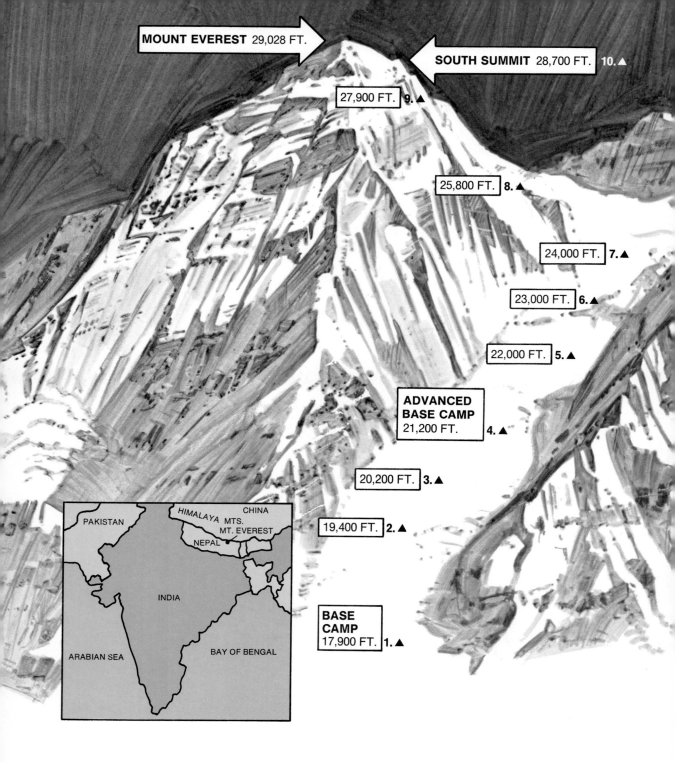

MOUNT EVEREST 29,028 FT.

SOUTH SUMMIT 28,700 FT. 10. ▲

27,900 FT. 9. ▲

25,800 FT. 8. ▲

24,000 FT. 7. ▲

23,000 FT. 6. ▲

22,000 FT. 5. ▲

ADVANCED
BASE CAMP
21,200 FT. 4. ▲

20,200 FT. 3. ▲

19,400 FT. 2. ▲

BASE
CAMP
17,900 FT. 1. ▲

PAKISTAN

HIMALAYA MTS.

CHINA

MT. EVEREST

NEPAL

INDIA

ARABIAN SEA

BAY OF BENGAL

184

FIRST UP EVEREST

Showell Styles

The small yellow tent clung to a ledge on a mountain ridge five miles high. Inside it lay two brave men. One was Edmund Hillary, a New Zealander. The other man was Tenzing Norkay, a Sherpa tribesman from Nepal. Soon these two would try to reach the summit of Mount Everest. If they succeeded, they would be the first to climb the highest mountain in the world.

People had been looking for a way to climb Everest for many years. Seven times, teams had tried and failed. Thirteen men had died trying to reach the top of Everest. Now, on the shadowy glacier 8,000 feet below the little tent, Colonel John Hunt and his men waited in their advanced base camp. Hunt was the leader of the team. All their hopes were with the two men who were making the eighth try.

It had taken Hillary and Tenzing two hours to carve a ledge for their tent out of the ice and rock 27,900 feet above sea level. The ledge was on Everest's southeast ridge and 1,100 feet below the summit. The two men had climbed many days to reach this point. Before that a team of 200 men had worked for eleven weeks to get within striking distance of the top. Hillary and Tenzing had been chosen to make the final, dangerous climb to reach the summit.

At four o'clock in the morning, Edmund Hillary unfastened the flap of the tent and looked out. The camp was still dark, but hundreds of icy peaks rising from the black valleys of Nepal glowed with the red of dawn. Their tent stood higher than all those peaks. Already they were the highest people in the world.

Hillary remembered that today was May 29, 1953. Was this to be their lucky day? Would he and Tenzing be the first to climb up Everest?

The air was so thin that they could speak only in gasps. In the night the temperature had been forty-eight degrees Fahrenheit below freezing. They had spent the dark hours bracing the tent against the fierce gusts of wind that could hurl them to their death on the glacier 8,000 feet below. Now, at dawn, the terrible wind had gone. They had a chance—a small chance—of climbing to the top and coming down alive. Hillary fastened the tent flap again, and they began to get ready for the climb.

These two were not ordinary men. At this height, in this cold, most men would have died before now. Hillary and Tenzing had trained themselves for the climb by living for weeks at a height of more than 12,000 feet.

Both men were skilled mountain climbers. Edmund Hillary was a tall, lean man, thirty-three years old. He took time off from his trade of beekeeping to climb in the New Zealand Alps and the Himalayas. Little Sherpa Tenzing was six years older. Only a year ago he had climbed as high as they were now before the mountain had beaten him. He was the toughest of a very tough race. Both men had courage and climbing skill. Both were determined that together they would be the first up Everest.

Hillary and Tenzing felt sick at the very thought of breakfast, but they made themselves eat sardines. They knew they must eat to build up energy for the many hours of climbing ahead of them. Drink was even more necessary, because

the thin, dry air quickly drained the moisture from
their bodies. They drank as much sweetened
lemon juice as they could.

Hillary's boots had frozen as hard as iron, so
he held them over the portable stove to thaw. At
6:30 A.M. the men put on their gear and crawled
out of the tent onto the dangerous slope of snow.

They looked like visitors from another planet.
They wore bulky suits padded with down, and
windproof suits over these. Hoods and snow
goggles covered the upper parts of their faces.
Oxygen masks hid nose and mouth. Only by
breathing oxygen all the time could they hope to
scale the last 1,100 feet. Each man carried on
his back a light metal frame like a small
toboggan. It held oxygen tanks and the valves to
control the rate of flow. Their lives depended on
the flow of oxygen as much as on the flow of
blood in their bodies—and they had been able to
carry up enough oxygen for only six or seven
hours' climbing.

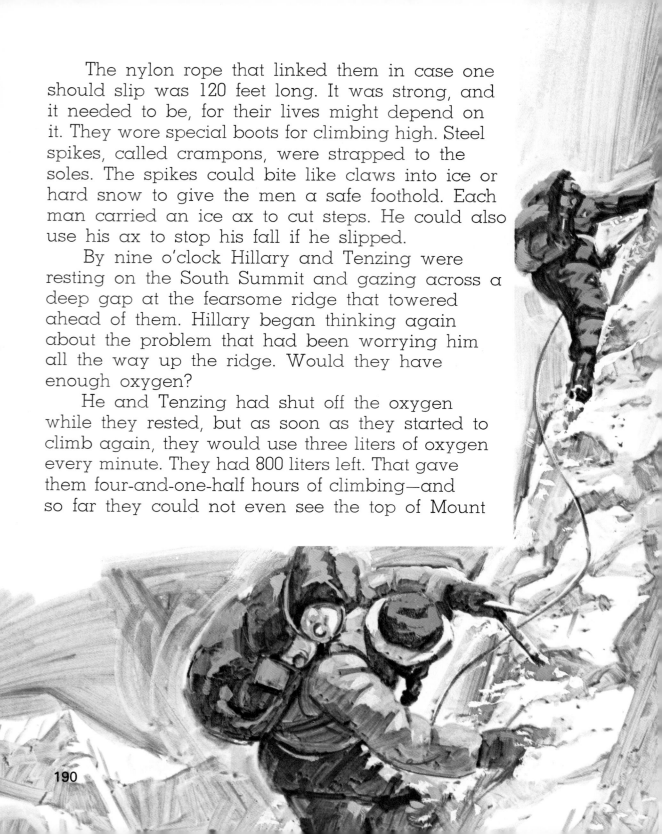

The nylon rope that linked them in case one should slip was 120 feet long. It was strong, and it needed to be, for their lives might depend on it. They wore special boots for climbing high. Steel spikes, called crampons, were strapped to the soles. The spikes could bite like claws into ice or hard snow to give the men a safe foothold. Each man carried an ice ax to cut steps. He could also use his ax to stop his fall if he slipped.

By nine o'clock Hillary and Tenzing were resting on the South Summit and gazing across a deep gap at the fearsome ridge that towered ahead of them. Hillary began thinking again about the problem that had been worrying him all the way up the ridge. Would they have enough oxygen?

He and Tenzing had shut off the oxygen while they rested, but as soon as they started to climb again, they would use three liters of oxygen every minute. They had 800 liters left. That gave them four-and-one-half hours of climbing—and so far they could not even see the top of Mount

Everest. Hillary had no idea how long the rest of the climb would take them. He figured that, if they could reach the top in two-and-one-half hours, they would have just enough oxygen to get back. He nodded to Tenzing, turned on the oxygen, and got to his feet.

Half past eleven. That was the oxygen time limit. If they had not reached the top then, they *must* turn back.

Two hours of dangerous climbing later, the men could not yet see the summit. It might still be hours away. Everest had tested the courage and skill of so many climbers in the past, and each time the giant mountain had won. Now it was the turn of Hillary and Tenzing to face the ordeal.

Hillary knew that they could go on for only another thirty minutes if they were to save enough oxygen to get back to the tent. If they did not turn back then, they risked almost certain death. If only they could move just a little faster!

He stopped cutting steps and tried to get a foothold with the spikes of his crampons. No, it wouldn't work—the margin of safety was gone if they did that. Once more he swung his ax. He must keep cutting the ladder of steps.

Behind him he felt the jerk of the rope that linked him to Tenzing. The Sherpa tribesman was moving more slowly now. Hillary knew that he, too, could not climb much higher. He had been cutting steps for two hours, at a height greater than any climber had reached before. His legs felt like lead, and his ax seemed to weigh a ton.

Only with the greatest effort of will could he force himself to go on.

Go on! Go on! The sharp words that could mean survival and triumph cut into his mind like the blade of his ax into the ice.

He topped another icy hump and saw above him still another. Wearily he swung the ax and dragged himself up step by step. It was nearly 11:30—they had almost reached the half-hour limit. In one minute more they must turn back, defeated, if they were to return alive. Then Hillary raised his head above the level of the snow hump—and he let out a great gasp of relief and triumph.

Edmund Hillary was looking down. Down the other side of Everest. He could see the North Col, where other climbers before him had been killed, and the terrifying North Face, where the famous mountaineer Mallory had died in 1924. Just in front of him a short, slender ridge of snow ran up a few feet to a snowy summit, the summit of Everest.

Seconds later the New Zealander and the Sherpa were standing together on the highest point of the earth's surface.

They shook hands and thumped each other on the back. The whole world would cheer them for this. The photographs Hillary began to take would appear in all the world's newspapers. But the important thing for Hillary and Tenzing was that they had done what they set out to do. Triumphantly they had beaten the great mountain. They were first up Everest!

LAST FLIGHT

Patricia Lauber

In late July, 1936, Amelia Earhart went out to Burbank, California, and began testing the plane that she proposed to fly around the world.

At the time, she was thirty-eight years old and one of the most famous women in the world. She had been the first woman to fly the Atlantic as a passenger; the first woman to fly solo across the Atlantic; the first woman to fly solo from Hawaii to California; the first woman to fly solo from California to Mexico City; and she was the winner of many aviation prizes and awards.

Somehow this was not enough. She yearned to do what no flyer—man or woman—had ever done. She was tired of being "the first woman to." She wanted to be "the first flier to." And so she had decided on a round-the-world flight.

People, it was true, had already flown around the world. But no flier had yet circled the earth by the longest route—at the equator. This was the task Amelia Earhart had set herself.

Her new plane was a twin-engined, all-metal Lockheed Electra. Behind the cockpit, the passenger seats had been cleared away and two big, extra fuel tanks bolted to the floor. A navigation room, with all the latest equipment, lay behind the fuel tanks.

The voice radio for sending and receiving messages with ground stations had a power of fifty watts. Its normal range was only 500 miles. For the parts of the flight when she would be flying over the ocean, she

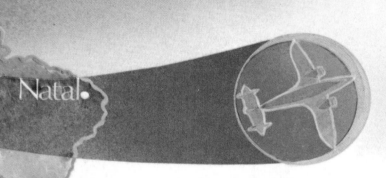

would need a much stronger radio to keep in touch with the ground. When the plane was out of touch with the ground, her navigator would have to work with instruments alone.

At 5:56 A.M. on June 1, 1937, the Electra raced down the runway at Miami, Florida, bound for California by the longest route possible. Amelia Earhart and her navigator, Fred Noonan, were on their way.

The first legs of the flight took them to Puerto Rico, Venezuela, Dutch Guiana, and Brazil. Natal, Brazil, was the take-off point for the long hop across the South Atlantic to Africa. Their destination was Dakar, 1,900 miles away.

Ahead lay long and difficult legs of the flight across Africa's 4,350 miles. Aviation maps of Africa were poor, and there were no radio beams to home in on. But Africa was crossed, then Arabia. On they went to Karachi, Calcutta, Akyab, Rangoon, Bangkok, and Singapore. From Singapore they flew to Bandung, Java, then a Dutch colony. Here one of the most important engine instruments failed. The flight was delayed until Dutch technicians fixed it.

The next leg took them to Surabaya. There the navigation instruments failed. Noonan could not get his most important long-range instruments to work. They backtracked to Bandung, where Dutch technicians worked for

two days on the navigation instruments.

Finally they were off again—Koepong, on the island of Timor; Port Darwin, Australia; Lae, New Guinea. They arrived in Lae on June 30.

They had now covered 22,000 miles in a month's time. The long hours of flying and the brief periods of rest snatched here and there were taking their toll. Pilot and navigator were weary. Yet the longest, most difficult leg of the flight was still to come—the 2,556 miles from Lae to Howland. "I shall be glad when we have the hazards of its navigation behind us," Amelia Earhart scribbled in the logbook that she was about to ship home.

Most of this long leg lay over open water. There would be almost no landmarks.

For the first 500 miles out of New Guinea, they could get radio bearings. For the last 500 miles, they could home into Howland on radio signals from the Coast Guard cutter *Itasca.* But for 1,500 miles they would be on their own. Given clear weather, they would use the stars by night and the sun by day for navigating.

Still, if all went well, twenty hours of flying should see Miss Earhart touching down on Howland.

At ten o'clock in the morning, the Electra roared down the runway at Lae. The date was July 2 in New Guinea. Their destination, Howland, lay on the other side of the international date line. The date in Howland was July 1. So this was, in a way, a flight into yesterday.

In the late afternoon, Miss Earhart talked by radio with Lae. She was then directly on course and proceeding to Howland.

That evening at Howland, the *Itasca's* radio equipment was given a final check. Everything was working well.

The arrangements were that the *Itasca* would broadcast the weather on the hour and the half hour. It would also use a telegraph key to send out a long series of A's, the signal that the Electra would home in on. At quarter to and quarter past the hour, Miss Earhart was to report in, using her call letters, KHAQQ.

Shortly after midnight the *Itasca* began trying to reach the plane. KHAQQ did not reply. This was not surprising, though. The Electra then was probably about 1,000 miles away and still out of radio range. However, there are times when radio waves skip and travel much longer distances. So the *Itasca* continued to send on the chance of making contact early.

At 2:45 A.M. KHAQQ came in. Because of static, listeners on the *Itasca* could make out only three words: "Cloudy and overcast."

Encouraged, the *Itasca* tried to talk with Miss Earhart. The attempt was unsuccessful. She gave no sign of having heard the messages.

At 3:45 A.M. Miss Earhart came in again. "*Itasca* from Earhart... *Itasca* from Earhart... Overcast... Will listen on hour and half hour...."

At 4:00 A.M., on schedule, the *Itasca* gave the weather. Then it asked: "What is your position? When do you expect to arrive at Howland? We are receiving your signals. Please acknowledge this message on your next schedule."

4:15 A.M.: No word from the Electra.

4:30 A.M.: The *Itasca* sent the weather.

4:55 A.M.: KHAQQ called in, but the *Itasca* could not make out what Miss Earhart was saying.

5:30 A.M.: The *Itasca* sent the weather both by voice and by key. By key it sent out the homing signal.

5:45 A.M.: No word from Miss Earhart.

6:00 A.M.: The *Itasca* repeated the weather and the homing signal.

6:15 A.M.: Miss Earhart called in. She believed they were about 200 miles from Howland, but she wanted the *Itasca* to check her position. She would whistle into her microphone so that the ship could take a bearing and tell her exactly where she was. But the whistle was lost in static and other radio noises. The *Itasca* could not take a bearing on it.

6:45 A.M.: Miss Earhart called in again. Her voice was clear and strong. "Please take a bearing on us and report in half an hour," she said. "We are about a hundred miles out." Again the *Itasca* could not get a bearing, for Miss Earhart did not whistle long enough. Almost an hour passed before she next broke radio silence.

7:42 A.M.: KHAQQ came in, Miss Earhart's voice high and troubled. "We must be on you," she said. "But we cannot see you. Our gas is running low. Been unable to reach you by radio. We are flying at altitude 1,000 feet."

The *Itasca* acknowledged her message and sent out the homing signal.

7:49 A.M.: *Itasca* to KHAQQ: "Your message OK. Please acknowledge."

7:58 A.M.: Apparently Miss Earhart had not heard the *Itasca,* for she broke in without acknowledging the ship's message. "KHAQQ calling *Itasca,*" she said. "We are circling but cannot hear you. Go ahead either now or on schedule time of half hour."

8:00 A.M.: The *Itasca* sent the homing signal. Miss Earhart replied immediately. She was receiving the signal but could not get a bearing on it. Again she asked the *Itasca* to take a bearing on her. Again the *Itasca* failed. Her whistling could not be heard clearly enough.

By this time the Electra had been in the air for twenty hours and should have been over Howland.

The *Itasca* continued to call.

8:45 A.M.: The *Itasca* heard Miss Earhart again. Her voice was loud, clear, and anxious. "We are in a line of position 157-337....We are running north and south," she said.

They were her last words.

The *Itasca* continued to call, but the Electra was not heard from again. By noon any possibility of seeing the Electra appear in the sky was gone. The plane could no longer have any fuel.

Amelia Earhart and Fred Noonan were down somewhere in the South Pacific.

The United States Navy, determined to find them, set in motion a great search.

The Navy believed that Miss Earhart had come down within a few hundred miles of Howland. The strength of her last radio signals indicated that she was then between 30 and 250 miles from Howland. A check of weather reports convinced the Navy that she was probably to the north of Howland. Her radio messages had been full of static, and there had been thunderstorms to the north.

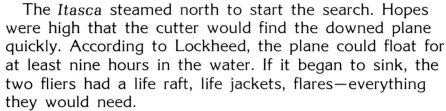

The *Itasca* steamed north to start the search. Hopes were high that the cutter would find the downed plane quickly. According to Lockheed, the plane could float for at least nine hours in the water. If it began to sink, the two fliers had a life raft, life jackets, flares—everything they would need.

The *Itasca* sent up a thick smoke screen so that the fliers could see the ship from afar and signal. When night came, the cutter played its searchlights against the sky, while the crew kept a constant watch for flares.

No trace was found of the two fliers. There was no sign of the plane, a raft, or wreckage. The watch saw no flares and heard no signal guns.

The days passed. The *Itasca* combed the area without success.

Meanwhile other ships were steaming full speed toward Howland to help with the search. On July 7 the battleship *Colorado* and the mine sweeper *Swan* joined the *Itasca*. Two days later the aircraft carrier *Lexington*, with sixty-three planes, sailed from Hawaii. So did four destroyers.

As the search became broader and broader, the Navy once more reviewed the few known facts. It was known that the Electra had had radio trouble. Noonan had had trouble with the navigation instruments.

At 2:45 A.M. on July 2, Miss Earhart had reported the weather as cloudy and overcast. There was no telling whether Noonan had been able to see the stars that night. If he hadn't, then they must have flown by compass alone. And a tiny compass error would grow into a big directional error during such a long flight.

Added up, the known facts told the Navy only one thing: The two fliers could be anywhere within twenty flying hours of Lae.

The last message from the Electra did not clarify matters. No one was sure what Miss Earhart had meant by "line of position 157-337." Probably it was a sun line, but a sun line is meaningless without a point of geographical reference. Her "we are running north and south" meant that she was conducting a search pattern for Howland or some other speck of land. It meant she did not know where she was.

For sixteen days ships and planes searched more than 250,000 square miles of the Pacific. And, at last, the Navy called off the search.

Amelia Earhart and Fred Noonan were missing and presumed lost. There was not the slightest clue as to where they had gone down or what had happened to them.

The two fliers came down somewhere in the South Pacific. If they were near Howland, the Navy ought to have found them. The Navy did not. Perhaps the Navy failed. Perhaps the fliers were not there to be found. It is impossible to tell.

There is no solution to the mystery of Amelia Earhart's last flight. It is only certain that, in the long night flight toward a tiny speck of land, she was somehow defeated by the vastness of the Pacific. The ocean claimed the plane that soared above it, just as it has claimed the many ships and people who have vanished from its surface.

Amelia Earhart left a letter for her husband in the event she did not return. She said in the letter: "I want to do it because I want to do it. Women must try to do things as men have tried. When they fail, then failure must be but a challenge to others."

HIGH FLIGHT

Oh, I have slipped the surly bonds of earth,
And danced the skies on laughter-silvered wings;
Sunward I've climbed and joined the tumbling mirth
Of sun-split clouds—and done a hundred things
You have not dreamed of—wheeled and soared and swung
High in the sunlit silence. Hov'ring there
I've chased the shouting wind along and flung
My eager craft through footless halls of air.
Up, up the long delirious burning blue
I've topped the wind-swept heights with easy grace,
Where never lark, or even eagle, flew;
And, while with silent, lifting mind I've trod
The high untrespassed sanctity of space,
Put out my hand, and touched the face of God.

—John Gillespie Magee, Jr.

205

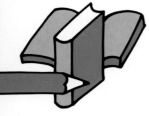

From Different Angles

The study of history and geography teaches us about the past. Knowledge of the past helps us live more effectively in the present.

Both history and geography are part of social studies. There are many books which contain social-studies information and thus help us learn about the past. The authors of these books present their information in several different ways. Below are some of the different kinds of social-studies writing.

Exposition is writing that explains facts. The author may discuss historical events and compare the events. Words may be defined and explained in detail. An example of exposition is "Following the Western Star."

Narrative is writing that tells a story. The author may describe a true experience. Sometimes, the story is narrated in the first person. An example of a first-person narrative is "Flying to the Moon."

A *diary* is a personal account of day-to-day events. The writer describes his or her daily experiences. The writer expresses personal feelings as well as factual details. "Kon-Tiki and I" is an example of a diary.

A *biography* is an account of a person's life. But a biography, unlike a diary, is written by another person. An example of a biography is "Ezra Meeker." An *autobiography* is also an account of a person's life. But an autobiography is written by the person whose life is being told.

206

Historical fiction is writing that mixes fact and fiction. The story may be based on real characters or actual events from history. However, the author will make up part of the action or conversation. "Sybil Ludington" is an example of historical fiction.

Read each paragraph below. On your paper, write the kind of writing each paragraph represents.

1. *May 4.* Our boat landed on the island. We unloaded the equipment and quickly set up camp. I am exhausted from the long journey. I will write more tomorrow.

2. Nellie Bly was born in 1867. Her real name was Elizabeth Cochrane. She was one of the first women to be a newspaper reporter. Nellie wrote many articles describing how poor people were forced to live and work. Later in life, she traveled around the world in seventy-two hours. She died in 1922.

3. The first traffic light was installed in Cleveland, Ohio, in 1914. In addition to red and green lights, it had a loud buzzer. The sounding buzzer was an extra safety device for motorists.

4. "Christopher Columbus," said Queen Isabel, "you want me to purchase three ships and finance your journey to Japan. You ask more than any other explorer," observed the queen. "Still, I think the risk is worth taking. You shall have your ships."

5. I remember when my father bought our first television. The product had just come out. We were the first people on our block to own a set. Many friends came over that afternoon.

JOURNEYS

Journeys can cover the short distance of a 100-yard dash, or they can span the globe. Journeys can yield fresh geographical findings about the land, climate, or forms of life in different places. A journey can be a challenging and enjoyable adventure. It can also involve taking a risk. But meeting the challenge and taking the risk can open up a whole new world of people, places, and ideas.

Thinking About "Journeys"

1. In "Flying to the Moon," what two sights impressed Michael Collins the most?
2. What did the Kon-Tiki crew recognize as the most serious threat to them on their journey?
3. What can geographers or historians learn from Thor Heyerdahl's journeys?
4. How did the weather lengthen the journeys in "The Lost Shepherd Girl" and in "Kon-Tiki and I"?
5. Think about "First up Everest" and "Last Flight." In what ways were the reasons for these journeys alike?
6. Think of journeys you have taken. What have you learned from these journeys?
7. Describe in one paragraph what it would be like to journey into outer space.

DIALOGUES

All your life, you are sharing your ideas with others. The most common way for you to communicate or share ideas is by using words. However, sometimes words may be misleading, or they may convey incomplete messages. Learning to read body language can add to your understanding of what someone is thinking or feeling. Gestures and facial expressions are an important part of the dialogues between people. Even the unspoken communication between a person and an animal is a kind of dialogue involving a sender and a receiver of messages.

In "Dialogues," you will read about communication between people of different ages and between friends. You will learn to recognize body language, and you will understand why it can be more revealing than verbal communication. You will read a play in which language is used for fun and nonsense. You will also learn how carefully a television news reporter must work in order to use language and communicate ideas accurately.

As you read, think about all the different ways of sharing ideas and feelings. Think about the things you do in your daily life. Which of them involve some form of communication?

The WORD MARKET

Norton Juster

Put the above two words together and you have the word *dictionopolis*, city of words. All the words in the world come from Dictionopolis. Does that seem strange? Well, Milo had experienced several strange things in the past few days. One minute, he was an ordinary boy in his own bedroom; the next minute, he was in a fantasyland called Dictionopolis.

Dictionopolis was a very odd place. For example, one of the first friends Milo made was a watchdog named Tock. Tock had a normal dog's head, feet, and tail. But his body was made out of a loudly ticking alarm clock. He could talk, too!

Tock and Milo were traveling through Dictionopolis when they came to the Word Market, where people buy and sell words.

As they approached, Milo could *see* crowds of people pushing and shouting their way among the stalls. They were buying and selling, trading and bargaining.

Above all the noise of the crowd could be heard the merchants' voices loudly advertising their products.

"Get your fresh-picked *if's, and's,* and *but's.*"

"Hey-yaa, hey-yaa, hey-yaa, nice ripe *where's* and *when's.*"

"Juicy, tempting words for sale."

So many words and so many people! They were from every place imaginable and some places even beyond that. They were all busy sorting, choosing, and stuffing things into cases. As soon as one was filled, another was begun. There seemed to be no end to the bustle and activity.

Milo and Tock wandered up and down the aisles looking at the wonderful assortment of words for sale. There were short ones and easy ones for everyday use. There were long and very important ones for special occasions. There were even some marvelously fancy ones packed in individual gift boxes for use in royal decrees and pronouncements.

"Step right up, step right up—fancy, best-quality words right here," announced one man in a booming voice.

"No, thank you," replied Milo. "We're just looking." They continued on through the market.

As they turned down the last aisle of stalls, Milo noticed a wagon that seemed different from the rest. On its side was a small neatly lettered sign that said "DO-IT-YOURSELF." Inside the wagon were twenty-six bins filled with all the letters of the alphabet from *A* to *Z.*

"These are for people who like to make their own words," the man in charge informed him.

"You can pick any assortment you like. You can also buy a special box complete with all letters, punctuation marks, and a book of instructions. Here, taste an *A*; they're very good."

Milo nibbled carefully at the letter and discovered that it was quite sweet and delicious—just the way you'd expect an *A* to taste.

"I knew you'd like it," laughed the letter man. He popped two *G*'s and an *R* into his mouth and let the juice drip down his chin. "*A*'s are one of our most popular letters. All of them aren't that good," he confided in a low voice. "Take the *Z*, for instance—very dry and sawdusty. And the

X? Why, it tastes like a trunkful of stale air. That's why people hardly ever use them. But most of the others are quite tasty. Try some more."

He gave Milo an *I*, which was icy and refreshing, and Tock was given a crisp, crunchy *C*.

"Most people are just too lazy to make their own words," he continued, "but it's much more fun."

"Is it difficult? I'm not much good at making words," admitted Milo, spitting the pits from a *P*.

"Perhaps I can be of some assistance——a-s-s-i-s-t-a-n-c-e," buzzed an unfamiliar voice. When Milo looked up he saw an enormous bee, at least twice his size, sitting on top of the wagon.

"I am the Spelling Bee," announced the Spelling Bee. "Don't be alarmed—a-l-a-r-m-e-d."

Tock ducked under the wagon, and Milo, who was not overly fond of normal-sized bees, began to back away slowly.

"I can spell anything—a-n-y-t-h-i-n-g," he boasted, testing his wings. "Try me, try me!"

"Can you spell *good-by*?" suggested Milo as he continued to back away.

The bee gently lifted himself into the air and circled lazily over Milo's head.

"Perhaps –p-e-r-h-a-p-s– you are under the misapprehension — m-i-s-a-p-p-r-e-h-e-n-s-i-o-n — that I am dangerous," he said, turning a smart loop to the left. "Let me assure–a-s-s-u-r-e– you that my intentions are peaceful—p-e-a-c-e-f-u-l." With that he settled back on top of the wagon and fanned himself with one wing. "Now," he panted, "think of the most difficult word you can and I'll spell it. Hurry up, hurry up!"

He jumped up and down impatiently.

"He looks friendly enough," thought Milo, not sure just how friendly a friendly bumblebee should be. Then he tried to think of a very difficult word. "Spell *vegetable*," Milo suggested, for it was a word that always troubled him at school.

"That is a difficult one," said the bee, winking at the letter man. "Let me see now . . . hmmmmmm . . ." He frowned and wiped his brow and paced slowly back and forth on top of the wagon. "How much time do I have?"

"Just ten seconds," cried Milo excitedly. "Count them off, Tock."

"Oh dear, oh dear, oh dear, oh dear," the bee repeated, continuing to pace nervously. Then, just as the time ran out, he spelled as fast as he could—v-e-g-e-t-a-b-l-e.

"Correct," shouted the letter man, and everyone cheered.

"Can you spell everything?" asked Milo admiringly.

"Just about," replied the bee with a hint of pride in his voice.

"BALDERDASH!" shouted a booming voice. From around the wagon stepped a large beetlelike insect dressed in a fancy coat, striped pants, checked vest, spats, and a derby hat. "I repeat—BAL-DERDASH!" he shouted again, swinging his cane and clicking his heels in mid-air. "Come now, don't be ill-mannered. Isn't someone going to introduce me to the little boy?"

"This," said the bee with complete disdain, "is the Humbug—a very dislikable fellow."

"NONSENSE! Everyone loves a humbug," shouted the Humbug. "As I was saying to the king just the other day—"

"You've never met the king," accused the bee angrily. Then, turning to Milo, he said, "Don't believe a thing this old fraud says."

"BAH!" said the bug, putting an arm around Milo. "Why are you listening to this silly spelling bee? What's the use of spelling? As soon as you learn to spell one word they ask you to spell another. You can never catch up. Take my advice, my boy, and forget about it. As my great-great-great-grandfather George Washington Humbug used to say—"

"You, sir," shouted the bee very excitedly, "are an impostor—i-m-p-o-s-t-o-r—who can't even spell his own name."

The Humbug waved his cane at the bee furiously. The Spelling Bee took up the challenge. He flew down and knocked off the Humbug's hat with his wing.

"Be careful!" shouted Milo as the bug swung his cane again, catching the bee on the foot and knocking over the box of *W*'s.

"My foot!" shouted the bee.

"My hat!" shouted the bug— and the fight was on.

The Spelling Bee buzzed dangerously in and out of range of the Humbug's wildly swinging cane. They menaced and threatened each other, and the crowd stepped back out of danger.

"There must be some other way to—"began Milo. Then he yelled, "WATCH OUT!" But it was too late.

There was a tremendous crash as the Humbug in his great fury tripped into one of the stalls, knocking it into another, then another, then another, then another, until every stall in the marketplace had been upset. The words lay scrambled in great confusion all over the square.

The bee got caught in the wreckage, and toppled to the ground. He knocked Milo over on top of him, and the two fell together. "Help! Help! There's a little boy on me," the bee shouted. The bug sprawled untidily on a pile of squashed letters. Tock, his alarm ringing loudly, was buried under a pile of words.

How Milo and Tock get out from under all those words is another story. The tale of their adventures fills a whole book called *The Phantom Tollbooth.*

WHERE'S MORTIMER ?

Jim Tobin

HENRY HOUND: Emily, I'm going downtown to visit Matilda, and on the way home I'm going to stop off at the park and dig up some...

EMILY HOUND: Good, Henry. Take the puppies with you. Matilda speaks human so well, it will be good practice for the puppies.

HENRY: But I wanted to stop at the park...

EMILY: Stop thinking about your stomach! The puppies need to practice their human or they'll never learn to get along in the world. Be a good dog and take them.

HENRY: No one is going to call me a lazy human. I'll take them. Jessie! Bessie! Mortimer! Mortimer?

MORTIMER: I'm coming.

HENRY: We're off to practice the human language. We'll walk downtown to see Matilda, an old family friend. She speaks human so well.

BESSIE: Do we have to go?

JESSIE: Can't we stay home and play watchdog and robbers?

HENRY: If I don't take you, I'll be in the peoplehouse all week. Come on.

217

MAN: Good boy, Spot.

BESSIE: What did he call you?

HENRY: Spot. He'll never learn. For years I've been training him to call me Henry. I guess Spot has something to do with this spot, but I don't call him Stomach just because... oh well. Puppies, remember that humans require endless patience and training. So if a human calls you Spot or Ruff, don't be annoyed. Remember, the doghouse wasn't built in a day. Besides, what can you expect from an animal that walks on two legs? Come on, run. Follow me.

JESSIE: What's the matter?

HENRY: Do you see that truck across the street? That's the dog catcher's truck.

MORTIMER: What truck?

JESSIE: Did you say trunk? I don't see any elephants.

BESSIE: Not elephants. Tree trunks. There are trees over there.

MORTIMER: Not that kind of trunk. Dad probably means some kind of suitcase.

BESSIE: I didn't pack. How far are we going?

JESSIE: Packs? Dogs and wolves travel in packs.

MORTIMER: Say, if there were a half dozen of us, would we be a six-pack?

HENRY: Just a minute. Stop all this and pay attention.

MORTIMER: Pay how much?

JESSIE: I can't pay till you give me my allowance.

HENRY: Pay *attention*, not money. Be quiet or the dog catcher will get us.

BESSIE: Get us what?

MORTIMER: Are we getting presents?

HENRY: No dog I know ever got a present from the dog catcher.

JESSIE: Dog catcher?

MORTIMER: Is that like baseball catcher?

BESSIE: Is daddy a pitcher?

JESSIE: Where's a pitcher? I'm thirsty. Give me some water, too.

HENRY: There is no water here. And there is no pitcher here. And I'm not talking about that kind of catcher. The dog catcher catches dogs and takes them to the pound.

JESSIE: Dog pound? They can't take me there. I weigh two pounds.

219

BESSIE: Pound? Isn't that like hitting something?

JESSIE: No one is going to pound on *this* puppy.

MORTIMER: I can go! I can go! I only weigh a pound.

BESSIE: Wait a minute. Dog pound. Is that like pound cake? Do they feed you there? Let's go.

JESSIE: No! Not pound like pound cake. I bet it's pound like pound sterling. It's probably an English bank.

MORTIMER: Did I hear bank? I don't see any water.

JESSIE: Well, there was a pitcher with water here about a minute ago.

HENRY: Stop talking! The dog pound is not a good place for us to be. Let's get going.

JESSIE: Dad! That dog catcher is heading this way!

HENRY: Oh, oh. Turn tail and run. Whew! We can stop now. We gave the dog catcher the slip.

JESSIE: What slip?

BESSIE: I didn't have any slip. Daddy, did you slip?

HENRY: No! Be quiet. Is everyone here?

BESSIE: Yes, except for Mortimer.
HENRY: Where's Mortimer?
JESSIE: Do you think the dog catcher caught him?
VOICE: Psssst.
HENRY: What was that?
VOICE: Psssst.
HENRY: What was that?
JESSIE: That was the garbage can talking.
BESSIE: You're wrong, Jessie. In human you don't say "The garbage can talking." You say "The garbage can talk."
JESSIE: I didn't mean that.
BESSIE: I didn't say you were mean.
HENRY: Don't be silly. Garbage cans can't...
VOICE: It's me!
BESSIE: What?
MORTIMER: I was in the garbage can.
BESSIE: The garbage can what?
JESSIE: What were you doing in there?
MORTIMER: I was hiding out.
HENRY: You mean hiding in, don't you? It's a good thing that the dog catcher doesn't have a dog's nose. He'd never lose Mortimer's scent.

JESSIE: Why would he lose it? He'd probably spend it.

BESSIE: Did Mortimer have money with him?

JESSIE: How come Mortimer had money? I didn't get my allowance yet. That's not fair.

MORTIMER: I don't see any fair. I saw trunks. I saw catchers. But I never saw any pitchers and I don't see any fairs.

BESSIE: Mortimer, how much money did you lose?

HENRY: I was not talking about Mortimer's money. I was talking about his odor.

BESSIE: How come Mortimer has his own door and I don't?

HENRY: Because you didn't hide in a garbage can.

BESSIE: Garbage can what?

HENRY: Forget it. Let's get on with our trip.

MORTIMER: Who tripped?

JESSIE: Bessie probably did. She slipped before.

BESSIE: I did not.

HENRY: OK. That's enough. We have to walk down this street now.

MORTIMER: Do we have to walk down or can we take an elevator?

BESSIE: How can we go down? I don't see any stairs.

JESSIE: Mortimer, if you took an elevator, what would you do with it?

MORTIMER: Is this a trick question?

JESSIE: Of course not. You said that you want to take an elevator. If you did take an elevator, what would you do with it?

MORTIMER: I don't have to answer trick questions.

HENRY: Come on. The traffic light is in our favor.

BESSIE: The traffic doesn't look light to me.

MORTIMER: The cars don't look so heavy. But some of those trucks sure do.

JESSIE: What favor is the light going to do for me?

MORTIMER: Did you say that lights come in flavors?

BESSIE: I want chocolate. I didn't get the pound cake that you talked about before, but this time I won't move until I get chocolate.

HENRY: You're right, Bessie. It is getting late. Let's get going and cross the street.

BESSIE: Where can you get a going?

MORTIMER: In a department store, of course. But what do you cross a street with?

JESSIE: Another street, I guess. You pick up the corners and . . .

HENRY: Just a little bit farther and we'll be at Matilda's. But where's Mortimer?

BESSIE: He was here a minute ago.

HENRY: Mortimer! Mortimer!

JESSIE: There he is, chasing that big cat.

BESSIE: Who does he think he is, the cat catcher?

HENRY: There's no such thing as a cat catcher. There are only dog catchers.

BESSIE: No one catches cats?

JESSIE: Maybe sometimes dog catchers catch cats.

HENRY: Why doesn't Mortimer leave that cat alone? He's such a bully.

BESSIE: I thought Mortimer was a puppy like Jessie and me.

JESSIE: How could you possibly compare Mortimer to me?

BESSIE: But he doesn't look like a bull.

HENRY: Mortimer, you should be ashamed of yourself for chasing that cat.

MORTIMER: But I didn't go near the cat. It came after me.

BESSIE: Oh no, no. Dogs and puppies come after cats. Look in any dictionary. *C* always comes before *D* in human.

HENRY: Why, Bessie, you learned your human very well. All you puppies did. Matilda will be very impressed with you. You all speak as well and as understandably as people do.

MORTIMER: What do we have to stand under?

JESSIE: What is your friend Matilda going to press me with?

BESSIE: I don't care what she presses me with as long as she doesn't pound me.

225

HENRY: Ah, here we are at last at Matilda's house. Let's go in.
BESSIE: Matilda has a mouse?
HENRY: Matilda, I brought my puppies to see you because I want them to hear how well you speak human.
MATILDA: Hello and welcome! Puppies want a cracker?
HENRY: Here she is, puppies, the animal who speaks human best, Matilda Parrot!

226

Puns, Anyone

A *pun* is a special kind of joke that is a "play on words." The humor in a pun is based on the fact that words may sound the same but have different meanings. Over ninety percent of our jokes are said to come from puns. A pun almost always gets a reaction: a laugh if it is good; a groan if it is bad. How do you react to the puns below? Do you know others?

Don't be a fool! You'll hurt yourself.

Don't worry. Just folly me!

Ann: When I woke up this morning, I was a little hoarse.

Fred: Oh? How fast did you gallop?

Peter: If I scrub hard, do you think I can get my face clean?

Mother: Let's soap for the best.

It's raining cats and dogs.

I know. I just stepped on a poodle.

Paw-Paw and Casey

Laurence Yep

Casey and her father had lived alone in the city and had depended on each other ever since the death of Casey's mother. Then, Barney, Casey's father, had to go into the hospital for several weeks, and Casey needed to stay with someone. She knew that the relatives who knew her considered her a troublemaker, so she wasn't surprised when she was "farmed out" to stay with her grandmother, whom she had never met.

Uncle Phil drove Casey into Chinatown and stopped his car in front of an old building. Casey thought to herself that all she knew about this grandmother was that she was to be called Paw-Paw, the Chinese word for one's "mother's mother."

Phil picked out the last doorbell and rang. He jabbed his thumb down rhythmically: three short—three long—three short.

"Why are you doing that?" I asked.

"Signaling your Paw-Paw," he grumbled. "It's got to be nine buzzes in that way or she doesn't open the door. She says her friends know what she means."

So did I. It was Morse code for SOS. The buzzer on the door sounded like an angry bee. Phil

opened the door. "Go on. Up three flights. Number nine," Phil said.

I walked into an old, dim hallway and climbed up the wooden steps. I stopped by the number nine room, afraid to knock. It could not be the right place because I could hear "I Want to Hold Your Hand" coming through the doorway. I scratched my head and checked the numbers on the other doors on the landing.

I shrugged. I knocked at the door. I heard about six bolts and locks being turned. Finally, the door swung open and I saw a tiny, pleasant, round-faced woman smiling at me. Her cheeks were a bright red. Her gray hair was all curly and frizzy around her head, and a pair of rimless, thick eyeglasses perched on her nose. She was round and plump, wearing a sweater even on a hot day like this, a pair of cotton black slacks, and a pair of open-heeled, flat slippers.

"Paw-Paw?" I asked.

"Hello. Hello." She opened up her arms and gave me a big hug, almost crushing me. It was funny, but even though Barney and I never went in much for that sentimental stuff like hugging and kissing, I suddenly found myself holding on to her. Underneath all the soft layers of clothing I could feel how hard and tough she was. She patted me on the back three times and then left me for a moment to turn down her radio. It was an old radio playing rock music.

Phil heaved his shoulders up and down in a great sigh and set the bag down. "Now, Momma—"

"Go on home," she said firmly. "We need time by ourselves."

Phil gulped. He turned and started down the steps.

"You mind your Paw-Paw, young lady. You hear me?" he shouted over his shoulder.

I waited till I heard the door slam. "Do you know what those buzzes stand for?"

"Do you?" Her eyes crinkled up.

"They stand for SOS."

"Yes, it's a good joke on such a learned man, no?" Her round red face split into a wide grin and then she began to giggle. When

230

she put her hand over her mouth, the giggle turned into a laugh.

I don't think that I had laughed in all that time since Barney's accident a month ago. It was like all the laughter I hadn't been able to use came bubbling up out of some hidden well. It burst out of the locks and just came up. Both of us found ourselves slumping on the landing, leaning our heads against the banister, and laughing.

Finally, Paw-Paw tilted up her glasses and wiped her eyes. "Philip always did have too much dignity for one person. Ah!" She leaned back against the railing on the landing before the stairwell, twisting her head to look at me. "You'll go far," she nodded. "Yes, you will. Your eyebrows are beautifully curved, like silkworms. That means you'll be clever. And your ears are small and close to your head and shaped a certain way. That means you're adventurous and you'll win much honor."

"Really?"

She nodded solemnly. "Didn't you know? The face is the map of the soul." Then she leaned forward and raised her glasses. She pointed to the corners of her eyes where there were two small hollows, just shadows, really. "You see those marks under my eyes?"

"Yes." I added after a moment, "Paw-Paw."

"Those marks—they mean I have a temper."

"Oh." I wondered what was to happen next.

She set her glasses back on her nose. "But I will make a deal with you. I can keep my temper under control if you can do the same with your love of adventure and intelligence. You see, people, including me, don't always understand a love of adventure and intelligence. Sometimes we mistake them for troublemaking."

"I'll try." I grinned.

I went and got my bag then and brought it inside Paw-Paw's place and looked around, trying to figure out where I'd put it. Her place wasn't more than ten by fifteen feet, and it was crowded with her stuff. Paw-Paw pulled aside a chair and told me to put my bag under the table next to the window.

231

Paw-Paw's radio was in a little cabinet built into the headboard of the bed. I sat down on the bed and looked at the radio dial. "Do you like rock music, Paw-Paw?"

"It's fun to listen to," Paw-Paw said, "and besides, *Chinese Hour* is on that station every night."

"*Chinese Hour?*"

"An hour of news and songs all in Chinese," Paw-Paw said. "They used to have some better shows on that station like mystery shows."

"I bet I could find some." I started to reach for the dial.

"Don't lose that station." Paw-Paw seemed afraid suddenly.

"Don't worry, Paw-Paw, I'll be able to get your station back for you." It was playing "Monster Mash" right then. I twisted the dial and the voices and snatches of songs slid past. Then I turned the dial back to her station, where "Monster Mash" was still playing. "See?"

"As long as you could get it back," Paw-Paw said in a worried way.

I fiddled with the dial some more until I got hold of *Gunsmoke.* It'd gone off the air three years ago, but some station was playing reruns. Paw-Paw liked that, especially the deep voice of the marshal. It was good to sit there in the darkening room, listening to Marshal Dillon and picturing him as striding down the dusty streets of Dodge

City. I got us some other programs, too—shows that Paw-Paw had never been able to listen to before.

Don't get the idea that Paw-Paw was stupid. She just didn't understand American machines that well. She lived with them in a kind of truce where she never asked much of them if they wouldn't ask much of her.

"It's getting near eight," Paw-Paw said, anxiously. It was only when I got the station back that she began to relax. "I was so worried that I would not be able to get back the station, I never tried any others. Look what I missed."

"But you have me now, Paw-Paw," I said.

"Yes," Paw-Paw smiled briefly. "I guess I do."

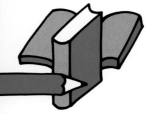

Get the Message?

There is an old saying: "Experience is the best teacher." In other words, it is often easiest to learn from things that happen to you personally. If you rode a bicycle with no hands and fell off, you would surely learn to be more careful next time.

Personal experience is one way to learn something about life. Another way is by reading stories. Things happen to the characters in a story, and the experiences of these characters can teach you about life, too.

The *theme* of a story is the idea or message of the story which is conveyed through the experiences of the characters in the story. It is the central point which the author wants to make about life and living.

Many children's stories have themes. For example, the theme of *The Three Little Pigs* is: "It is important to prepare for a safe future."

The theme of a story is not usually stated specifically in the story. To discover the theme, think about the following questions:

What kinds of characters did the author create?

What did these characters learn about themselves and about life?

What is the significance of the title of the story?

The answers to these questions will help you determine the theme, or idea about life, which the author has tried to present.

ACTIVITY A: Think about the characters and their experiences in "Paw-Paw and Casey." Read the themes below. Write the most appropriate theme on your paper.

1. Chinese radio programs are better than English radio programs.
2. Young people and old people can help one another.
3. Relatives never get along.

ACTIVITY B   Read the following story. Then answer the questions.

What Money Can't Buy

Jenny was the richest girl in her class. She loved to brag about the money her family had. She told about her fancy house and her large bedroom. She always showed off her new and expensive clothes.

After a while, nobody talked to Jenny. But Jenny didn't care. She thought she had everything she needed or wanted in her room: a color television, a record player, and a closetful of clothes.

Soon, a new restaurant opened in town. It was called "Friends." On opening day, every customer had to come with a friend.

Jenny was anxious to see the new restaurant. She asked many people in school to be her partner, but they all refused. Jenny couldn't get into the restaurant, so she cried in her bedroom all day.

As a result, Jenny realized why no one liked her. She stopped bragging about herself. Soon, she made many new friends.

1. What kind of girl was Jenny?
2. What did Jenny finally learn about herself?
3. What is the significance of the title of the story?
4. What is the theme of the story?

When I Became Friends With Phyllis

Alma Whitney

I started to become friends with Phyllis and told her a lie, both on the same day.

We met at camp last summer, right after I had graduated from the sixth grade. While I was in the sixth grade, I took a test to get into a special junior high. The school, Creston, is about fifteen miles from my house. But that didn't bother me. You see, Creston gives special training in art. I love art. I want to be an artist when I grow up. I thought Creston was just the school for me.

So when I got the letter from Creston saying that I had not been accepted, I was very disappointed. I had already begun to imagine myself wearing a blue and gold Creston sweatshirt and carrying my books all covered in Creston covers. I had begun to imagine the way the kids from the local junior high would look at me and admire me for having been accepted at a special school.

"Cheer up," my parents told me. "You can try again next year, you know. And anyway, things don't always go the way we plan in this world."

I felt terrible. Kids in school kept asking me how I had made out on the test. And I had to keep telling them. But Creston didn't accept anybody from my school last year. So everyone who applied was in the same miserable boat.

But that was not true at camp. You see, Creston is right in the middle of New York City. It takes kids from all over the city. And so does my camp. Some of the kids at camp who were my age *had* to have gotten into Creston. One of them was Phyllis.

"Hi."

"Hi."

"My name is Phyllis. What's yours?"

"Pamela," I said.

"That's the biggest suitcase I've ever seen in my life," Phyllis said, eyeing my luggage. "Need any help getting it to your bunk? I already took mine to my bunk. I came on the first bus."

"Oh, gee, thanks. I'm in Rookery. What bunk are you in?"

"Rookery," said Phyllis. "Dumb name, isn't it?"

That's how we started to become friends.

We lugged the suitcase down a gravel path to a little wooden cabin. We would share that cabin with four other kids for the next eight weeks.

"Where do you live, Pamela?" Phyllis asked. And she opened the suitcase that was already on her bed.

"Way out in Queens," I answered. "Almost at the end of the city. What about you?"

"I live in the Bronx. Real close to the city."

"Are you in junior high yet?" I asked.

"I'm starting in September," she said. "I'm really excited about it. I'm going to this place called Creston. And I'm going to learn a lot about art."

It would have been easier if Phyllis had been nasty or snooty or mean or anything. But there she was. She was a really nice, friendly person. She had helped me carry my suitcase. She was almost my friend. And she, of all people, had gotten into Creston.

"Oh, sure," I said, sounding cool. "I know about Creston. As a matter of fact, I took the entrance exam."

"You did?" Phyllis said. "What happened?"

Well, *I* knew what happened. But something inside me didn't want Phyllis to know what had happened.

"It's kind of complicated," I said. And I tried to think of something complicated that would make sense.

"You see, they didn't reject me." BEGINNING OF LIE. "But they didn't accept me either. They wrote me a special letter. They said they would like me to come to Creston but that I live too far away. They just don't think it's right for me to travel so much." END OF LIE.

"Oh," said Phyllis. Then we both got very busy unpacking.

Now why did I have to tell Phyllis that story? Where did the idea come from? It had never occurred to me before. I decided to tell Phyllis the truth. But not at that exact moment. I'd tell her right after supper.

After supper that night, the counselors put on a show for us. That wasn't the time to tell the truth to Phyllis.

And after the show, we walked to the bunk with the rest of the girls. That wasn't the time to tell Phyllis. There was a lot of gabbing after lights out, so that wasn't the time to tell Phyllis. And after the gabbing stopped, it got so quiet that everyone would have heard me even if I had whispered. So that wasn't the time to tell Phyllis. But I would find the time—some other time.

Do you know how fast eight weeks can go by? Well let me tell you, they can go by pretty fast. Especially when you are busy. And were we busy! We had arts and crafts and basketball and baseball and tennis. And we went swimming twice a day, every day, except when it rained.

Phyllis and I did just about everything together, even when we were with the other kids. We did a lot of drawing that summer. Sometimes we would draw as we sat on our beds talking and waiting for lights out. And sometimes, during free-time, we would sit in the woods in back of the cabin. Then we'd draw the trees, or the sky, or the rocks, or each other. But the funny thing was, as much as we were together, I never got around to telling Phyllis the truth. No moment ever seemed like the right one to tell her.

Then, all of a sudden, it was two days before the end of camp. Kids were starting to exchange phone numbers and addresses and to make plans to visit each other. The rowboats were pulled off the lake and turned upside down on the beach for the winter.

It was free-time, and Phyllis and I decided to go for a walk. We walked to the lake and sat down on one of the overturned boats.

"Do you ever think about memories?" I said.

"Hmmm," Phyllis said.

"Well, soon this whole summer is going to be a memory. A memory of the time right before junior high."

Now why did I say that? I guess the whole thing was on my mind even more than I thought. I would tell her. Not right now. But before we went home.

Then Phyllis spoke. "Pamela, you know you can try for Creston again in the spring."

"Cres . . ." I began to say, staring at my sneakers.

"Your drawings are really good. They're just as good as mine. Don't feel bad about not getting in. Maybe just too many kids applied this year."

We sat there a while longer, tossing pebbles into the lake, and not saying anything.

So she knew. I wonder how long she had known without telling me. But actually, she never did tell me. I mean, she never said, "Pamela, that's not true. You never got into Creston."

I guess when someone's a friend they can tell when you're telling the truth and when you're covering up. And that's what I had been doing, covering up.

Two days later, we were on our way home from camp. And as we saw fewer and fewer trees and more and more buildings, we made plans to visit each other as soon as possible.

I HAVE STARTED JUNIOR HIGH AND I LOVE IT

I have French and math and English and social studies and art and gym and band. Well, not really band yet. I signed up to play clarinet on the first day of school. Every week I take a group lesson. The teacher says we'll probably start band in February if we're good enough.

My art teacher thinks my drawings are terrific. I told her about not getting into Creston, and she said I should definitely try again. She's even going to help me a couple of afternoons a week so I have a better chance this year.

Phyllis really loves Creston. She says she gets to paint every day. She says I'll love it if I get in this year. She even found out when the test is—April 23.

Last weekend I went to sleep over at Phyllis's house. In the afternoon, a friend of Phyllis's from Creston came over to meet me. Her name was Joyce.

"Where do you go to school?" Joyce asked me.

And without even feeling bad, I said, "I go to Merryweather. It's right near my house. I wanted to go to Creston, but I didn't get in. So I'm taking the test again this year. Maybe this time I'll make it."

"I hope so," said Joyce.

"I do, too," I said, smiling at Phyllis.

"I do, too," she said.

Communicating

Communicating's more than merely talking.
Communicating's when a thing unsaid
Is heard and shared and given deeper meaning.
It's like good bread

And cheese. Now either, by itself, is splendid
And yet, when you combine and taste the two,
They add to one another a fresh flavor.
The same is true

Of minds that meet and match. There's something extra,
A gleam, a swiftness neither knew before.
Talking stays in one room. Communicating
Opens the door.

—Jean Little

YOUR BODY SPEAKS OUT

"I'm not angry," says your friend. Still you wonder, is she? What makes you wonder? Perhaps it's not what she says. It's what she does. She frowns. Her face is tight and her fists are clenched. People sometimes say how they really feel with their bodies. Eyes, faces, arms, legs talk. This is called body language.

Today a number of people are studying body language. They believe that body signals may help in communicating a message. Sometimes body signals may tell more than words can. So, if your friend says, "I'm not angry," you may want to read her body signals to be sure.

Understanding body language is not easy. It may differ from one country to another. That's because people's customs and values are different.

Body language signs may have different meanings at different times, too. For example, a smile may be a sign of happiness. Or it can be a sign of anger or nervousness. A smile may even cover up sad feelings.

But even when body signals are understood, they may tell only part of a story. Read the body signals in the photos on these pages. What stories do they tell?

At a party, a group of people talk. Three have their arms crossed and heads tilted. Each person is like a mirror image of the others. This may mean that all three agree. In this picture, one person is sending different body signals. Which one? What might this mean?

2

Hand crooked back, this boy looks out of the corners of his eyes. Perhaps he is wondering about something sad. Or is he showing doubt? loneliness? dislike? What do you think? What does his body say?

Boys jump. Their bodies say how they feel. Do you jump for joy? Is jumping how your body says it's happy? How else does it show the feeling? Look at people around you. Do their bodies show how they feel?

What is this girl doing? Does her body give you any clues? Is she making mischief? Is she pretending to be an animal? Is she trying to be scary? What do you think she is looking at? If you're not sure, let your body do what hers is doing.

BODY LANGUAGE IN CODE

Two women talk. They are sitting. One smiles and winks her right eye. She crosses one leg over the other. The other woman crosses her legs the same way. This might show that she agrees with the first woman. The second opens her eyes wide. She lifts her eyebrows and folds her hands. These actions might be recorded in code. Here are its symbols:

○ = eye open   ∩∩ = eyebrows lifted   ＼／ = frowning brow

— = eye winking   ⅄ = legs crossed   ↓ = crouch

⌐ = frown   ≢ = folded hands   ✗ = arms crossed

⊍ = smile   ↑ = jump   L = sit

𝒪 = head tilted to right

In code, the smiling woman would look like this:

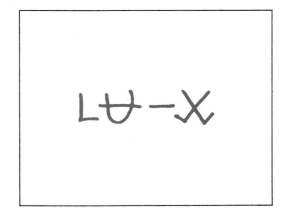

What symbols would you use to show the second woman?

Codes that record body actions are used by some dancers. Some say that actors and business-people may also one day use such a code.

Watch for body messages in the schoolyard, in class, at home, on a bus. You might record what you see in code. If you need more symbols, create some.

Read it Backward

There are many words in the English language that can be read forward and backward. Some of them spell two different words. If you write the word forward, it spells one word. If you write it backward, it spells another word. Here are some examples:

stop — pots   deer — reed

laid — dial   strap — parts

net — ten   devil — lived

Other English words spell the same word forward and backward. These words are called *palindromes.* The word *palindrome* comes from Greek and means "to run back again." Here are some examples of palindromes:

peep — peep   level — level

mom — mom   wow — wow

bib — bib   noon — noon

Sometimes a whole sentence can be made into a palindrome. But it is difficult to make up this kind of sentence. One of the most well-known examples speaks of the island of Elba where the famous French general, Napoleon, was once imprisoned. Written forward, the sentence reads:

Able was I ere I saw Elba.

Now write it backward! Napoleon did not make this statement when he was sent to Elba after his defeat in the battle of Waterloo. But he could have — if he had spoken English and if he had been interested in making up palindromes.

Can you think of some words or sentences that can be read forward and backward?

A Mother Writes to Her Child

Dina Anastasio

Dear Jenny,

Tonight at dinner when I asked what you had done in school today, you replied, "nothing." My first reaction was to give you a lecture about communication—to tell you that people who live together must make an effort to talk to each other. But then I saw your sad face, and I said nothing. I wondered what it was that had made you sad. Your school work? your teachers? an unthinking friend? And then as we ate our dinner, I remembered another dinner that took place a long, long time ago.

When I was in the sixth grade, as you are, we moved to a new city. It was in November, when school friendships had already been made and work patterns already established. From the first day, I was behind in my schoolwork, for this school was more demanding than the last. But as the fall turned to winter, I began to catch up. Soon I no longer had this problem.

The problem of making friends, however, did not go away. Somehow I just could not break into

any of the groups that had formed during the years and months before I had moved to that town.

At first no one was really mean. I guess you could say they were polite, if a bit stand-offish. Some of them even allowed me to walk home with them. I say "allowed" because, looking back, that is just what they did. I can't remember anyone ever actually inviting me to join them, but then they never said "go away," either.

Then one day when I had been at the school for about a month, everything changed. It happened while I was walking home from school with some of the girls. If I remember correctly, there were four of us, and a few of the other girls in the class were walking about a half block behind.

All of a sudden Harriet, the leader of the group behind us, began calling the name of one of my companions.

"Jane," she called. "Hey, Jane, come back and walk with us."

At first Jane hesitated, for she didn't understand just what was happening. But then she seemed pleased. She walked back to join Harriet and her friends.

A few minutes later Harriet called out another name, and the girl that was walking beside me turned and was gone.

This happened two more times until I was alone, and they were all behind me. They were laughing happily and whispering in tones that were not quite loud enough for me to hear.

I straightened my back and held my head high. And I walked on.

That night at dinner my mother asked what I had done that day and, even though (or maybe because) it had been the most awful day of my life, I said, "nothing." She was a wise lady, wiser than I, I'm afraid. She asked no more questions, for which I was very grateful.

Even cruelty, I have found, becomes boring. In time Harriet and her friends found other forms of entertainment.

But then another new girl joined our class. Harriet had a new victim. Her name was Diane, and we began walking home together.

One day as we approached my house, a voice behind us called my name. It was Harriet, of course. For the first time since I had come to this town, she invited me to join her. For a moment I wanted, more than anything in the world, to go back and become one of them. But then I looked at Diane's face. I realized that I didn't want to be back there at all.

Diane and I remained friends for a long time. When I was in the eighth grade, I moved to another town, where the people were kind, and I made lots of friends. At dinner when my parents asked me what I had done that day, I often told them. Although once in a while, I still said, "nothing."

Love, MOM

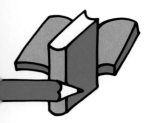

Words, Words, Words

A dictionary is a book that contains information about words. The words are listed in alphabetical order. Look at the dictionary guide words and entry for the word *moment*. This word also appears in the glossary of this book.

---

moldboard / Monaco

> **mo · ment** (mō′mənt) *n.* **1.** a short period of time: *I'll be back in a moment.* **2.** a particular point in time, especially the present time: *The moment he spoke we recognized his voice.* **3.** importance; significance: *This is a question of great moment.*

Guide words appear at the top of each page of the dictionary. They show the first and last words on a page, which helps you locate a particular word. The guide words shown above are *moldboard* and *Monaco*.

The *entry word* is the word for which information is given. It is printed in heavy, dark type and is divided into syllables. The entry word above is *moment*.

The *syllables* in the entry word are separated by a dot. The word *moment* has two syllables.

The *pronunciation* of the entry word appears in parentheses. Symbols are used to show how to pronounce the word. A dictionary has a *pronunciation key* that explains how these symbols are used.

If the entry word has two or more syllables, an *accent mark* appears with the pronunciation symbols. This mark indicates which syllable is stressed when you say the word. The first syllable of *moment* is stressed.

An abbreviation shows the *part of speech* of the entry word. It follows the word's pronunciation. An *n.* is the abbreviation for *noun,* so the word *moment* is a noun. Other abbreviations are

pron.	pronoun	*adj.*	adjective
v.	verb	*adv.*	adverb

The *definition* of the word follows the part of speech. When a word has more than one definition, each definition is numbered. Sometimes, a sample sentence or phrase using the word follows the definition. The word *moment* has three meanings and three sample sentences.

ACTIVITY A **A** dictionary page shows the guide words *candle/carrot.* On your paper, write those of the following entry words that would appear on that page.

1. candy
2. cannon
3. carry
4. candid
5. captain
6. cart

ACTIVITY B Use the glossary at the back of this book to answer the four questions for each of these words.

alarm   hostess   memory   position   temper

1. How many syllables are in the word?
2. Which syllable is stressed?
3. What part of speech is the word?
4. How many definitions are listed for the word?

ACTIVITY C Look up the word *stall* in the glossary. Then read the sentences below and determine how the word *stall* is used in each sentence. On your paper, write the definition that applies to the word's use in each sentence.

1. The man sold dishes in a <u>stall</u> at the fair.
2. The animal broke out of its <u>stall</u> and ran away.

the meeting

Johanna Reiss

The Upstairs Room is the true story of Annie de Leeuw and her sister Sini. They are Jewish girls living in Holland during World War II. At this time, the Nazis were persecuting the Jewish people. Some Jews went into hiding to try to save themselves. A farmer, Johann Oosterveld, and his wife, Dientje, hid Annie and Sini.

The girls spent over three years with the Oostervelds. Most of that time they stayed in an upstairs room of the Oosterveld's farmhouse. But on a very few occasions, the girls were taken out of the house.

One of these occasions was in late winter of 1944. Then Annie was taken by Dientje to meet a young girl hiding with a farmer nearby. Dientje wanted Annie to meet the girl so that she might have someone her own age to talk to for a while.

In the portion of *The Upstairs Room* that you are going to read, you will see how the meeting between the two girls worked out. Try to put yourself in Annie's position. What would you have said to the first person your age that you met in two years?

I glanced at my sister Sini. Would she be mad because of what Dientje just said? That I was going out tonight. Just me and Dientje. We really were going out. We'd have to take the bike to get there, to the farmer Dientje used to work for. He was hiding ten Jews. That was a lot. One of them was a girl my age, Dientje said. I'd probably like her. Sure. Wasn't it nice that Dientje had been told about them? But what if the weather weren't good?

"Dientje, what if it's raining?"

"Don't worry, we'll go anyway."

"What's her name?"

"Whose name?"

"The girl's."

"I don't know. You're glad you're going out, aren't you?" Dientje beamed.

I nodded. "How long will we stay?"

"Not too long. Maybe an hour."

"You look fine," my sister said when it was time to leave.

I walked down the stairs from our room. At the bottom, I looked up. I waved at Sini.

"You can come," Dientje's husband said softly.

Outside, Dientje was holding her bike. She wasn't going to turn the bicycle lamp on, she said. Then nobody would be able to recognize her.

I climbed on the back of her bike. Dientje put her right foot over the bar and pushed off. One, two pumps, then she sat down. "Put your arms around my middle. Hold on."

I knew we were going over a sandy road. Every once in a while the bike sank into a little hole. I could feel Dientje strain to get out of it. Was it a narrow road?

Around the town that I came from all the side roads like this one were narrow. Were there any trees along the road? Carefully I stuck out my right arm. I didn't touch anything. My hands were cold. I put them inside Dientje's pockets.

"The path is getting very narrow here. Be sure to hold on."

Of course, I would. I didn't want to fall.

The air smelled good. I opened my mouth wide. Come in air, it's all right, it's me. Gratefully I rubbed my cheek against Dientje's coat.

"Good evening." Dientje walked into the stable, holding my hand. "How've you been? This is Annie."

"I see, I see. Well, why don't we go talk to Mimi?"

We followed the farmer into a room at the back of the stable. "Here's somebody to visit you," he announced.

The girl in the corner must be Mimi. She looked my age. From across the room we looked at each other. What would I say? I backed up and leaned against Dientje's chair. She was busy listening to the farmer and his wife.

"The baker must think something is going on here," he said. "Everyday I come to the bakery with a large basket. 'Boy, you're eating well these days,' he's already said to me more than once. 'Ja,' I said, 'my kids sure have appetites.' But I worry plenty over it. He might find out."

Where did the ten people sleep? Did they have a hiding place? I looked around. Our room was cozier—just my sister Sini and me. I wondered whether she missed me.

"Isn't she a little thing?" Dientje asked. "You should see her eat. Like a bird."

I wriggled uncomfortably.

"I don't know what's the matter with her tonight. At home she isn't so bashful. You should hear her sometimes. C'mon, Annie, talk to what's her name? Mimi. She looks like a nice girl. Go on."

"Mimi, you're not shy. Talk to Annie," the farmer's wife said.

Mimi laughed sheepishly.

"Aren't you going to say anything to each other?" Dientje wanted to know.

I felt my face getting red. I was sure that everybody was waiting to see whether we would start talking.

"Well, that wasn't a success," Dientje said a little while later. "Let's go home."

"Bye, Mimi," I said on my way out.

"Now, why didn't you start talking earlier? This is the first thing you've said to each other."

Ashamed, I nodded. It was silly. But what was there to say? I didn't even know her.

With a sigh of relief, I climbed back on the bike. Once again I wrapped my arms around Dientje's middle. It sure did smell good outside. It was getting to be spring.

ZLATEH THE GOAT

Isaac Bashevis Singer

At Hanukkah time the road from the village to the town is usually covered with snow, but this year the winter had been a mild one. Hanukkah had almost come, yet little snow had fallen. The sun shone most of the time. The peasants complained that because of the dry weather there would be a poor harvest of winter grain. New grass sprouted, and the peasants sent their cattle out to pasture.

For Reuven the furrier it was a bad year, and after long hesitation he decided to sell Zlateh the goat. She was old and gave little milk. Feyvel the town butcher had offered eight gulden for her. Such a sum would buy Hanukkah candles, potatoes and oil for pancakes, gifts for the children, and other holiday necessaries for the house. Reuven told his oldest boy Aaron to take the goat to town.

Aaron understood what taking the goat to Feyvel meant, but he had to obey his father. Leah, his mother, wiped the tears

263

from her eyes when she heard the news. Aaron's younger sisters, Anna and Miriam, cried loudly. Aaron put on his quilted jacket and a cap with earmuffs, bound a rope around Zlateh's neck, and took along two slices of bread with cheese to eat on the road. Aaron was supposed to deliver the goat by evening, spend the night at the butcher's, and return the next day with the money.

While the family said good-bye to the goat, and Aaron placed the rope around her neck, Zlateh stood as patiently and good-naturedly as ever. She licked Reuven's hand. She shook her small white beard. Zlateh trusted human beings. She knew that they always fed her and never did her any harm.

When Aaron brought her out on the road to town, she seemed somewhat astonished. She'd never been led in that direction before. She looked back at him questioningly, as if to say, "Where are you taking me?" But after awhile she seemed to come to the conclusion that a goat shouldn't ask questions. Still, the road was different. They passed new fields, pastures, and huts with thatched roofs. Here and there a dog barked and came running after them, but Aaron chased it away with his stick.

The sun was shining when Aaron left the village. Suddenly the weather changed. A large black cloud with a bluish center appeared in the east and spread itself rapidly over the sky. A cold wind blew in with it. The crows flew low, croaking. At first it looked as if it would rain, but instead it began to hail as in summer. It was early in the day, but it became dark as dusk. After awhile the hail turned to snow.

In his twelve years Aaron had seen all kinds of weather, but he had never experienced a snow like this one. It was so dense it shut out the light of the day. In a short time their path was completely covered. The wind became as cold as ice. The road to town was narrow and winding. Aaron no longer knew where he was. He could not see through the snow. The cold soon penetrated his quilted jacket.

At first Zlateh didn't seem to mind the change in weather. She too was twelve years old and knew what winter meant. But when her legs sank deeper and deeper into the snow, she began to turn her head and look at Aaron in wonderment. Her mild eyes seemed to ask, "Why are we out in such a storm?" Aaron hoped that a peasant would come along with his cart, but no one passed by.

The snow grew thicker, falling to the ground in large, whirling flakes. Beneath it Aaron's boots touched the softness of a plowed field. He realized that he was no longer on the road. He had gone astray. He could no longer figure out which was east or west, which way was the village, the town. The wind whistled, howled, whirled the snow about. It looked as if white imps were playing tag on the fields. A white dust rose above the ground. Zlateh stopped. She could walk no longer. Stubbornly

she anchored her hooves in the earth and bleated as if pleading to be taken home. Icicles hung from her white beard, and her horns were glazed with frost.

Aaron did not want to admit the danger, but he knew just the same that if they did not find shelter they would freeze to death. This was no ordinary storm. It was a mighty blizzard. The snowfall had reached his knees. His hands were numb, and he could no longer feel his toes. He choked when he breathed. His nose felt like wood, and he rubbed it with snow. Zlateh's bleating began to sound like crying. Those humans in whom she had so much confidence had dragged her into a trap. Aaron began to pray for himself and for the innocent animal.

Suddenly Aaron made out the shape of a hill. He wondered what it could be. Who had piled snow into such a huge heap? He moved toward it, dragging Zlateh after him. When he came near it, he realized that it was a large haystack which the snow had blanketed.

Aaron realized immediately that they were saved. With great effort he dug his way through the snow. He was a village boy and knew what to do. When he reached the hay, he hollowed out a nest for himself and the goat. No matter how cold it may be outside, in the hay it is always warm. And hay was food for Zlateh. The moment she smelled it she became contented and began to eat. Outside the snow continued to fall. It quickly covered the passageway Aaron had dug. But a boy and an animal need to breathe, and there was hardly any air in their hideout. Aaron bored a kind of a window through the hay and snow and carefully kept the passage clear.

Zlateh, having eaten her fill, sat down on her hind legs and seemed to have regained her confidence in people. Aaron ate his two slices of bread and cheese, but after the difficult journey he was still hungry. He looked at Zlateh and noticed her udders were full. He lay down next to her, placing himself so that when

he milked her he could squirt the milk into his mouth. It was rich and sweet. Zlateh was not accustomed to being milked that way, but she did not resist. On the contrary, she seemed eager to reward Aaron for bringing her to a shelter whose very walls, floor, and ceiling were made of food.

Through the window Aaron could catch a glimpse of the chaos outside. The wind carried before it whole drifts of snow. It was completely dark, and he did not know whether night had already come or whether it was the darkness of the storm. Thank goodness that in the hay it was not cold. The dried hay, grass, and field flowers exuded the warmth of the summer sun. Zlateh ate frequently; she nibbled from above, below, from the left and right. Her body gave forth an animal warmth, and Aaron cuddled up to her. He had always loved Zlateh, but now she was like a sister. He was alone, cut off from his family, and wanted to talk, He began to talk to Zlateh. "Zlateh, what do you think about what has happened to us?" he asked.

"Maaa," Zlateh answered.

"If we hadn't found this stack of hay, we would both be frozen stiff by now," Aaron said.

"Maaa," was the goat's reply.

"If the snow keeps on falling like this, we may have to stay here for days," Aaron explained.

"Maaa," Zlateh bleated.

"What does 'Maaa' mean?" Aaron asked. "You'd better speak up clearly."

"Maaa. Maaa," Zlateh tried.

"Well, let it be 'Maaa' then," Aaron said patiently. "You can't speak, but I know you understand. I need you and you need me. Isn't that right?"

"Maaaa."

Aaron became sleepy. He made a pillow out of some hay, leaned his head on it, and dozed off. Zlateh too fell asleep.

When Aaron opened his eyes, he didn't know whether it was morning or night. The snow had blocked up his window. He tried to clear it, but when he had bored through to the length of his arm, he still hadn't reached the outside. Luckily he had his stick with him and was able to break through to the open air. It was still dark outside. The snow continued to fall and the wind wailed, first with one voice and then with many. Sometimes it had the sound of devilish laughter. Zlateh too awoke, and when Aaron greeted her, she answered, "Maaa." Yes, Zlateh's language consisted of only one word, but it meant many things. Now she was saying, "We must accept all that is given us— heat, cold, hunger, satisfaction, light, and darkness."

Aaron had awakened hungry. He had eaten up his food, but Zlateh had plenty of milk.

For three days Aaron and Zlateh stayed in the haystack. Aaron had always loved Zlateh, but in these three days he loved her more and more. She helped him keep warm. She comforted him with her patience. He told her many stories, and she always cocked her ears and listened. When he patted her, she licked his hand and his face. Then she said, "Maaa," and he knew it meant, I love you too.

The snow fell for three days, though after the first day it was not as thick and the wind quieted down. Sometimes Aaron felt that there could never have been a summer, that the snow had always fallen, ever since he could remember. He, Aaron, never had a mother or father or sisters. He was a snow child, born of the snow, and so was Zlateh. It was so quiet in the hay that his ears rang in the stillness. Aaron and Zlateh slept all night and a good part of the day. As for Aaron's dreams, they were all about warm weather. He dreamed of green fields, trees covered with blossoms, clear brooks, and singing birds. By the third night the snow had stopped, but Aaron did not dare to find his way home in the darkness. The sky became clear and the moon shone, casting silvery nets on the snow. Aaron dug his way out and looked at the world. It was all white, quiet, dreaming dreams of heavenly splendor. The stars were large and close. The moon swam in the sky as in a sea.

On the morning of the fourth day Aaron heard the ringing of sleigh bells. The haystack was not far from the road. The peasant who drove the sleigh pointed out the way to him—not to the town and Feyvel the butcher, but home to the village. Aaron had decided in the haystack that he would never part with Zlateh.

Aaron's family and their neighbors had searched for the boy and the goat but had found no trace of them during the storm. They feared they were lost. Aaron's mother and sisters cried for him; his father remained silent and gloomy. Suddenly one of the neighbors came running to their house with the news that Aaron and Zlateh were coming up the road.

There was great joy in the family. Aaron told them how he had found the stack of hay and how Zlateh had fed him

with her milk. Aaron's sisters kissed and hugged Zlateh and gave her a special treat of chopped carrots and potato peels, which Zlateh gobbled up hungrily.

Nobody ever again thought of selling Zlateh, and now that the cold weather had finally set in, the villagers needed the services of Reuven the furrier once more. When Hanukkah came, Aaron's mother was able to fry pancakes every evening, and Zlateh got her portion too. Even though Zlateh had her own pen, she often came to the kitchen, knocking on the door with her horns to indicate that she was ready to visit, and she was always admitted. In the evening Aaron, Miriam, and Anna played dreidel. Zlateh sat near the stove watching the children and the flickering of the Hanukkah candles.

Once in a while Aaron would ask her, "Zlateh, do you remember the three days we spent together?"

And Zlateh would scratch her neck with a horn, shake her white bearded head and come out with the single sound which expressed all her thoughts, and all her love.

Personification

Giving human characteristics to things that are not human is called *personification.* For example, if you said, "The toast jumped out of the toaster," you would be using personification. Toast cannot jump. Jumping is something people do. Therefore, when you say the toast jumped, you are using personification.

Is personification used in the following sentence?

The sun is shining.

The answer is *no.* But in the following sentences, personification *is* used to describe the sun.

The sun is smiling on us.
The sun hid its face from us.

Read the sentences that follow. Some of them are examples of personification; others are not.

Find the sentences that are examples of personification.

1. The box is on the floor.
2. Does the car have enough gas?
3. The leaves danced across the yard.
4. Snowflakes tickled my face.
5. Big drops of rain fell on the ground.
6. The clothes swam around in the washing machine.
7. The day is crawling by.

Use personification to complete the following sentences.

1. A train came _____ down the track.
2. Ann and Jenny could hear the motor _____ .
3. The wind _____ through the trees.
4. The plant_____ the water we poured on it.

TWO WERE LEFT

HUGH B. CAVE

On the third night of hunger, Noni thought of the dog. Nothing of flesh and blood lived upon the floating ice island except those two.

In the breakup Noni had lost his sled. His food, his fur, even his knife were gone. He had saved only Nimuk, his devoted dog. And now the two on the ice watched each other. Each kept his distance.

Noni's love for Nimuk was real, very real. It was as real as the hunger and cold nights. And it was as real as the pain of his injured leg in its homemade brace. But the men of his village had killed their dogs when food was scarce, hadn't they? And without thinking twice about it.

And Nimuk, he told himself, when hungry enough would seek food. One of us will soon be eating the other, Noni thought. So...

He could not kill the dog with his bare hands. Nimuk was powerful and much fresher than he. A weapon, then, was needed.

Removing his mittens, he unstrapped the brace from his leg. When he had hurt his leg a few weeks before, he had made the brace from bits of harness and two thin strips of iron.

Now he kneeled. He put one of the iron strips into a crack in the ice. He began to rub the other against it with firm, slow strokes.

Nimuk watched him. It seemed to Noni that the dog's eyes glowed more brightly as the night passed.

He worked on, trying not to remember why. The strip of iron had an edge now. It had begun to take shape. His task was finished at daylight.

Noni pulled the finished knife from the ice. He touched its edge. The sun's glare reflected from it. It stabbed at his eyes and momentarily blinded him.

Noni straightened himself.

"Here, Nimuk!" he called softly.

The dog watched him.

"Come here," Noni called.

Nimuk came closer. Noni read fear in the animal's look. He read hunger and suffering in the dog's breathing and awkward walk. His heart wept. He hated himself and fought against it.

Closer Nimuk came. Now Noni felt a thickening in his throat.

He saw the dog's eyes. They showed Nimuk's suffering.

Now! Now was the time to strike!

A great sob shook Noni's kneeling body. He cursed the knife. He threw the weapon far from him. With empty hands outstretched, he moved toward the dog. Then, he fell.

The dog growled. He circled the boy's body. And Noni was sick with fear.

In throwing away his knife, he had left himself defenseless. He was too weak to crawl after it now. He was at Nimuk's mercy. And Nimuk was hungry.

The dog circled him and was creeping up from behind.

Noni shut his eyes. He prayed that the attack might be swift. He felt the dog's feet against his leg. He felt the hot rush of Nimuk's breath against his neck. A scream gathered in the boy's throat.

Then he felt the dog's hot tongue licking his face.

Noni's eyes opened. He stared unbelieving. Crying softly, he drew the dog's head down against his own....

The plane came out of the south an hour later. Its pilot was a young man of the coastal patrol. He looked down and saw the large ice island. And he saw something flashing.

It was the sun gleaming on something shiny which moved. The pilot was curious. He descended, circling the island. Now he saw a dark, still shape. It appeared to be human. Or were there two shapes?

He set his plane down in the water and investigated. There were two shapes, boy and dog. The boy was unconscious but alive. The dog whined but was too weak to move.

The gleaming object which had trapped the pilot's attention was a knife stuck point first into the ice. It was a little distance away and quivering in the wind.

This conversation between two autumn leaves comes from the book **Bambi,** the story of a young deer and the forest life around him.

Fall

Felix Salten

The leaves were falling from the great oak at the meadow's edge. They were falling from all the trees.

One branch of the oak reached high above the others and stretched far out over the meadow. Two leaves clung to its very tip.

"It isn't the way it used to be," said one leaf to the other.

"No," the other leaf answered. "So many of us have fallen off tonight we're almost the only ones left on our branch."

"You never know who's going to go next," said the first leaf. "Even when it was warm and the sun shone, a storm or a cloudburst would come sometimes, and many leaves were torn off, though they were still young. You never know who's going to go next."

"The sun hardly shines now," sighed the second leaf, "and when it does, it gives no warmth. We must have warmth again."

"Can it be true," said the first leaf, "can it really be true, that others come to take our places when we're gone and after them still others, and more and more?"

"It is really true," whispered the second leaf. "We can't even begin to imagine it, it's beyond our powers."

"It makes me very sad," added the first leaf.

They were silent a while. Then the first leaf said quietly to itself, "Why must we fall?"

The second leaf asked, "What happens to us when we have fallen?"

"We sink down...."

"What is under us?"

The first leaf answered, "I don't know. Some say one thing, some another, but nobody knows."

The second leaf asked, "Do we feel anything, do we know anything about ourselves when we're down there?"

The first leaf answered, "Who knows? Not one of all those down there has ever come back to tell us about it."

They were silent again. Then the first leaf said tenderly to the other, "Don't worry so much about it, you're trembling."

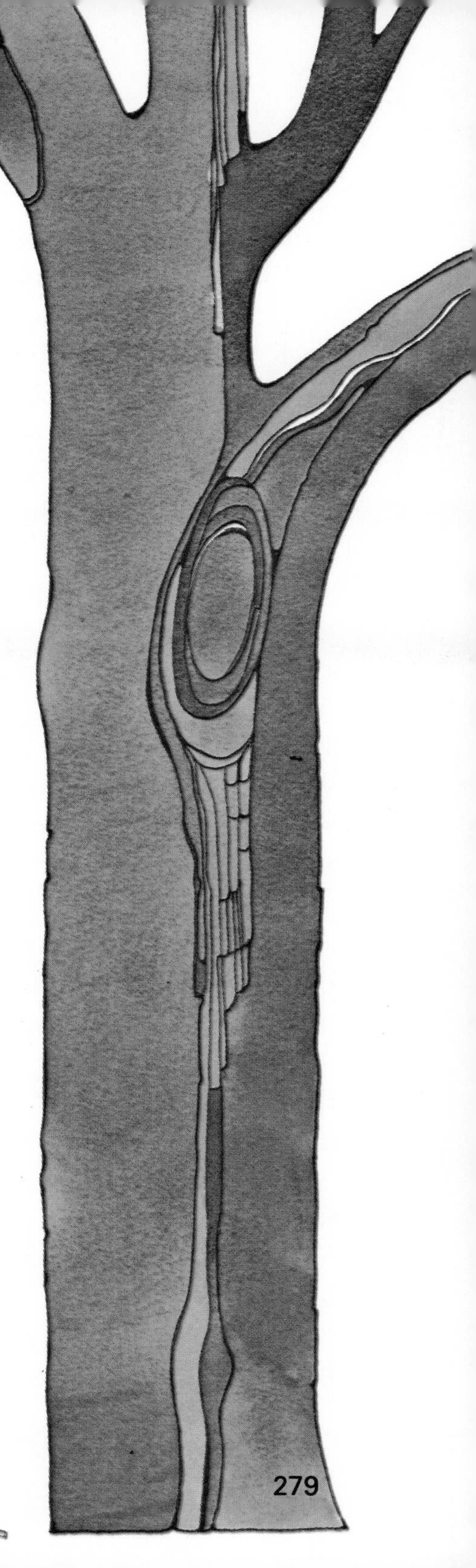

"That's nothing," the second leaf answered, "I tremble at the least thing now. I don't feel so sure of my hold as I used to."

"Let's not talk any more about such things," said the first leaf.

The other replied, "No, we'll let it be. But—what else shall we talk about?" It was silent, but went on after a little while, "Which of us will go first?"

"There's still plenty of time to worry about that," the other leaf said reassuringly. "Let's remember how beautiful it was, how wonderful, when the sun came out and shone so warmly that we thought we'd burst with life. Do you remember? And the morning dew and the mild and splendid nights . . ."

"Now the nights are dreadful," the second leaf complained, "and there is no end to them."

"We shouldn't complain," said the first leaf gently. "We've outlived many, many others."

"Have I changed much?" asked the second leaf shyly.

"Not in the least," the first leaf said. "You think so only because I've gotten to be so yellow and ugly. But it's different in your case."

"You're fooling me," the second leaf said.

"No, really," the first leaf answered eagerly, "believe me, you're as lovely as the day you were born. Here and there may be a little yellow spot. But it's hardly noticeable and makes you only more beautiful, believe me."

"Thanks," whispered the second leaf, quite touched. "I don't believe you, not altogether, but I thank you because you're so kind. You've always been so kind to me. I'm just beginning to understand how kind you are."

"Hush," said the other leaf, and kept silent itself, for it was too troubled to talk any more.

Then they were both silent. Hours passed.

A moist wind blew, cold and hostile, through the treetops.

"Ah, now," said the second leaf, "I . . ." Then its voice broke off. It was torn from its place and spun down.

Winter had come.

DAYDREAMS

Dina Anastasio

As you can see, many inventions have made our lives much easier. Maybe you can build some other inventions here in shop class.

Pat Garcia, famous inventor.

283

WOMAN IN THE NEWS

Alma Whitney

There are people whose job it is to communicate something to an audience.

Melba Tolliver is one of these people. Ms. Tolliver is a news reporter for a television station in New York. She appears on an evening news program.

Ms. Tolliver grew up in Ohio and came to New York to study nursing. She has been working in television since 1966.

In the following interview, Melba Tolliver talks about what it is like to work at communicating. And she talks about the importance of her work.

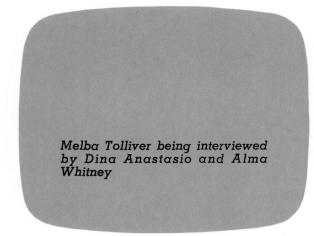

Melba Tolliver being interviewed by Dina Anastasio and Alma Whitney

Q. *Were you interested in becoming a television reporter when you were growing up?*

A. No, I never thought about it at all. I think people are influenced in the careers they choose by the people they know or can identify with. I grew up at a time when there were no black men or women reporting the news on television. I had no reason to think it was a career I could ever have.

Q. *How did you get into television work?*

A. It was kind of a Cinderella story. I left nursing after several years and took a job as a secretary at a television station. One day the reporters went out on strike. The station had to find someone to fill in for a reporter who was the hostess on a news program. I was asked to do the job and I did. I continued doing the show for about a week, until the woman returned to work. There was a lot of talk about what I had done. And some people at the station became interested in me.

Q. *Was that all? Did you go from being a secretary to a television reporter just like that?*

A. No, that wasn't all. At the time I filled in on that program, the television stations were being criticized for not having many minority-group members on programs. The company decided to set up a training program for minority-group members. I was placed in the program. For eighteen months, I worked in different departments in the news section of the company. I also studied reporting for a while. Then I was hired as an on-camera reporter for the station.

Q. *What do you try to communicate to your viewers?*

A. There are two things. I want to tell people about things that have happened that I think are important. And I want people to feel that the news is happening to real people, people who have feelings just like the feelings of the people who watch the program. Whenever I do a story, I try to focus on some person who is involved with the story.

Melba Tolliver with a former co-worker, Gil Noble.

Q. *Could you give us an example?*

A. Yes, I once did a series of news stories called "Profiles." I would select a topic that I thought many people were concerned about. And I would then tell the story by talking to somebody who was involved in it. One thing that comes to mind is a story I did about American Indians and what their life is like in America today. I interviewed a Mohawk Indian who had come from a reservation to work in the city. This man told me things I could never have learned from reading books. He told me about the dreams he had for his children. He told me what it feels like to be a foreigner in his own country. We talked about wrong ideas people have about American Indians. For example, many people think that they are not afraid of heights. That is because many of them have come to the city and taken jobs as construction workers on tall buildings. But this man told me that American Indians take those jobs because they pay better than safer jobs. Many American Indians are poor. They come to the cities to work. Then they can send money to their families. Naturally, they want to get a job that pays well. But many people think they take the dangerous work because they are fearless.

Q. *What do you think you communicated to your audience by doing that particular story?*

A. I communicated some facts about American Indians today. I think I got a lot of people to realize they had feelings that they could share with American Indians.

For instance, what it feels like to have people look at you because you look different. That is certainly a feeling I have had in my life, and I know many of the viewers of the program have had it, too.

Q. *In your work, you get to talk to some very well-known people. Do you find this exciting?*

A. It is always interesting for me to meet people and talk to them. But I think that too many people believe that a well-known person must be more interesting or exciting than an unknown person. I find that the most extraordinary people are ones that you're likely never to have heard of. But these people are doing important, valuable things that really mean something in this world. I feel I can really communicate something important to my audience by talking about these people.

I once did a story about a woman named Mrs. Clara Hale who lives in New York. Mrs. Hale became interested in raising foster children. She took many, many foster children into her home and brought them up. And do you know, she

sent almost all of these children to college. I think Mrs. Hale is extraordinary and exciting, even though she's not what people might call famous.

Q. *Since you have started working for television news, have you seen any changes in the business?*

A. Yes, and I imagine it is the same in almost every business. As newer, younger people come to a job, they sometimes question the way things are done. And they want to change things. But things don't change overnight. They take a long time. However, there are certainly more minority group people and women working on news programs than there were when I started. And this has meant change. You might have to listen very carefully to notice it, but it is there.

Q. *Do you mean that women report news differently from the way that men do?*

A. Yes, in a way. Women and men may report the same types of stories. But women may report stories in a slightly different way from the way men do. Suppose you are doing a story about Washington. You are talking about Congress. Most of the people in Congress are men. A man reporting the story may say, "today congressmen were busy working on a new plan for clean air." But a woman reporting the story may observe, "today the men and women in Congress," or "today congressmen and congresswomen were busy working on a new plan for clean air." You see, women reporting the news are not going to make the news different. But they are going to be very careful to make sure women are mentioned when they are involved in a story. People will get used to hearing little changes like this in reporting. And people will get more and more used to women being involved in important things, as they actually are.

Q. *Do you feel that being black influences the way you report a story?*

A. It influences my reporting in much the same way that being a woman does. As a black, I may observe things that someone who is not black might not see.

Q. *What advice can you give to young people who want to have careers as television reporters?*

A. I don't think there is any direct path that one can take to get a job as a reporter on television. People come in by so many different doors. Look at me! I started as a secretary. But as soon as a young person decides that he or she is interested in news reporting, the person should investigate the different jobs that have to do with news. There are jobs in filming and editing. There are jobs for writers and producers. If you limit yourself to being a television reporter or nothing else, you may very well be nothing else. Young people can gather experience writing for their school newspapers and by studying journalism in school.

Q. *What qualities do you think make a good reporter?*

A. In the first place, people who want to be reporters must want to tell a story. They have to want to communicate something to others. And, just as important, they have to have endless curiosity. Reporters must always want to know the whys and hows of things. Reporters should not stop searching and questioning until they are satisfied that every detail of a story has been uncovered.

A Reporter's Questions

In "Woman in the News," Melba Tolliver says that reporters must "have endless curiosity." The basic questions a reporter must ask are the five *W's: Who? What? Where? When? Why?* The answers to these questions give reporters the essential information they need to write their stories.

The first part of a news story is written to catch the attention of the audience or the reader. It also gives the major facts of the story — the five *W's*. In preparing her story on American Indians, Ms. Tolliver had to answer the basic questions.

Who?	American Indians
What?	Their lives and the work they do
Where?	On reservations and in cities
When?	Today
Why?	To support their families

Can you use the information above to write the beginning of a news report that catches the audience's attention and gives the important facts?

Now choose one of the following topics:

- a person in sports
- an event in your school
- an interesting person in your neighborhood

Use the five *W's* as a guide in gathering information on your topic. Then try your hand at writing an interesting, factual news story. **Remember:** A good reporter asks the right questions and finds the answers that are accurate and interesting.

THE QUESTION

1

If I could teach you how to fly
Or bake an elderberry pie
Or turn the sidewalk into stars
Or play new songs on an old guitar
Or if I knew the way to heaven,
The names of night, the taste of seven
And owned them all, to keep or lend—
Would you come and be my friend?

2

You cannot teach me how to fly.
I love the berries but not the pie.
The sidewalks are for walking on,
And an old guitar has just one song.
The names of night cannot be known,
The way to heaven cannot be shown.
You cannot keep, you cannot lend—
But still I want you for my friend.

—Dennis Lee

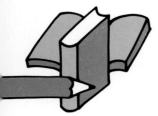

Quote, Unquote

Sometimes an author wants to report the exact words a person has said. These exact words are called a *quotation*. The author uses *quotation marks* to show where the quotation begins and ends. Opening quotation marks are placed before the quotation. Closing quotation marks are placed after the quotation.

The speaker's name and the word indicating that something has been said may come before the quotation.

> Paul said, "Our friends are here."

Notice that a comma is placed before the opening quotation marks. A period is placed inside the closing quotation marks at the end of the sentence. The first word of the quotation is capitalized.

The speaker's name and the word indicating that something has been said may come after the quotation.

> "They are right on time," he commented.

In this case, a comma is placed inside the closing quotation marks. A period is placed at the end of the entire sentence. The first word of the quotation is capitalized. The first word after the quotation is not capitalized unless it is a proper noun.

If a quotation ends with a question mark or an exclamation point, these marks are placed inside the closing quotation marks.

> Irene asked, "How did you get here?"
>
> "What a trip we had!" they exclaimed.

The speaker's name and the word indicating that something has been said may interrupt the quotation. If a *single* sentence is being interrupted, one comma is placed inside the first part of the quotation, and another comma is placed after the word indicating that something has been said. The first word in the last part of the quotation is not capitalized unless it is a proper noun.

"Sit down," she offered, "on the sofa."

If two separate sentences are being interrupted, one comma is placed inside the first part of the quotation, and a period is placed after the word indicating that something has been said. Then, the first word in the last part of the quotation is capitalized.

"Thank you," they answered. "We are very tired."

Write each sentence correctly on your paper.
Use quotation marks and other punctuation where needed.

1. Julio asked why were you late
2. Our taxi cab never came Linda explained
3. We had to take a bus to the station she added
4. The train she said was almost ready to leave
5. Was the trip long Paul asked
6. It seemed like forever Linda exclaimed
7. Roger asked where can I go swimming
8. The pool in the park Paul said opens tomorrow
9. Is it crowded there Frank asked
10. It's not crowded in the morning Paul replied
11. What fun it will be Roger shouted
12. I hope it's hot Frank said rain would spoil our fun

DIALOGUES

People have always needed to communicate with others and have always found ways to do so. In "Dialogues," you read about how people use poems, letters, pictures, and conversations to communicate with each other. You also learned how body language plays an important part in spoken communication among people and in communication between people and pets. There are many different ways to communicate, but the result is the same—shared thoughts, ideas, and feelings.

Thinking About "Dialogues"

1. How did knowing that a word can have more than one meaning help you to understand the humor in "Where's Mortimer?"
2. Why didn't Pamela tell Phyllis the truth about Creston?
3. Why do you think it is important to know how to "read" body language?
4. How did Zlateh and Aaron communicate?
5. In "Woman in the News," what did you learn about the features of a good news report?
6. How do you use different ways of communicating in different situations?
7. In "Fall," you read a conversation between two autumn leaves. Now write a dialogue between two leaves in spring.

INROADS

People have always wanted to learn about the world and find ways to improve life. By studying the past, we have learned how forms of life have developed and changed over the centuries. Sometimes we have learned from past mistakes. Sometimes we have learned from our own experiments. Still, many mysteries remain to be solved. In a search for answers, the inroads made by science and medicine are helping to make our lives better now and in the future.

Some of the selections in "Inroads" tell about discoveries that have helped answer scientific and medical questions. A group of people work together to identify and preserve a living fossil discovered in the sea. A pioneer in the field of medicine performs the first open-heart surgery. A doctor finds the cause of a patient's carrot-colored skin. Other selections discuss questions that still need to be answered, such as whether there is life on other planets.

As you read, think about how developments in science and medicine have helped you or someone you know.

WHAT IF YOU MADE A MUSEUM?

BY MARGERY FACKLAM

What if someone gave you a huge empty building and said, "Make a museum."

"What for?" you might ask. "Who needs a museum?"

Everyone needs a museum. Museums save things because scientists and other people want to study them. Learning about stars or birds or rocks can help us live better lives.

"How's that?" you might wonder. While it's true that each of us need not know about birds, it's good that someone does know. The people who built the first aircraft learned

about flight by studying the way air moves around birds' wings as they fly. Men and women who study birds can tell us how to get rid of mosquitoes without using poison. They know what kinds of bushes to plant in a yard so that birds that eat mosquitoes will want to live there.

Studying stars is important for space flights. Collecting things from ancient Egypt or from ancient tribes helps us learn about people who lived differently from the way we live now.

Sometimes we learn that they had good ideas. Even though they didn't call it ecology, ancient tribes knew a lot about living with the land. They

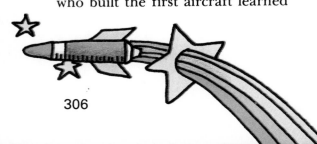

knew that they shared the land with plants and animals. So, they didn't go around chopping down too many trees or killing more animals than they could eat.

Sometimes we collect objects, such as ancient pottery, just because we are curious and we like to see things that will never be made again. It is important to collect objects.

"OK," you might finally say. "It's important to have collections. But how do I start to make my museum?"

You might be a guest on a television program, and you could tell people about your museum and ask them to send things. Then you could sit back in your director's chair and wait for your museum to grow —and it would grow.

People would send you fossils and falcons, minerals and masks, bird nests and fishing nets, weeds and wigwams, pieces of pottery and parts of peace pipes.

307

The zoo director might call one day and say, "Our orangutan died. Do you want him?"

A woman might phone and say, "We have an empty wasps' nest. Can you use it at your new museum?"

So your museum would grow until one Monday morning you would walk into your big building and it wouldn't be empty any more. The place would look like an enormous attic, crammed full of thousands of things. You wouldn't be able to remember whether the sharks' teeth were in the box under the birds' eggs or next to the wasps' nest. You would not remember who had given what.

Right then you might holler, "Hey, wait a minute! This isn't a museum!" Only no one would hear you, because no one works in your museum.

Walking around your museum-that-isn't-a-museum, tripping over boxes, you'd have a problem. You'd wonder how you could get the mess in order. Whom should you hire to help?

You would need someone to make a list of all things and put a number on each one. The person you would hire to get things in order would be called the *registrar*. The registrar keeps track of everything in the museum. A registrar is a person who registers things.

First he or she might pick up several pieces of a broken bowl and give them all a number. Then each piece would have to be numbered

with a kind of ink that doesn't wash off. Finally, the registrar would put the same numbers on a card and type:

> 1. Twelve pieces of pottery from Arizona
> Collected by Karl Kramer, February 21, 1976
> Numbers 1a, 1b, 1c, 1d, 1e, 1f, 1g, 1h, 1i, 1j

A dead bat might be the next thing in your pile of objects.

When the registrar had finished you would feel satisfied that things were in order. Everything would have a number and a card, just like the books in the library.

Then the registrar would interrupt your contentment. "The bat is on a shelf next to the pieces of pottery, and the rocks are in a cupboard with insects. The Indian baskets are in a box with the sea urchins. Everything has a number, but the place is still a mess. Two wooden spears are broken, too."

To solve these problems, you would hire one person to take care of the rocks, another to take care of the animals, and another to take care of things such as Indian baskets and

wooden spears. These people would be called *curators*.

Curators are people who take care of collections. The curator of zoology studies and takes care of animals. The curator of geology studies and takes care of rocks and fossils.

You can have as many curators as there are things to study. You can have a curator for just about every kind of science there is. Or, if yours is a small museum, you might have only one.

Curators also repair broken objects in their collections. They store things carefully so that nothing will be hurt by too much heat or light or insects or dampness.

Curators are the keepers of the treasures of the earth—things we see every day and things that will never be on this earth again.

What's Next?

Almost as soon as you think your museum is finished, it will be old-fashioned.

Science doesn't stand still. Every day there are discoveries, inventions, ideas, new ways of doing old things, new ways of building exhibits.

When you visit a museum now, you walk past the exhibits. Maybe

someday you will sit in a comfortable chair and all the exhibits will move by you on a huge conveyor belt.

Today, in some museums, you can push a button and smell the salty sea air of an ocean exhibit. You can push a button and hear the gulls scream or the wind screech. You can hear the monkeys howl in a jungle or the owl hoot in the freezing Arctic.

At the Boston Children's Museum, you can go into a manhole and crawl under the city streets to see the old trolley tracks, the water pipes, and the bundles of wires.

You can learn a tribal dance or try on a tribal costume at a People Center in New York City's American Museum of Natural History. At the Ontario (Canada) Science Center, you can feel as though you are docking a space capsule, and you can blow glass or look through a microscope. You can play games with a computer or stand in an exhibit and feel your hair stand on end as 300,000 volts of harmless static electricity pass over your body.

Museums change because people change. But no matter what new ways there will be to store information, museums will always have collections.

A LINK WITH THE PAST

ELEANOR CLYMER

When a fishing trawler docked in East London, South Africa, in 1938, it had a very peculiar catch on board. There, among the sharks and the food fish, was a type of fish that nobody in that area had ever seen before.

The 127-pound, 5-foot-long fish had been caught in the waters off the coast of South Africa. It stayed alive much longer than the other fish on-board did. And when the trawler's captain tried to touch it, the creature almost bit the captain's hand.

Miss Latimer, the curator of the local museum, was called to look at the fish. She, too, had never seen anything like it. Miss Latimer was amazed by many things about the fish, like its strange thick scales and the bony plates which covered its head. But most of all, Miss Latimer was astonished by the creature's fins, which looked like legs. As one of the sailors said, the thing looked "more like a lizard than a fish. . . ."

Miss Latimer looked through all the books that she had on living fishes, but could find no description of a fish that resembled the one caught that day. So she did what many people do when they are faced with something for which they can find no answer. She consulted someone else. Miss Latimer wrote to Dr. James Smith to see if he could help her discover what the creature was.

Dr. Smith's reaction may give you some idea about how scientists feel when they come across a very unusual discovery.

When he received Miss Latimer's letter, Dr. James L. B. Smith was a professor at the University of Grahamstown, about a hundred miles from East London, a town in South Africa. Officially he was a professor of chemistry. But that was only half his life. The other half was fish!

Dr. Smith could never spend as much time as he would have liked studying the fish of the Indian Ocean off South Africa. He had to earn a living. And since professors of chemistry were in more demand than professors of ichthyology, it was chemistry that Dr. Smith taught. However, every minute that Dr. Smith could spare from his classes was given to the study of fish. He published papers

about fish, and people came to him with fish they
had caught and could not identify. He helped
commercial fishers as well as amateurs
by classifying fish and explaining their habits.

Dr. Smith had to work very hard to keep up
with his two interests. But he did it. He went out
in fishing vessels with the crews, braving bad
weather and seasickness for a chance to look over
the "rubbish" that they couldn't sell and would
throw overboard. He went to remote places to talk
to farmers and fishers and lighthouse keepers.

He worked with the curators of museums and
was appointed Honorary Curator of Fish of
many of them.

He also became interested in paleontology, the study of life in past ages. He studied fossils as well as living fishes. And in his spare moments, when he had time to dream, he dreamed of someday discovering something very rare and marvelous that would amaze the scientific world.

By 1938, Dr. Smith was the best-known ichthyologist in South Africa. He was an authority on African fishes. And so it was to him that Miss Latimer decided to write.

Dr. Smith and his wife were spending the Christmas holidays at their house at Knysna, about 250 miles from Grahamstown. The professor had been looking forward to this holiday for some time.

It was peaceful in Knysna. There was no telephone closer than the neighborhood shop. The post office was in the village, but the mail did not come regularly. In a few days there would be examination papers to correct. But for the present there was nothing to do but fish in the lagoon and work in his laboratory, which were Dr. Smith's favorite forms of relaxation.

In the midst of all this peace and quiet, something happened that was like a bomb exploding.

On January 3, 1939, a friend came to see the Smiths. He brought with him a stack of mail that had been piling up at the post office. There were Christmas cards, bills, letters from friends, and, as always, some letters asking for help in identifying fish.

Dr. Smith picked up one from the East London Museum. He knew it was from Miss Latimer because she had written to him many times. He opened the letter. This is what he read and the drawing he saw:

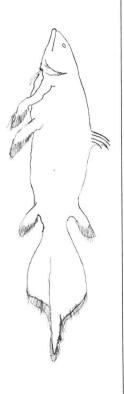

East London,
South Africa
23 December 1938

Dear Dr. Smith,

I had the most queer-looking specimen brought to notice yesterday. The captain of the trawler told me about it, so I immediately set off to see the specimen, which I had removed to our taxidermist as soon as I could. I, however, have drawn a very rough sketch, and am in hopes that you may be able to assist me in classing it.

It is coated in heavy scales, almost armorlike. The fins resemble limbs and are scaled right up to a fringe of filament. The dorsal fin has tiny white spines down each filament. Note drawing inked in red.

I would be so pleased if you could let me know what you think, though I know it is difficult from a description of this kind.

Wishing you all happiness for the season.

Yours sincerely,
M. Courtenay-Latimer

It seemed like a routine request. But then Dr. Smith turned the page and looked at the drawing of the fish. He stared at it. He had never seen such a thing in all his life. A fish with legs! His first thought was that this was some kind of ridiculous mistake. Or maybe it was a joke. But no. Miss Latimer was very careful and serious. It would not be like her to play jokes.

Then he thought she might have made a mistake in her drawing. And yet . . . and yet . . . somewhere he *had* seen such a fish. But where? Not in the sea. Not on the deck of a boat. No—wait. Now he had it: in a book—a book on fossil fish! The drawing was a picture of a fossil fish, anywhere from 70 to 300 million years old! Miss Latimer had sent him a picture of a coelacanth! (SEE-la-Kanth)

But how could it be? The letter said that the fish had been caught *alive* in the waters off South Africa.

He stared at the picture. He would not have been more astounded if Miss Latimer had sent him a picture of a living dinosaur!

"What's the matter?" asked Mrs. Smith.

Dr. Smith shook his head. "Don't think me crazy," he said. "But Miss Latimer has sent me a picture of a living fish that has been extinct for 70 million years. I have to see this fish at once. I'll have to go to East London right away."

But such a trip was really impossible. East London was 350 miles away, over terrible roads.

Trains were few and far between. And in a few days he would have to start work on his examination papers. That was his job, and it came first.

"Well, I'll have that fish sent here," he said. "That will be the best way. Then I can work on it in the laboratory."

His wife looked at the letter. "Do you see when this was written?" she said. "It may be too late."

The letter was dated December 23. Now it was the third of January. What must Miss Latimer be thinking? She had expected to hear from him at once. Why, the fish might be completely spoiled by now! What had the taxidermist done with it? Had he thrown away the insides? Had he saved the gills and the skeleton?

Dr. Smith rushed to the neighborhood shop to try to telephone Miss Latimer. But it was not an easy matter to make a long-distance call from Knysna.

It was now one o'clock in the afternoon. The call could not possibly be put through before five o'clock. At five o'clock the museum where Miss Latimer worked would be closed for the day, and she had no phone at home. So Dr. Smith rushed off to the village. If he couldn't telephone, he could at least send a telegram. And so he did:

> MOST IMPORTANT PRESERVE
> SKELETON AND GILLS FISH DESCRIBED

For even if the soft parts were destroyed or

decayed, a great deal could be learned from the bones.

He arranged for a telephone call to Miss Latimer to be put through the next day and rushed home to write a letter. A coelacanth! A living fossil! The more he thought about it, the more he wanted to believe that it was true. He wrote to Miss Latimer instructing her to take very good care of the fish until he could examine it.

The next day he rushed back to the shop to see if he could get his call through to East London. After waiting three hours, the call finally came through, and Dr. Smith heard Miss Latimer's voice.

He was almost afraid to ask what had happened to the fish's insides, but he managed to stammer out his question. His heart sank when he heard the answer. Yes, the insides had been thrown away. It was impossible to keep them. The garbage wagon had taken them away.

Dr. Smith was desperate. He wanted to take a plane to East London and dig through the rubbish with his own hands. But it was too late. The garbage had been dumped far out at sea.

At last he finished talking and hung up. The phone call had been very expensive. Everyone in the shop was amazed. They had all been standing there, drinking in every word and waiting to learn whether someone in the professor's family had died. But the call had been about a dead fish! It was plain to see what the villagers thought of a man who would pay so much money to talk about a dead fish. He was obviously not quite right in the head.

Dr. Smith was inclined to agree with them. After all, he was jumping to conclusions on the basis of one tiny sketch. He was behaving quite unlike a serious scientist. He had to have books in order to verify his conclusions. But there were no books on fossil fish in the village of Knysna. He sent a telegram to a friend at a museum in Cape Town, asking for a well-known book on the subject.

Two days later the book arrived. It was Volume II of a work entitled *Catalogue of Fossil Fishes in the British Museum*.

Dr. Smith checked the book and found the picture he was looking for. There could be no doubt. The fish that Miss Latimer had drawn must be a coelacanth, though every paleontologist in the world would swear that the last coelacanth had died 70 million years ago!

Somehow, unknown to the human race, coelacanths had survived all this time and were alive somewhere in the ocean. For if one had been found, there must be others.

Why had nobody ever seen one before? It was too big a fish to go unnoticed for long. That raised another question: why was it so big? The fossil coelacanth had been a little fish, about a foot long —never more than 20 inches.

However, in 70 million years, the little fish might have evolved into a big one. And if its outside appearance was so much like that of the fossil, perhaps its inner parts were, too. Think what it would mean to scientists to study not just the bones and teeth of a fossil, but the nervous system, the breathing apparatus, the stomach, the brain, and the muscles!

He wrote to Miss Latimer again. Please, he begged, please try to remember all you can about the fish. What was its air bladder like? Had she remembered to have the skull and the jawbones preserved intact? He would need to know how the jaw was attached to the skull. Had she kept any other parts of the skeleton? Were the gills preserved so that he could learn how the animal breathed? Could she perhaps send him the skin?

A letter arrived from Miss Latimer six days later. The strange specimen was being mounted and looked very well. As for the skeleton, there *wasn't* any.

```
      The backbone was a column of
soft, white, gristlelike mate-
rial, running from skull to tail--
this was an inch across and filled
with oil, which spouted out as cut
through. The flesh was plastic
and could be worked like clay. The
stomach was empty....
      The gills had small rows of
fine spines but were unfortu-
nately thrown away with the body.
```

> Mr. Center has almost mounted
> the specimen now and is not
> doing it badly at all--the oil is
> still pouring out from the skin,
> which seems to have oil cells
> beneath each scale.
>
> The scales are armorlike,
> fitting into deep pockets.

Miss Latimer was very unhappy.

> I have done every possible
> thing to preserve and not lose any
> points, and I feel worried to
> think in the end I allowed the
> body and gills to be discarded.
> They were kept for three days, and
> when I did not hear from you, I
> gave the order for disposal.

Dr. Smith wrote again. Please, he asked, offer a reward for another specimen. And be sure to have a large tank ready in case one should be found. The fish was to be preserved in a strong formalin solution. He would pay for everything. And please, if possible, send him a photograph of the fish and one of the scales to examine.

Some photographs that Miss Latimer had had taken of the fish had not come out. But she did send Dr. Smith three of the fish's thick scales. The scales were almost exactly like those of the fossil fish. Dr. Smith decided to name the fish Latimeria, in honor of Miss Latimer.

It was the middle of February before it was possible for Dr. Smith to make the trip to East London.

Dr. Smith was in such a state of excitement that he did not stop for anything. He rushed to the museum.

He saw no one and nothing except the fish he had come so far to examine. There it was, mounted, its mouth open, its fins more like legs than anything else.

Dr. Smith put out his hand and touched it gently. There was no doubt in his mind.

It was a coelacanth!

The discovery of the coelacanth in 1938 was just the beginning of Dr. Smith's search for another living fossil. After fourteen years, he finally found another one and was able to examine the insides of the fish.

Why all this fuss about a fish that was supposed to have been extinct for 70 million years?

The discovery of the coelacanth gave people a glimpse of what life was like on the earth millions and millions of years ago. Without such a discovery, the history of the earth would remain an even bigger mystery than it is today.

Other Living Fossils

ELEANOR CLYMER

Latimeria is not the only living fossil that has been found. There are others that have been found which tell us what life was like on the earth millions of years ago.

The Lingula is a living shellfish which is somewhat like a clam. Fossils judged to be 600 million years old have been found of shellfish that are almost exactly like Lingula.

These crinoids, sea lilies, look like flowers. They are really related to sea urchins and starfish. Crinoids have survived on earth for 600 million years.

The horseshoe crab is not really a crab but is related to the spider. Horseshoe crabs have been on earth for 350 million years.

One of the insects that has kept its ancient form is the cockroach. It has remained unchanged for the 325 million years it has been on the earth.

Here is a lungfish. The lungfish still buries itself in the mud as its ancestors did 300 million years ago.

Oysters look little different today than their ancestors would have looked 200 million years ago.

This lizardlike creature which lives on islands off New Zealand is called Sphenodon. The Sphenodon has changed little from the 200-million-year-old fossils of it which have been found.

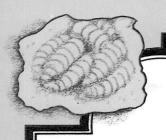
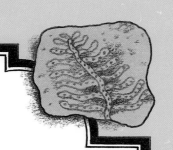

LANGUAGE AND FOSSILS

When a fossil is discovered, it is important to be able to name the time when the plant or animal lived. Therefore the history of the earth has been divided into time periods according to when different types of life existed. To name these divisions, we have borrowed some words from the Greeks.

There are five important divisions:

Cenozoic—the past 60 million years, when mammals have been dominant

Mesozoic—the 100 million years before Cenozoic, when reptiles were dominant

Paleozoic—the 300 million years before Mesozoic, when fish and land invertebrates were dominant

Proterozoic—millions of years before Paleozoic, when sea invertebrates were dominant

Archeozoic—long before Proterozoic, when one-celled animals were dominant

The suffix **-zoic** on these words comes from the Greek *zoon*, meaning "animal." The prefixes come from *kainos*, meaning "new"; *mesos*, meaning "middle"; *palaios*, meaning "old"; *proteros*, meaning "earlier"; and *archaios*, meaning "ancient."

If you found an animal fossil from the Paleozoic era, would it be a very old or a recent animal?

What is a fossil anyway?

It's any remains or impressions of an extinct plant or animal that's preserved in the earth's crust.

What does fossil mean?

It's from an old Latin word *fossilis*, meaning "dug up." 'Cause they are, you know.

A Medical Pioneer

DR. DANIEL HALE WILLIAMS 1856-1931

ALMA WHITNEY

One summer day in 1893 a young man who had been stabbed in the chest was brought to Provident Hospital in Chicago. The patient had lost much blood and seemed to be getting closer to death every hour. Dr. Daniel Hale Williams, Director and Chief Surgeon of the hospital, was called in to examine the man.

None of the doctors or nurses present at the examination would have been the least bit surprised if Dr. Williams had said, "This man has a stab wound which probably reaches his heart. We will give him the usual treatment for such wounds —keep him cool, make sure he has complete rest, and give him painkillers."

But he didn't say that. Dr. Williams knew that this usual treatment would not help the man. Patients treated in this manner died. Instead the doctor turned to his staff and made a surprising statement: he intended to open the man's chest and repair the damage that had been done when he had been stabbed.

This photo shows an operation in a ward at Bellevue Hospital in New York City in the 1870s.

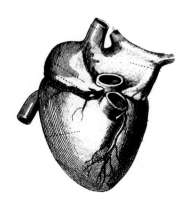

The doctors and nurses in the room were surprised and concerned. In those days no surgeon dared to operate on the chest of a patient. In the first place, most of the techniques of modern medicine were unknown. There were no X rays and no blood transfusions. There was none of the machinery that is used in present-day heart operations. Some doctors still operated in their street clothes, without sterilizing their instruments or the equipment in the operating room. Patients often developed infections after being operated on. Since drugs had not yet been discovered that could cure such infections, these patients usually died.

But Dr. Williams practiced modern techniques of surgery. At this time such methods were beginning to be discussed by scientists all over the world. He never operated without first sterilizing his instruments and applying germ-killers to everything in the room in which he would operate. His surgery was almost always successful because his patients did not develop infections.

But even with his past successes, Dr. Williams had never operated on a patient's heart. If the operation failed, Dr. Williams might be criticized by members of the medical profession all over the world for taking such a chance.

The operating room was prepared for the patient, and the operation began. Dr. Williams opened the patient's chest and found that the knife had struck the heart and badly cut the pericardium, the sac surrounding the heart. Deciding not to touch the heart itself, Dr. Williams proceeded to sew up the pericardium. As he worked, the six doctors in the room watched attentively and wondered what the outcome of the first open-heart surgery would be.

The answer came a few days later. There was no sign of infection. Instead all of the patient's life signs returned to normal. Several weeks later the man who had been brought to Provident Hospital on the brink of death walked out of the hospital to continue his life. He lived for many years.

Dr. Daniel Hale Williams made history with his heart operation. It was a medical first. But the operation was not the first contribution that this doctor had made to his profession or to his people.

The very hospital in which Dr. Williams performed his historic operation was also a first.

Before Dr. Williams founded Provident Hospital in 1891, he had been forced to perform operations in his patients' homes. Because of racial prejudice, black doctors like himself could not get jobs at hospitals. So they had to treat their patients in the patients' homes. Black patients who were admitted to hospitals were assigned to special wards. Many people felt these wards did not offer the quality of treatment available to white patients.

Dr. Williams decided that the time had come to start a hospital that would be run by blacks and whites together. At his hospital blacks and whites would receive equal care. Black doctors would have a chance to work in a hospital. And there would be a training program open to black nurses. Provident Hospital, the first interracial hospital in the United States had all of these features. Within a year Provident Hospital was on its way to becoming an outstanding medical facility.

In 1894, less than one year after Dr. Williams' history making operation, he was appointed Chief Surgeon at Freedman's Hospital in Washington, D.C. When the doctor took the job he found the hospital to be in a run-down and poorly managed state. Dr. Williams organized a department of surgery for the hospital and then set about bringing to the hospital leading doctors of all races who agreed to volunteer their services. He created an internship program for black doctors and a training program for black nurses. Under Dr. Williams' direction the number of patients who recovered af-

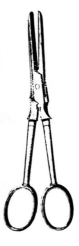

ter treatment at Freedman's reached an all-time high.

Several years later, Dr. Williams returned to Chicago and to his post as Chief Surgeon at Provident hospital.

Williams became the first black doctor on the staff of St. Luke's Hospital in Chicago in 1912. He went on to become one of the charter members of the American College of Surgeons in 1913. And he later joined with black doctors all over the United States to form the National Medical Association.

When Dr. Daniel Hale Williams died in 1931, he had long been thought of as one of the greatest doctors in the United States.

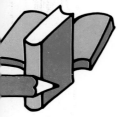

Metrics Up Front

The United States is beginning to convert to the metric system of measurement. You may have noticed that road signs frequently give distances in kilometers as well as in miles. Food packages show grams as well as ounces. Liquids are sold in liter bottles as well as in quart bottles.

Just as our system of measurement uses the yard, the quart, and the ounce, the basic units in the metric system are the *meter*, the *liter*, and the *gram*. The words for these units are often used with special prefixes. Look at the chart for the meaning of each prefix and for examples of some of the words that can be formed.

Metric Prefix	Meaning	Example
milli-	one thousandth	milligram
centi-	one hundredth	centimeter
deci-	one tenth	decimeter
deka-	ten	dekameter
hecto-	hundred	hectogram
kilo-	thousand	kilometer

When these metric prefixes are combined with the words for the basic metric units, they have meanings such as these:

A *milligram* is one-thousandth of a gram.
A *kilometer* is one thousand meters.
A *centimeter* is one-hundredth of a meter.

ACTIVITY A   Use the chart of metric prefixes to answer these questions. Write the answers on your paper.

1. How many grams equal one kilogram?
2. How many milliliters equal one liter?
3. How many centimeters equal one meter?
4. How many milligrams equal one gram?
5. How many liters equal one kiloliter?
6. How many meters equal one kilometer?
7. How many centigrams equal one gram?
8. How many deciliters equal one liter?
9. How many millimeters equal one meter?

ACTIVITY B   Use the chart of metric prefixes to answer these questions. Write the answers on your paper.

1. If *gon* means "side," how many sides does a *dekagon* have?

2. A *penny* is a coin that is worth one-hundredth of a dollar. What else do we call this coin?

3. *Grams* are used to report weights. *Milligrams* report very small weights, while *kilograms* report large weights. In which of these metric units would you report the weight of:
   a. an elephant
   b. a straight pin

THE
ORANGE
MAN

BERTON ROUECHÉ

On December 15, 1960, Dr. Richard L. Wooten, a doctor in Memphis, Tennessee, was told that a patient, Elmo Turner, was waiting to see him.

Dr. Wooten remembered Turner, but did not remember much about him. He asked the nurse to fetch Turner's folder and to then send Turner in. The folder refreshed Dr. Wooten's memory. Turner was fifty-three years old, married, and a plumber. Over the past ten years, Dr. Wooten had seen him through pneumonia and other troubles.

There were footsteps in the hall. Dr. Wooten closed the folder. The door opened, and Turner came in. Dr. Wooten had risen to greet him. But for a moment he could only stand and stare. Turner's face was orange, a golden, pumpkin orange. His hands were orange, too.

Dr. Wooten found his voice. He gave Turner a friendly good morning and asked him to sit down. He remarked that it had been a couple of years since their last meeting.

Turner agreed that it had. He had been away. He had been working up in Alaska. He and his wife were back in Memphis on a matter of family business. He thought he ought to pay Dr. Wooten a visit. There was something that

338

kind of bothered him. Dr. Wooten listened with half an ear. His mind was searching for a disease which could color its victims orange. But as far as he knew, there was none.

Turner was saying that he was worried. He had pain in his abdomen. Dr. Wooten waited for Turner to say something about his strange color. But Turner had finished.

Dr. Wooten asked Turner to come into the examining room. His color would wait. His abdominal pain came first. Dr. Wooten thought that the cause of Turner's pain was probably also the cause of his strange color.

Soon Dr. Wooten had learned all he could from the examination. He had also learned that Turner's body was as orange as his face. For the doctor to learn more, Turner would have to have a series of X rays. That would require a couple of days in the hospital. Turner said he was willing to do whatever had to be done.

Dr. Wooten called the hospital and made arrangements for Turner to be admitted that afternoon. Then Turner got up to go.

But Dr. Wooten waved him back. There was one more thing. It was about the color of his skin. How long had it been like that? Turner looked blank. Color? What color? What was wrong with the color of his skin? He was honestly confused. He didn't know about his color. He really didn't.

That meant that Turner's change of color had not come on suddenly. It had come on so slowly that Turner never realized it was happening. Dr. Wooten asked no more questions. The matter would keep until he had more information to work on.

The next day X rays were taken of Turner. They showed that an empty sac had developed in his abdomen. It was Dr. Wooten's belief that the sac would disappear if left alone.

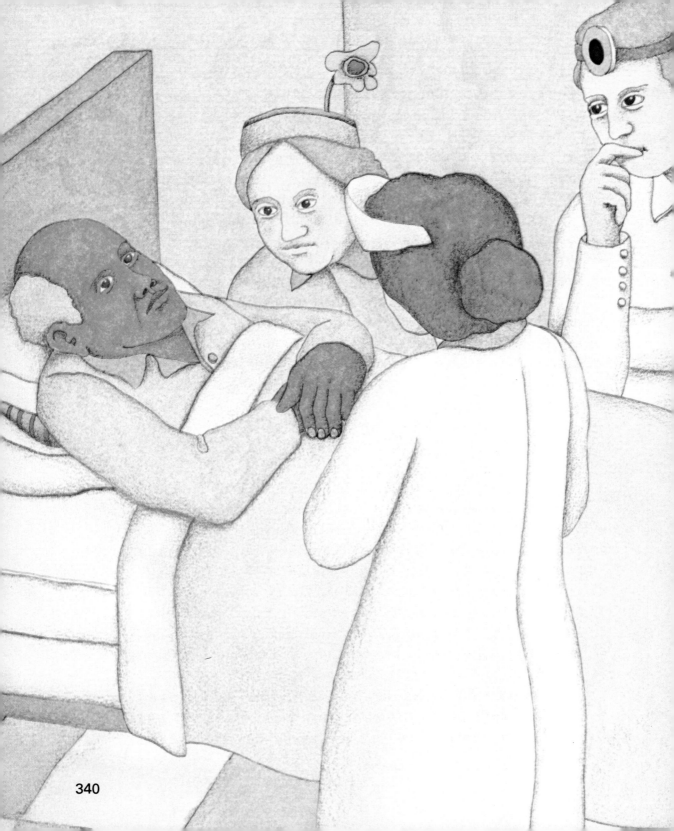

But Dr. Wooten did not want Turner to leave the hospital. The sac did not explain the color of Turner's skin. Turner still said he saw nothing wrong with his color. But Dr. Wooten insisted that he have further medical tests made. The results of two of these tests might explain Turner's skin color. One test checked the blood for the presence of bilirubin. Bilirubin is a pigment, a coloring that can make people look yellow. The other test was for a condition called hemochromatosis. Hemochromatosis could cause its victim's skin to turn bronze. Dr. Wooten did not really expect much from either of these tests. Turner was neither yellow nor bronze. But the doctor wanted to be sure.

The test results came in that afternoon. They showed that Turner's bilirubin was normal. And he did not have hemochromatosis.

Dr. Wooten walked slowly to Turner's ward. What was it? What was coloring Turner's skin orange? Maybe it had something to do with his diet.

When Dr. Wooten came into the ward, he found Turner's wife at his bedside. Turner had changed his mind.

Maybe Dr. Wooten was right about the color of his skin. There must be something peculiar about it. There had been a parade of doctors and nurses past his bed since early morning. Mrs. Turner hadn't noticed anything strange about her husband's skin color. But now she had to admit he did look kind of orange.

Dr. Wooten turned to the subject of diet. What, for example, did Turner have for breakfast? Turner said his breakfast was always the same. He had orange juice, bacon and eggs, toast, coffee. And what about lunch? Well, that didn't change much either. He ate a lot of vegetables—carrots, rutabagas, squash, beans, spinach, turnips, things like that.

Mrs. Turner laughed. That, she said, was putting it mildly. He ate carrots the way some people eat candy. Dr. Wooten sat erect. Carrots, he was suddenly aware, were rich in carotene. So were eggs, oranges, rutabagas, squash, beans, spinach, and turnips. And carotene was a powerful yellow pigment. What, he asked Mrs. Turner, did she mean about the way her husband ate carrots?

Mrs. Turner laughed again. She meant just what she said. Elmo was always eating carrots. Eating carrots and drinking tomato juice. Turner gave an embarrassed grin. His wife was right. He guessed he did eat a lot of carrots.

So that was it! Turner's skin color had changed because of what he ate. Carrots were rich in carotene, which is yellow. And tomatoes contained a red pigment. And yellow and red make orange!

Turner was discharged from the hospital. He was instructed not to eat carrots, other yellow vegetables, or tomatoes in any form. Four months later, Turner reported to Dr. Wooten that his skin was back to its normal color.

BLENDING WORDS

A number of words in our language have been formed by combining parts of two other words to make one new word. This combining process is called *blending*. A well-known example of a blended word is the word *smog*. The word *smog* was made from the blending of parts of the two words *smoke* and *fog*. Two other examples of blended words are *motel* and *brunch*.

$$\text{motorist} \ + \ \text{hotel} \Rightarrow \text{motel}$$
$$\text{breakfast} \ + \ \text{lunch} \Rightarrow \text{brunch}$$

See if you can match each new word on the left with the pair of words on the right that was blended to make the new word.

New Words	Blends
telecast	flame + glare
heliport	hocus pocus + bunkum
splatter	transfer + resistor
chortle	Europe + Asia
transistor	squint + pinch
Eurasia	sky + hijack
telethon	helicopter + airport
hokum	television + broadcast
sky-jack	prim + sissy
prissy	chuckle + snort
squinch	splash + spatter
flare	television + marathon
clash	clap + crash

SMOKE + FOG = SMOG

Can you think of other pairs of words that might be blended to form some useful new words?

PURDY'S
SUNDRIES
&
DRY GOODS

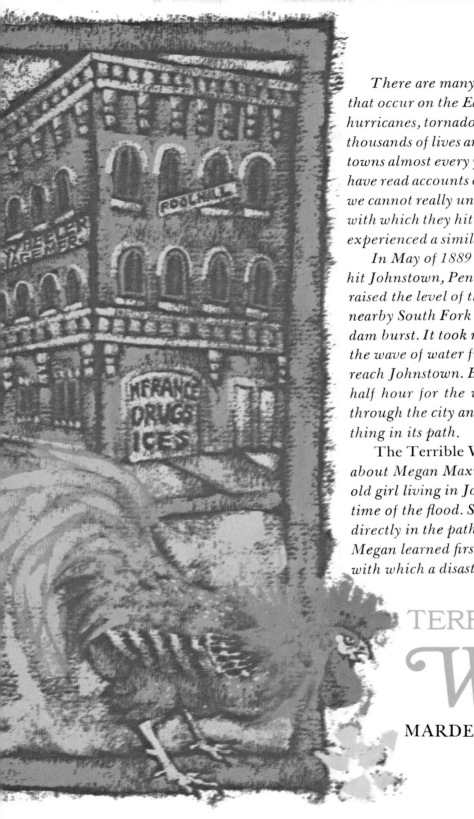

There are many natural disasters that occur on the Earth. Earthquakes, hurricanes, tornadoes, and floods claim thousands of lives and wreck entire towns almost every year. Although we have read accounts of such disasters, we cannot really understand the force with which they hit unless we have experienced a similar one.

In May of 1889 a severe rainstorm hit Johnstown, Pennsylvania. The rain raised the level of the water in the nearby South Fork Dam so much, the dam burst. It took nearly an hour for the wave of water from the dam to reach Johnstown. But it took only one half hour for the wave to roar through the city and destroy everything in its path.

The Terrible Wave is a story about Megan Maxwell, a fifteen-year-old girl living in Johnstown at the time of the flood. Since her house was directly in the path of the wave, Megan learned first-hand the force with which a disaster can strike.

THE TERRIBLE Wave

MARDEN DAHLSTEDT

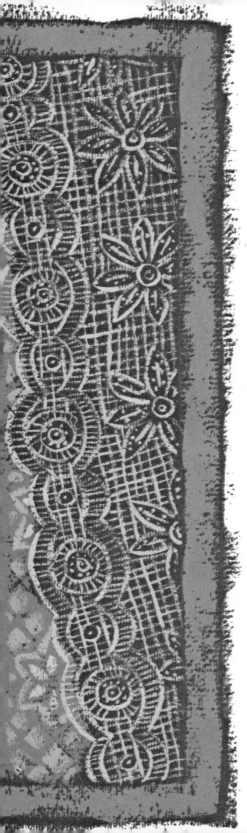

4:07 P.M., FRIDAY, MAY 31

Megan was, in fact, one of the few people in Johnstown that day who actually saw the gigantic wave that destroyed the entire city.

At first all she could see was a mean black mist. It rolled toward the house like billowing smoke. For a moment Megan thought there must be a huge fire somewhere.

But the noise convinced her it was something else. There was a deep, heavy rumbling, mixed with a grinding sound, like some enormous mill wheel churning.

The black fog curled swiftly over the house. Then the air seemed to clear for one split second. There, almost on top of her, was a huge wall of debris-filled water, much higher than the house!

347

Megan spun around. She could see a soft film of plaster dust begin to fall from the ceiling as gently as snow.

Suddenly there was a tremendous crash. It sounded as if the whole house had been caught in a vast grinding machine. Megan saw the boards of the attic floor split open. A surge of oily, yellow water gushed up, foaming at the edges like old lace.

Then it seemed as if the air were filled with flying objects. Trunks whirled by, along with wicked-looking boards splintered with nails. Showers of broken glass brought a thousand tiny arrows. Linens flapped like strange, white birds. Chairs with legs torn off went whistling by. Everything in the attic seemed to be whirling through the air.

Megan ducked her head and shielded her body with her arms against the debris. The floor beneath her feet heaved mightily and then suddenly dropped.

Wildly Megan reached up, her hands grasping for anything to cling to. She found herself swinging from a rough board, the lower half of her body submerged in water.

How long she clung there in the darkness she would never know. She was choking and spitting as the evil water surged about her, splashing over her face.

After what seemed a lifetime in the thunderous blackness, Megan lifted her head. Far above her, she could see a glimmer of dirty, gray light.

She wasn't even thinking now. Painfully she began to crawl toward the light with a kind of blind animal instinct. Clinging with one hand, she would reach out with the other until she found some new thing to grasp. And so, inch by inch, she worked her way through the tangle of shattered wood toward the tiny wedge of light above her. The crack of snapping boards and the terrible thunderous roar still filled her ears.

The wedge of light suddenly widened. There was a long hiss and gurgle of rushing water. Megan felt herself being pushed, as if by a mighty hand, through the jagged crack between darkness and light. The force of the movement sent her flying. Flailing her arms, she rushed through the rainy air.

The feeling of total helplessness she felt was the worst thing of all. Even the jagged boards she had been clinging to had been comforting compared to this. With a sickening thud, she landed, sprawling on something horribly soft and squashy.

Too frightened to move, she simply lay there, her eyes closed, her breath coming in great choking sobs.

Her mind had completely stopped functioning. Drawing her knees up under her chin, she circled them with her arms. She curled herself up small, whimpering like an animal in pain.

Finally, bit by bit, her brain began to register again. The first thing she became aware of was the cold. It was incredible, biting deep down into her bones. She hugged herself tighter, trying to fight it. Slowly she realized that her clothes were soaking wet. Rain beat down heavily and without mercy upon her, flattening her long hair against her shoulders.

Finally she noticed the smell. It was horrible, a sour and rotten stench. Instinctively she raised her head to get away from it. With her head up, she finally opened her eyes.

She was crouched on a sodden, mud-stained mattress!

The mattress itself seemed to be buoyed up by a tangle of broken boards and tree branches. The combination made a kind of crazy, lopsided raft. It was floating on a sea of fearfully churning, dark water that seemed to stretch in all directions.

Before she could get her bearings, something heavy crashed into the side of the mattress. The mattress tilted with a sickening lurch. Megan made a frantic grab for the edge, her fingers digging deep into the spongy cotton. The thing that had caused the lurch was carried away on the current. The "raft" righted itself.

Gasping, Megan saw that the object that had struck the raft had been the great, dark bulk of a horse. Megan watched in fascinated horror as the horse's lifeless body spun down the rushing current, bobbing up and down like some horrible toy.

The makeshift raft somehow continued to float. Megan discovered that if she was careful she could get on her hands and knees without tilting it too much. This made it easier to see. Although darkness seemed to be falling fast, Megan began to search in vain for some familiar object.

She had no idea where she was. For a moment she believed that the world must have come to an end, and that she was the last person left alive on earth. These thoughts raced each other through her stunned mind. She crouched on her knees, clutching the swaying mattress, too frightened even to cry out.

The din around her was tremendous. The sounds were entirely inhuman—cracking, grinding, roaring, together with the dreadful sucking, sloshing noise of the dark water which surrounded her.

And then Megan heard a human voice!

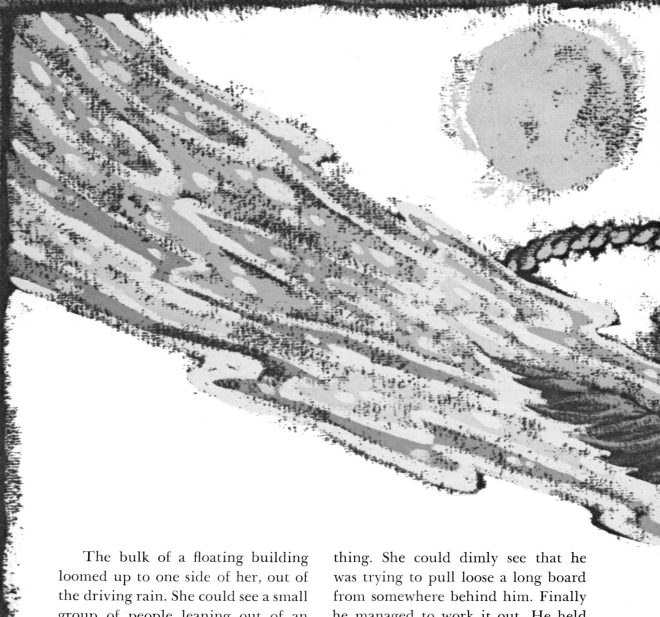

The bulk of a floating building loomed up to one side of her, out of the driving rain. She could see a small group of people leaning out of an opening in the building. They were waving their arms and shouting.

"Over here . . . over here. . . ."

A man was struggling with some-thing. She could dimly see that he was trying to pull loose a long board from somewhere behind him. Finally he managed to work it out. He held onto one end and thrust the other toward her across the gulf of swirling water.

"Grab onto this," he shouted.

Holding the mattress with one hand, Megan reached out with the other.

"Grab it, and hang on for dear life," he yelled. "We'll pull you in. . . ."

The end of the board was about a yard's length away from her. Cautiously Megan edged nearer to the rim of the tilting mattress. The board was about a foot away now.

And then, quite suddenly, a fierce eddy of water caught her small raft, swung it around, and sent it spinning off in the opposite direction.

She heard a wail from someone in the group. Her rescuers seemed to vanish in the rainy mist.

After a few moments the motion ceased. Megan once again dared to raise her head and look about. The eddy had carried her to a quiet stretch of water, and the mattress was floating peacefully, as if on a pond. The awful lurching had stopped.

A piano drifted beside her, its white keys looking like a great, grinning mouth. Megan stared at it. It was a nightmarish world. Nothing seemed real anymore.

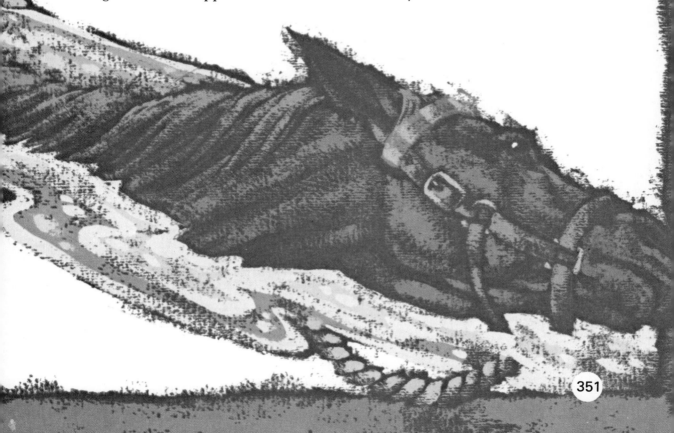

And then Megan saw a sight that would stay with her for the rest of her life. Later, out of the whole horrible, confused time, she would remember this sight most clearly.

About 20 yards from where she floated on quiet water, there seemed to be a rapidly flowing current. Barrels and boards, rooftops, fences, trunks, and debris were rushing swiftly past her.

Suddenly a large platform appeared. It might have been the floor of a house. In the center of it was an open Saratoga trunk. Kneeling about the trunk in a circle were a man, a woman, a boy, and a girl. They were busily packing the trunk with articles of food and clothing.

Megan recognized them. It was Mr. Mussante, the fruit vendor from whom her mother always bought fresh produce. He came to their street each Friday morning, his handcart piled high with golden lemons, clusters of rich purple grapes, crinkle-skinned melons, and mounds of apples. Megan knew his wife, too, Mama Mussante, who knelt beside him now, and Vito and Angela, his merry-eyed children. She had often seen them when she went with her mother to the small, sweet-smelling, little store with its strings of red onions hanging from the ceiling.

"Oh, Mr. Mussante," Megan called at the top of her lungs. "Help me . . . please . . . it's me, Megan Maxwell."

She watched, unbelieving, as the floor was carried past her. The Mussante family never raised their eyes from their task. They continued packing their trunk. They sailed out of sight, still busily working.

Megan had been aware for the past several minutes that the mattress beneath her was becoming dangerously soggy. It was so heavy with water that only the tangle of branches and boards underneath was keeping it afloat.

I've got to get off this thing soon, Megan thought desperately.

Feeling was beginning to return to her numbed mind. She realized her dangerous position. And now came a strong will to survive.

Just then a small white house came into view. A man was sitting astride the peaked rooftop. His long legs were dangling on either side of the slope. He was clinging to the remains of a brick chimney that reared up in the middle.

The rooftop looked at that moment large and safe and comfortable.

In desperation Megan lay on her stomach, and with her hands she tried to paddle the mattress toward the rooftop.

The man looked at her, a long, sad, searching glance, and just shook his head. The house drifted past her.

"Oh, you terrible, awful man," shouted Megan. "I hate you . . . I hate you. . . ."

She dropped her face against the mattress and wept.

Megan's whole body shook with the violence of her sobs. She was thoroughly frightened. For the first time in her life she was completely alone. She had no idea where her family might be.

Slowly she became aware that her body was not being shaken by sobs alone. The mattress was heaving under her. Once again she raised her head and looked about.

The debris under the mattress shifted and lurched to one side. The mattress tilted steeply. Gasping, Megan clutched for the high side. She crawled slowly across the spongy mass.

To her astonishment, she found herself looking directly into a human face!

The current had carried her close to a long wooden building that was floating along like an ark. From the narrow windows in its side, Megan could see at least twenty people staring at her. She stared back.

The face she had looked into belonged to a young man.

The young man turned to some men who stood behind him. He pointed toward Megan. The men shook their heads. They seemed to be arguing about something. Megan could not hear what they were saying. The distance between the building and her mattress was growing wider.

Then she saw the young man climb onto the windowsill. For one long second the young man stood poised on the window ledge. Then Megan saw his body arc, drop, and disappear into the yellow water.

In her terror, she was puzzled by the whole scene. Suddenly Megan felt an enormous lurch at one side of her mattress raft. She gave a sharp cry and turned around.

A wet, dark head appeared, sleek as a seal. Then the rest of a soaking body followed. Working his way on his stomach like a snake, he inched his way to the center of the mattress. It was the young man from the building!

"By golly," he panted, "it's not much of a craft you've got here."

Megan stared at him astounded, unable to speak.

The young man crawled to a sitting position. Shaking water from his eyes like a huge dog, he peered about. Their distance from the building was growing wider. The building's win-

dows were still crowded with heads. A faint cheer went up.

"Toss a line," yelled Megan and the young man.

A few heads vanished from the windows and after a long moment reappeared. A coil of rope curled through the air. It fell short, and one of the men dragged it back through the water for a second try.

But at that moment came a grinding crash!

The mattress began to spin madly. It went reeling off in a sickening rush of water.

When the movement finally stopped, the young man raised his head.

357

Megan opened her eyes.

Where the wooden building had been was only a crazy pile of timbers. A railway coach lay jammed against it. There was no sign of any people.

The young man gripped Megan firmly by the arm.

"Don't look," he said in a shaky voice. "And since it looks as if we're going to be riding this thing together for a while, you'd better tell me who you are. I'm Brian O'Meara."

"How do you do," she answered. "I'm Megan Maxwell."

"Well, now, I'm pleased to make your acquaintance," said Brian with an odd formality.

Megan was about to speak again, when suddenly Brian pointed.

"Look," he cried.

Bearing down on them rapidly was a large farm wagon. It was floating along nicely like a large, solid raft. Crouched in the center of it were two women and an old man.

Brian reached for Megan's hand.

"You grab hold of me around the waist and hang on," Brian said. "We're going to get on that wagon."

The wagon was nearly beside them now. The old man had seen them and seemed to sense what they were trying to do. He crawled to the edge of the wagon and stretched out his arm.

"Catch hold of me, lad," he called.

With a great heave Brian pushed against the mattress and flung himself and Megan headlong onto the wagon.

The force of their leap had knocked the old man flat. For a moment the three of them lay in a heap. Finally, panting, they crawled up to a sitting position. Brian grinned at Megan.

Megan smiled back. The wagon bed was wet, but firm and comforting. It felt so good to have something solid under her.

The old man was looking at both of them.

"It's rather a good thing we happened by," he said. Megan and Brian looked to where he was pointing. The pile of debris beneath the mattress had broken up. The mattress sank into the darkening water without a sound.

The old man began to crawl toward the center of the wagon.

"Come away from the edge," he cautioned. "There will be less chance of it tilting."

Megan and Brian slid carefully across the splintery planks to where the old man had joined the two women. The older woman paid no attention to them. The other lay on her back, her eyes closed. She was

young and pretty. A man's heavy tweed coat had been wrapped around her.

"Is she . . . is she . . . dead?" Megan whispered. "No," replied the man. "She's hurt." His voice trailed off. He looked at Brian and Megan. "I'm glad you're here," he said simply. Brian stretched out his hand. "Brian O'Meara, sir. And this is Megan Maxwell."

The old man and the young people shook hands formally.

"My name is Septimus Shaw. And may I present Mrs. Alderson"—he nodded to the middle-aged woman, who still paid them not the slightest heed—"and this poor girl—well, I don't know her."

It was only much later, when she thought about it all, that Megan was filled with wonder at this curious little scene of grave introductions carried on at the height of one of the world's greatest disasters. At the time it had seemed the natural thing to do.

EPILOGUE

The Johnstown flood was especially tragic because it could have been avoided. The dam that broke had originally been built of stone. It was built to create a reservoir.

When the dam needed repairing, however, the repairs were carried out without scientific engineering procedures. Mud and straw were used to fill in places where the dam needed mending. As a result, the tremendous lake above Johnstown came to be held in place by little more than a wall of earth.

The unusually heavy rains that preceded the flood raised the level of the lake. The earthen dam was strained until it burst.

The dam was never rebuilt, and the lake that once existed was gone forever. In later years flood walls were built along some of the rivers around Johnstown. And this time the walls were built by qualified engineers.

CAN YOU EXPLAIN IT?

LEE GEBHART AND WALTER WAGNER

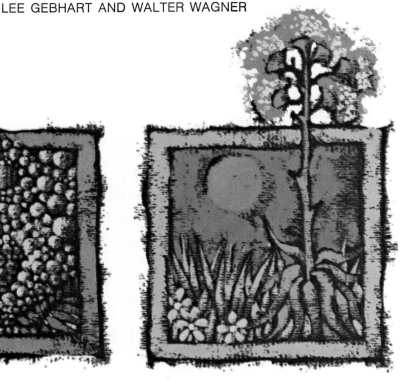

Toad of the Hills

From the valleys of the Andes Mountains in South America often come reports of the existence of the giant Sapo De Loma, or "Toad of the Hills." The creature and others of its kind are supposed to be poisonous and large enough to devour fair-sized birds. Neither traders, explorers, nor scientists have ever seen one, so it is not known whether the toads' existence is fact or legend.

The Late Bloomer

In the tropics of South America there is a type of plant called *Agave,* which takes a very long time to bloom. The plant's seeds develop into a set of pointed leaves, which remain dormant for from ten to thirty years. Then suddenly the plant produces a 20-foot high flowering spike, which lasts only briefly. The cause of this plant's behavior is unexplained.

Monsters of the Deep

Do monstrous sea serpents exist? Ancient and even modern mariners have reported sighting "monsters" that appeared to be 100 feet long. Legends say that such creatures have encircled small vessels and have dragged them to the depths of the ocean. Yet no actual proof of such giants has ever been found. Or has it? In August, 1967, Richard Gagne, the son of a Maine fisher, discovered the 23-foot-long remains of a serpentlike creature. Scientists have not been able to identify the creature, and so the preserved skeleton is still a mystery.

Four Eyes

"Four-eyed" fish have been found in the rivers and lakes of Central America. Actually the fish have only two eyes. But these are divided into distinct halves. These eyes seem to function like bifocal glasses. The fish swim at the surface of the water, hunting food that is floating. The upper part of their eyes are exposed above the water and are focused for air viewing. The lower halves, short-sighted like ordinary fish eyes, remain submerged, watching for enemies. Scientists now wonder if there may be other creatures with bifocal vision.

Volcanic Water

Erupting volcanoes normally spout streams of hot lava. But in 1541, a volcano in Guatemala poured forth a vast flood of water. Following three days of unceasing earthquakes, the torrent swept down from the 12,000-foot slopes of the volcano with such force that it destroyed the city below. Over one thousand inhabitants of the city were drowned. There has never been an acceptable explanation for why this volcano spouted water.

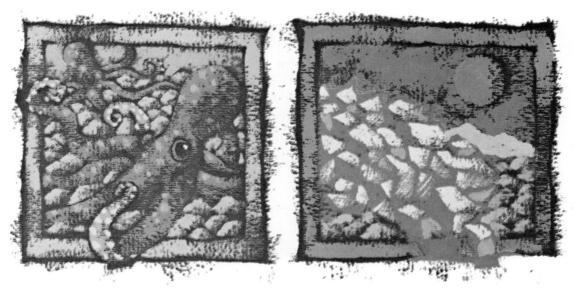

Octoplague

Great flights of crop-destroying locusts have been reported since biblical times. But plagues have been known to come from the sea, too. Strangest of these is the phenomenon of swarms of octopuses that suddenly appear along shorelines. These swarms have been known to wipe out shoreline populations of crabs and lobsters. One such occurrence was in 1899 on the coast of France. Every rock for miles was covered with the tentacled creatures. A year later, the coast of England was attacked. Similar invasions have taken place in Scotland and Japan. Marine biologists are still puzzled by the invasions.

Ice from the Sky

Violent thunderstorms have been known to produce hailstones as big as hens' eggs. But scientists are puzzled by incidents in which chunks of ice weighing up to 25 pounds each have fallen from the sky. Three such incidents occurred in California in 1968. And there have been others occurring for over a century. Usually irregular in shape, the strange chunks are streaked with tints of blue, yellow, or green. No satisfactory theory has been offered to explain the phenomenon.

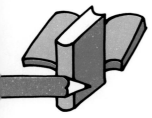

In Conclusion

A *syllogism* is a way of reasoning used to reach a conclusion. A syllogism has three statements. The first two statements are facts. The third statement is a conclusion drawn from the facts. The conclusion in a true syllogism must follow a pattern. Read the two syllogisms below. Which one has the correct conclusion?

Fact 1: All animals need oxygen.
Fact 2: An elephant is an animal.
Conclusion: An elephant needs oxygen.

Fact 1: All animals need oxygen.
Fact 2: A daffodil needs oxygen.
Conclusion: A daffodil is an animal.

You know that the second syllogism does not have a correct conclusion. It is incorrect because the facts do not follow the right pattern.

What *is* the right pattern? Look at the first syllogism. The underlined words are the same or almost the same. This syllogism follows the right pattern.

Now look again at the second syllogism. The underlined words are *not* the same or almost the same. This syllogism does not follow the right pattern. Therefore, its conclusion is based on faulty reasoning.

Read the syllogisms on the next page. Watch for the correct pattern and the correct conclusion in each one. Then, on your paper, write whether each conclusion is correct or incorrect.

1. **Fact 1:** Baseball teams must have at least nine players.
   Fact 2: The New York Yankees is a baseball team.
   Conclusion: The New York Yankees must have at least nine players.

2. **Fact 1:** Baseball teams must have at least nine players.
   Fact 2: The Los Angeles Rams must have at least nine players.
   Conclusion: The Los Angeles Rams is a baseball team.

3. **Fact 1:** A table is a four-legged piece of furniture.
   Fact 2: Pam is sitting on a four-legged piece of furniture.
   Conclusion: Pam is sitting on a table.

4. **Fact 1:** A table is a four-legged piece of furniture.
   Fact 2: David is sitting on a table.
   Conclusion: David is sitting on a four-legged piece of furniture.

5. **Fact 1:** Citrus fruits contain Vitamin C.
   Fact 2: An orange is a citrus fruit.
   Conclusion: An orange contains Vitamin C.

6. **Fact 1:** Citrus fruits contain Vitamin C.
   Fact 2: A potato contains Vitamin C.
   Conclusion: A potato is a citrus fruit.

7. **Fact 1:** All mice eat cheese.
   Fact 2: Nancy eats cheese.
   Conclusion: Nancy is a mouse.

8. **Fact 1:** All mice eat cheese.
   Fact 2: Roger is a mouse.
   Conclusion: Roger eats cheese.

IS SEEING BELIEVING?

NED POTTER

In 1947, a private pilot named Kenneth Arnold called the United States Air Force with a strange report. Arnold said that he had been flying near Mount Rainier, Washington, when he saw nine disk-shaped objects moving across the sky.

Nobody else saw the objects. And nobody could explain what they might have been. But because of the description Arnold gave of their appearance, the disks became known as "flying saucers."

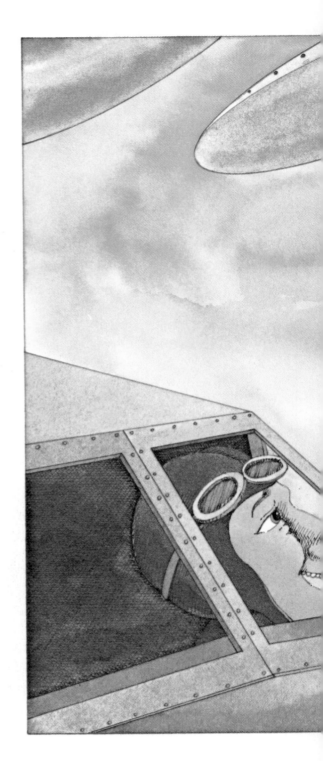

Soon after Arnold's "discovery," people all over the world began to report that they were seeing strange things in the sky. Disk-shaped and cigar-shaped objects were the most commonly reported. Sometimes people said that these objects made a hissing or whirring noise. Every now and then, someone claimed to have seen blinking lights moving across the sky. People began to call the things they saw UFO's, which stands for Unidentified Flying Objects.

Since 1947, over ten thousand UFO reports have come in to police stations, Air Force headquarters, and observatories all over the United States. In many of these cases, the UFO's became IFO's, or Identified Flying Objects.

A call comes into the Air Force.

"I've just seen a disk-shaped flying thing that's glowing," says a frightened voice at the other end of the telephone.

The Air Force checks it out. A plane has just flown over the location described by the caller. Because it is sunset, the underside of the plane

seems to glow in a peculiar way. The caller is relieved to hear the explanation.

Weather balloons floating through the air have also been reported as UFO's. Sometimes the moon, seen through the window of a moving train or car, can appear to be "following" the traveler and can be reported as a UFO.

There occurs in nature a phenomenon called "ball lightning." Air that is charged with great quantities of electricity can sometimes gather into a ball. The glowing ball that forms can travel across fields, into people's houses, or along electrical lines. If you were to witness "ball lightning" on the move, you might think that you had seen a UFO.

UNEXPLAINED

Although many UFO's are now IFO's, there are still a number of sightings that have never been explained. Here are a few.

Two New Hampshire police officers reported that their police car was chased for several miles by a giant object with colored lights, flying at treetop level.

A highway investigator in California reported sighting a hat-shaped object sailing over a field, kicking up dust on the ground. He tried to use his car's radio to call for help, but the radio wouldn't work. It did start to work, however, when the UFO disappeared.

A Colorado farmer reported that he saw something land in a field where his horses were grazing. When the farmer had gotten up the courage to investigate, he found the skeleton of a dead horse with all of the flesh removed.

During the 1957 International Geophysical Year, many people involved in the Brazilian Navy's scientific station in the South Atlantic reported seven sightings of the same UFO. Photographs of the object were taken by different members of the team at different times. The pictures were all the same. The team also reported that they received strange radio signals during the sightings.

In 1965, Commander James McDivitt reported sighting an object orbiting a few miles from his Gemini 4 spacecraft. Some scientists claim that McDivitt probably saw one of the thousands of satellites that daily circle the Earth. But the Air Force keeps careful track of all objects in space. The Air Force did not know of any object that was near enough to Gemini 4 to be seen by McDivitt.

Two Canadian nurses on duty in a hospital reported seeing an occupied flying saucer outside a window in the hospital. One of the nurses said that the occupants were human in appearance and wore headgear and dark clothing. Other nurses in the hospital went to a different window to catch a glimpse of the spacecraft. These nurses said they saw the saucer-shaped object and watched it as it circled several times and flew away.

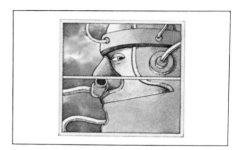

What is going on? What are these UFO's that never become IFO's?

Some people have suggested that they might be secret military aircraft from other countries. But this is very unlikely. With modern radar equipment and intelligence work, such things are just too hard to keep secret.

Well, what about UFO's just being things that people think they see but really don't? This is a possibility when only one person reports a particular UFO. One person can be mistaken, as is often the case. But when many people who have never met each other and who live in different places all report seeing the same thing at about the same time, it is hard to believe that they are all mistaken.

Of course, there is always the possibility that somebody is just making up a UFO report, even if he or she claims to have photographs of the object. Photographs can be doctored to appear to show UFO's when they really don't. But, in any case, until a UFO report can be proven false, there is always a possibility, no matter how small, that it is true.

Could UFO's be spacecraft from another planet? Visitors from outer space? "Little green people?" These ideas are straight out of science fiction. But it is a scientist's job to consider *all* possible answers.

First of all, is there life on other planets besides the Earth? To that question, most scientists answer yes. There are many millions of stars like our sun in the universe. It is probable that at least some of them have planets circling around them the way the Earth orbits the sun. Even if only some of the stars in the universe have planets, there could be thousands of forms of life in outer space.

But could these forms of life visit Earth? Stars are so far apart that even light, traveling at 186,000 miles per second, takes years to go from one star to another. Alpha Centauri is the star nearest our sun. If there were life on a planet near Alpha Centauri, it would take at least four years for that life to reach us if it traveled at the speed of light. At the speeds at which *our* spacecraft can travel, it would take twenty thousand years for life from a planet near Alpha Centauri to reach us.

Some people believe that beings on another planet may be far more advanced in space travel than we are, and may be able to travel at the speed of light. Some people believe that beings on another planet may live so long that a twenty-thousand year trip might be possible for them.

These ideas are constantly discussed. But people know so little about what exists beyond the Earth that, for the moment, these ideas are only guesses.

Then how can we explain the UFO's which have never become IFO's? The answer is, we *CAN'T!*

So we wait. We gather evidence by recording sightings. We try to sift out the possible from the impossible. We continue to explore the universe with our telescopes and spacecraft to learn as much as we can. And we tell people how not to mistake a normal object for a UFO. And maybe some day we will have an answer.

Kitty O'Neil

VIRGINIA O. SHUMAKER

Vrooooommmmm! The race car trembles as it stands on the track, ready to go. A man beside the car hand-signals the countdown to the driver. Five . . . four . . . three . . . two . . . one . . . zero . . . GO! For a split second, the car seems to stand still in space. The next moment, it is gone. In another moment, it is just a speck down the track.

When the run is completed, the automatic speed timers have clocked the car at almost 600 miles (960 kilometers) per hour! She has done it! Kitty O'Neil has just traveled faster than any woman in the world—*much* faster. Traveling in a rocket-engine car called the *Motivator*, she has sped down the dry lake bed in Utah at more than 200 miles (320 kilometers) per hour faster than the previous record holder.

At the end of the race, the driver climbs out of the car's tiny cockpit. She shakes her hair free after taking off her helmet. Smiling at those around her, Kitty happily accepts their congratulations. She watches people carefully as they speak to her, answering their questions and commenting on the car's performance.

Kitty O'Neil is an unusual person. Besides breaking world land speed records, she performs dangerous tricks as a stunt woman. She is also completely deaf. But she has never let her disability stop her from doing whatever she has wanted to do.

Kitty was born in Texas. Her mother is Cherokee. Her father was Irish. Kitty's father died shortly after her birth. While still an infant, she had several serious diseases at once which impaired her hearing.

Kitty's mother was determined that her child lead as normal a

life as possible. Mrs. O'Neil began to take courses in how to teach children with hearing defects. She wanted to learn the best way to communicate with Kitty.

She taught her daughter how to read lips and how to speak. She encouraged Kitty to try many different activities. Kitty took piano and cello lessons, which she could enjoy by feeling the vibrations of the instruments. She learned how to swim at an early age; and when she was twelve, she began to compete as a swimmer.

Then Kitty turned to diving. Balance is a critical part of diving, and a person's sense of balance comes from the inner ear. Because of her deafness, Kitty's swimming instructors felt diving would be impossible for her. But they were wrong. Soon she was winning diving awards and training with Dr. Sammy Lee, an Olympic diving champion who worked only with exceptional divers.

Dr. Lee had to work out some special ways of communicating with Kitty while she was on the diving board. When working with his other students, he would call out as they were diving to tell them the exact moment at which they were to start a complicated twist or turn. Since Kitty couldn't hear his shouts, he fired blanks from a gun at the instant a movement should begin. Kitty felt the vibrations of the loud noise and responded in mid-air. By the time she left high school, Kitty not only graduated with academic honors, but also left with five trophies and fifteen gold medals for her diving performances. She went on to win many more diving awards.

Having mastered diving, Kitty began to explore other sports. She raced boats, sky dived, and in 1970, won the record as the world's fastest woman water-skier.

After marrying stunt man, Duffy Hambleton, Kitty decided to try stunt work herself. A stunt person often "stands in" for a performer when a dangerous trick is called for in a movie or TV show. Stunt people dress like the actors or actresses and keep their faces from the cameras so the audience won't notice the difference.

378

Kitty, as a very successful stunt person, has hung from roofs and been in a rolled-over car. Once, she even fell 105 feet (31.5 meters) from a cliff into a river.

Then the *Motivator* came along. Kitty heard about the rocket-engine car and knew she wanted to be the one to set a new women's world record. The last women's land speed record had been set at 308 miles (493 kilometers) per hour in 1965. Kitty broke that record fairly easily at 322 miles (515 kilometers) per hour, but she didn't want to stop there. She wanted to set a record that would be hard to break for a long time. On her last run, she raced close to 600 miles (960 kilometers) per hour. It took her over five miles just to stop the car!

What's next? Kitty hopes to race faster than sound. Sound waves travel at about 770 miles (1,232 kilometers) per hour. If she can beat that speed, she will be the first woman to break the sound barrier.

Kitty says, "Mostly I want always to have a goal, some dream that I can try for."

Gull Number 737

JEAN CRAIGHEAD GEORGE

Luke Rivers' father was a famous ornithologist, or bird scientist. The Rivers family spent five summers on an island off the coast of Rhode Island, where Luke helped his father study a large colony of herring gulls living nearby. But during the sixth summer, a national emergency occurred. Herring gulls, flocking at Boston's Logan Airport, caused a serious plane crash. Scientists and airport officials feared similar accidents would

occur unless they found a way to keep the gulls off the runways while planes were landing and taking off.

Dr. Rivers flew to the airport to help. He brought Luke along to gather information about the birds. Several other scientists joined them, including Dr. Allard and Dr. Olsen.

As the scientists and Luke knew, herring gulls could "talk" to each other using different cries and noises. They had, for example, an alarm cry that warned of danger and sent the birds soaring high into the air.

Dr. Olsen had made a tape recording of gulls crying out in alarm. He hoped to play this recording over loudspeakers so the gulls on the runway would hear the cry and respond by flying away.

It took a week to install and pretest the recording. Then it was time to test it. Several scientists from Washington and three airline presidents were coming to watch the test. Dr. Rivers said Luke could join the group. Luke was very pleased, for he would be the youngest witness to this important experiment.

When the day arrived, both Luke and his father got up early. Luke dressed quickly, but his father took so long getting ready that Luke decided to go to the dining room and start breakfast. He ordered a big glass of orange juice and was adding bacon, eggs, and waffles to the list when Dr. Allard entered the empty room. Luke's heart beat faster. He did so admire the kindly scientist.

"Good morning, Luke," Dr. Allard called to him.

Luke stood up, knocking his silverware to the floor as he jerked his hand forward in greeting.

"Are you ready for the big test?" Dr. Allard inquired.

"Of course," Luke said. "It's exciting."

Dr. Allard ordered a breakfast almost as big as Luke's, then stretched back in his chair. "Do you think it'll work?" he asked Luke seriously.

"Not for long," Luke answered. He felt very sure of himself.

"Why not?"

"Dad thinks the calls are too weak. Dr. Olsen had to make the tapes late in the nesting season, when the gulls are less wary. The tapes will scare them off for a few days, but then I'll bet a dollar these smart old Boston gulls will catch on and come right back to loaf on the airstrips."

"You know a lot for a young man," Dr. Allard said.

Luke chuckled. "I've worked with my Dad so long that I know a good full-blown alarm cry when I hear one. As a matter of fact, my Dad can get a more violent cry in any season than the cry on these tapes. All he has to do is walk out the lab door, and the 'haha's' are fierce. Sometimes I think they can be heard in England."

"Why is that?" Dr. Allard asked, curiously.

"Well, it's a family joke that Dad is the most hated man on Block Island. He has more enemies than anyone we know —all gulls. He has invaded their nesting sites so much that they regard him as their chief enemy. Those tapes should have been made with Dad on Block Island, head bare, coat off."

"Hmmm," said Dr. Allard. "Have you told this to Dr. Olsen?"

"No, I never thought of it 'til just now."

"I'm sure that's just what should be done. If this tape fails, I'll recommend your idea."

While they were eating, the sky had lightened. In the faint light of dawn, seven men and a boy climbed to the conning tower high above Logan Airport. They checked their watches, lifted their binoculars, and waited. At 4:45 A.M., Airways Flight 11 was to take off for Washington, D.C.

The jet was loaded and standing by at 4:40. It was ready to taxi down gull-filled Runway 7. Luke saw through his binoculars that all his white and gray friends, almost eight hundred of them, were just awakening on the airstrip. Some preened; others began to gossip in soft "mew" voices.

"Flight 11 to tower," the jet captain said over the radio.

"We're ready to take off. Let the birdies sing."

"Tower to Flight 11. Okay. I'm starting the tape."

Engineer Carl Moody flicked the switch on the tape recorder at his left. Around the boxes, birds looked to the right and left. They got on their wings. More got up. Then more and more, until in three minutes, the whole flock was flying out over the bay.

"They're leaving," the traffic controller said to the pilot of Flight 11. "They're leaving! Hold your engines until the air is clear.

Okay, go!'' The jet screamed forward and sped down Runway 7.

"Beautiful day!" the pilot cried. "And not a bird in the sky!"

"Bravo!" the people in the conning tower shouted.

Several days later, Luke climbed to the conning tower.

"How's the tape working?" he asked Carl Moody.

"Haven't you heard?" he said.

"No, I've been chasing sandpipers and ducks. What's happened?"

"The gulls all walk over to the speaker box and stand around. They listen in fascination to the gull in the box. They love him!"

"No! No! Aren't they afraid any more?"

"Not in the least."

Luke turned and jumped down the steps. He had to find his father and Dr. Olsen. They were out on Runway 4 trying to get a new "hahahaha" tape. He ran all the way, following the beach that flanked the runways.

A club of gulls was sitting along the beach. A few were stretching their necks to see who was boss. Some were sleepily contemplating their feet. As he approached Runway 3, a warning yell behind him announced that a jet was about to take off. Luke ran into the weeds and lay down. He hated to be so close to the awful noise, but better on the ground than standing.

As he lay curled on his side, he could see three sharpshooters who had been posted along the bay stand up and shoot off blank cartridges. They were back to the

old method of scaring gulls. The guns boomed, the birds flew away, and the jet ripped forward.

As Luke and his father suspected, the tapes hadn't worked for long. Soon the birds were as much a problem as they had been before. But what about Luke's idea? Could his father raise a *really* loud alarm cry from among the gulls near their cottage? The scientists decided to try it out. Several of them flew by helicopter to the Rivers' remote island cottage to make the recording.

The afternoon was devoted to wiring the gullery for sound. A few birds still had young, so Dr. Rivers was hopeful of rousing a strong alarm cry. He stayed in the lab while the others took care of the wiring, as he did not want any of the birds to see him until everything was ready.

Mr. David, Airways president, was enjoying the unusual afternoon away from the office. He joined Luke and Dr. Olsen and glanced at the white wings in the sky.

"They don't seem any nastier than the Boston gulls," he observed. Then he chuckled. "Want to bet our birds are meaner than your birds?"

"Yes," replied Luke. "There's no Boston bird as mad at anyone as Larus, the lead gull, is at my father. Dad was nervous the day he banded him, and he must have scared the dickens out of him. After all, Larus was the first bird Dad had banded. Larus must have felt Dad's nervousness, and he responded. Animals are very sensitive to people's feelings, you know."

Neither man offered any comment, so Luke went on, "Anyway, I think after Larus got to be president of the gulls he passed his anger on to others. I can come out here in August when the nesting season's done without a hat or raincoat...but not Dad."

"I can't really quite believe they dislike your father more than they do you or me or Mr. David," Dr. Olsen said.

Luke was so surprised he hardly knew what to say. "Don't you think gulls can tell one person from another?"

"Not to that point," Dr. Olsen said, firmly.

"Heck," said Luke, "they can tell each other apart two or three miles away; a mere human face would be nothing to them."

"You can tell people apart, but you can't tell birds apart," Dr. Olsen said. "It would be nice if you could, then you wouldn't have to band them."

Luke did not want to argue. "Time will argue for me," he said to himself. "When Dad walks out on that gullery, Dr. Olsen will wonder *why* the birds scream, not *if* they scream." He grinned privately. It was nice to feel confident.

The engineers made the routine tests and then called, "We're ready!" They laughed. "Now where's the star?"

Now Luke was annoyed. No one in the party believed that these gulls would fuss louder at his father than at any other person in the world. He wondered why they had come if they were in such doubt.

"Dad!" he called. He hurried down the lighthouse dune and over the trail to the lab. Luke's sister, Chinquapin, rushed up from the water, and their mother came outside from the kitchen. Here was solidarity. "At least *we* all believe in Dad." He glanced

back at Dr. Olsen and Mr. David, the engineers and the pilot. "You just wait," he thought grimly.

Dr. Rivers put on a black slicker, took a pith helmet, and started out. He checked his watch and said to Luke, "The time is right, isn't it?"

"Yes. Larus has been around the lighthouse every day at this time ever since I've been home."

"Well, he better not let us down today."

Dr. Rivers lifted his binoculars to study the gulls on the roof of the building. He paused as he focused, then smiled. "He's the one nearest the light," he said, and started walking toward the dune where the recording party waited.

"Some show," Luke's mother giggled. "I never thought I'd have a bird matinee idol for a husband."

Chinquapin giggled, too, and folded her arms over her chest. "Our hero," she said. "Some kids watch their fathers get Best Citizen of the Year Awards, but not the Rivers children. They watch their father walk bravely across a dune, head high, chest out, to be screamed at by a gull."

Luke chuckled warmly at his sister and wiggled his shoulder a few inches closer to her as they leaned against the wall together. They waited in utter confidence.

Luke kept his eye on the lighthouse. The bird near the light grew nervous as the black figure walked toward Yank Hill. Several times he lowered his wings to fly, then thought better of it and relaxed.

"Go on!" Luke said aloud. He could see Dr. Olsen waiting with patient resignation against the lighthouse wall. His father walked on. The technicians were at their station, but they were not on the alert.

Larus was now concentrating fully on the black figure. The bird pulled himself up tall and thin. "Good," Luke thought. "He's flattened his feathers to his body. He's scared."

"His wings are drooped," Chinquapin breathed excitedly.

Then with a thrust, Larus dropped on his wings. Luke saw his father remove his helmet and take off his coat. Larus broke into a reverberating distress call. The air sounded with his "HA HA HA HA HA HA HA!" His voice was so desperate that three other gulls began to scream, too. The noise was deafening.

Dr. Olsen straightened up. The technicians at the tape-recording machine were so surprised that they fumbled their dials. The gulls were now circling and crying, and Luke could see that they were getting ready to strike their enemy. His father was unprotected! The gulls folded their wings and plunged. Dr. Rivers' arms went up to cover his face, and he dropped to the ground, as gulls ripped down on him.

Luke found himself running to help. He knew the wrath of the birds, even if Dr. Olsen did not.

Dr. Rivers grabbed up the black raincoat and ran into the lighthouse, waving the helmet to fend off the birds. Luke could see a red gash on his forehead.

"Are you all right?" he demanded.

"Yes. Sure," his father said with a shrug. "It's not deep. How was it?"

"Splendid! Bravo!" called Dr. Olsen. "I can't believe it!"

He rushed to shake Dr. Rivers' hand, his face beaming with delight. "You're marvelous. I think this will do the trick. Any gull who hears this tape is going to take off for China."

Luke looked at him and thought, "There's one big thing about scientists that's a pleasure to see; they never mind being proved wrong."

The engineers came over to his father with renewed respect.

"This is the hottest record in the nation!" one of them said, and the laughter mingled with "Hahahaha."

More About Gulls

The dangerous problem of gulls on airport runways is not just a part of "Gull Number 737." For many years, airport officials have tried to deal with this situation in different ways—some, successful; some, unsuccessful.

Suppose you wanted to find out more about airport problems with gulls or about gulls in general. Two sources of factual information are encyclopedia articles and newspaper articles.

GULL is a long-winged bird about the size of a pigeon. Most gulls make their homes near the ocean, but they also live on the Great Lakes and other inland waters. Gulls are close relatives of another kind of sea bird, the tern.

Adult gulls are generally pearl-gray above and white below. The feathers of some species also show some black, brown, or gray. The colors change with the season and with the age of the birds. Young birds look grayish or brownish. Some kinds become white the second year, while others may not grow their adult

The Great Black-Backed Gull, above nests along the northern Atlantic Coast. The black-headed gull, below, breeds along the coasts of the Gulf of Mexico, but winters in South America.

feathers until they are four years old. Most gulls have broader wings, squarer tails, and larger, stockier bodies than terns. Gulls look less graceful in flight than terns, but they can swim better. Ocean gulls often rest by floating on the water.

American Gulls are migratory birds. They fly to warm regions in the winter, and fly back north to breed in the summer. They build their nests on the rocky ledges of islands or in marshes. Large colonies may be seen where their breeding places have not been disturbed. The female gull lays one to four grayish or greenish-brown spotted eggs. Soft fluffy feathers, called *down*, cover the young birds when they hatch.

Gulls eat fish and other water animals, insects, rotten meat, and the eggs and young of other birds. When they live around harbors and shore waters, they are useful scavengers. They devour any kind of food or garbage that floats. Inland gulls destroy many insects. Salt Lake City residents erected a monument to the gulls that destroyed millions of grasshoppers in 1848 and saved the crops of the settlers.

Scientific classification. Gulls belong to the gull family, *Laridae*.

See also BIRD; FRANKLIN'S GULL; JAEGER; KITTIWAKE; TERN.

Two Tried To Move Birds

NEW YORK——Two men at Kennedy International Airport tried unsuccessfully on Wednesday to move a flock of seagulls from a runway. A short time later, a jet hit some of the birds and one engine burst into flames.

Shotgun blasts were fired at the birds as "they were on or crossing" the runway. But "some of them came back" before the plane took off.

Several gulls were sucked into the plane's right engine as it took off.

The pilot had been cautioned about bird activity around the airport. He managed to brake the jet to a screeching halt near the end of the runway as flames came from the right engine. The 10 crew members and 139 passengers escaped down emergency chutes about 1:15 P.M.

GULLS BEING DYED IN AVIATION STUDY

ROCKPORT, MASS.——As the herring gulls wheel over the fishing piers or dumps, a bright green bird will stand out from the others with their sober gray backs.

Sometimes, the odd bird will be not green but red. Somewhat more rarely, it will be a bright yellow. In every case, the uninformed person is likely to stare and follow the bird on its swoops and dips.

The gulls have been dyed. The trapping, dyeing, and tracing has been done by college students. They are working under the direction of the Massachusetts Audubon Society. The data are for the Fish and Wildlife Service of the Department of the Interior and for the Federal Aviation Agency.

The main purpose of the study is to help learn when, why, and how often the big gulls group at airport runways.

Between Narragansett Bay and Portland, Me., each of five nesting areas has been given a different color. From south to north, these are blue-violet, yellow, red, green, and black.

Navy Ousts Seagulls

SAN FRANCISCO (UPI)——The Navy has won its two-week battle with a flock of seagulls for runway space at nearby Moffet Field. The gulls landed on the airstrip Oct. 19. Huge helicopters swept over the runway at regular intervals Tuesday. The birds left in search of less hectic surroundings.

ACRONYMS

A number of words in our language are *acronyms*. An *acronym* is a word formed by combining the initial letters or syllables of a name, title, or group of related words. For example, *radar* is an acronym for *ra*dio *d*etecting *a*nd *r*anging. Another acronym you probably know is *ZIP*, as in *ZIP Code*, which means *Z*oning *I*mprovement *P*lan.

Acronyms are a fairly recent addition to our language. The popularity of acronyms in America began around the time of World War II. At that time, many government agencies were known by their initials. Then, the military services began to use them, too. Soon, everyone was using them.

Below is a list of interesting acronyms. You might already know some of them. Can you figure out how they were formed?

PAL—Police Athletic League
WHO—World Health Organization
UNICEF—United Nations International Children's
　　　　　　Emergency Fund
NATO—North Atlantic Treaty Organization
NOW—National Organization of Women
CARE—Cooperative for American Relief Everywhere
NASA—National Aeronautics and Space Administration
SAC—Strategic Air Command
scuba—self-contained underwater breathing apparatus
laser—light amplification through simulated emission of
　　　　　radiation
snafu—situation normal all fouled up
fubb—fouled up beyond belief

ORDERS

Muffle the wind;
Silence the clock;
Muzzle the mice;
Curb the small talk;
Cure the hinge-squeak;
Banish the thunder.
Let me be silent,
Let me wonder.

—A. M. Klein

The Bare Bones

To write a report, you must first find information in different sources. You must take notes on the articles you read. Your notes may be phrases or complete sentences. But you must be sure not to copy the information word for word. Write the notes in your own words.

Here are phrase notes taken from an article. The article told how scientists were solving forestry problems.

> Forestry Problems
>
> Fire, main problem
>   lookout stations spot fires
>   fire fighters parachute into area
>   bulldozers shovel ditches
>   fire lanes cleared
>
> Bark beetle, a problem
>   careful use of pesticides
>   birds and other insects destroy beetles
>
> Waste, a problem
>   old trees removed for new ones
>   diseased trees destroyed
>   machines and helicopters plant seeds

After taking notes, it is a good idea to arrange them in an outline. An outline helps you organize the information. On the next page is an outline made from the above phrase notes. Notice how each phrase has been shortened into one or two key words.

```
┌─────────────────────────────────────────────────────────┐
│                  Forestry Problems                       │
│                                                          │
│  I. Fire Problem         II. Bark-beetle Problem         │
│     A. Lookout stations      A. Pesticides (careful use) │
│     B. Parachutists          B. Birds, insects           │
│     C. Bulldozers       III. Waste Problem               │
│     D. Fire lanes            A. Old, new trees           │
│                              B. Diseased trees           │
│                              C. Machines, helicopters    │
└─────────────────────────────────────────────────────────┘
```

ACTIVITY A On your paper, write an outline that organizes the following phrase notes. The notes were taken from an article about vitamins.

Vitamin A: helps us grow; keeps eyes and skin healthy; found in milk, butter, yellow vegetables

Vitamin B₂: keeps skin and muscles healthy; helps body change food to energy; found in meat, dairy, green vegetables

Niacin: prevents disease called *pellagra*; keeps stomach and intestines working; found in lean meat, fish, liver

ACTIVITY B On your paper, take phrase notes on the information in the following paragraphs. Then make an outline.

How Fish and Birds Differ

Fish are cold-blooded animals. They must live in the water. They have no lungs, but breathe through gills. Many fish are covered with scales, but they have two pair of fins for swimming.

Birds, on the other hand, are warm-blooded creatures. They survive on land. Birds have wings that enable them to fly, and they are covered with feathers.

INROADS

Science helps us to understand the past and live in the present. It also helps to shape the future. By studying ancient forms of life, scientists have been able to relate life today to life in the past. Scientific discoveries and developments have lengthened our lives and made them more comfortable. Today, scientists continue to search for solutions that will make inroads into the mysteries that still puzzle us.

Thinking About "Inroads"

1. In "A Link with the Past," how did sharing information lead to making an important scientific discovery?
2. Why are certain objects chosen for display in museums?
3. How was Dr. Daniel Hale Williams a pioneer in the medical field?
4. In "Unexplained," the author says that "it is a scientist's job to consider *all* possible answers." How does this description fit the doctor's search for a solution in "The Orange Man"?
5. How could science have helped to prevent the Johnstown flood? How did science help prevent a similar tragedy?
6. What developments in science have changed or improved your life?
7. On your way to school, observe someone at work. Describe in a paragraph an invention that would help that person to do his or her job.

EXPRESSIONS

From earliest times to the present, people have had a need and a desire to express themselves. This need has often inspired people to create beautiful and imaginative things. When the need for expression is combined with a special talent, a person may create a dance, a song, a painting, a poem—you name it!

In "Expressions," you will read fictional and nonfictional selections about creative people with varied backgrounds and talents. You will read about a painter, a poet, a sculptor, and a photographer. You will learn about the people who express themselves through dance. But you will also read about some people who express themselves in uncommon and rather special ways: a boy who builds a fort out of scraps of wood and junk, and a girl who builds a ship in a bottle.

As you read, think of all the different ways that people share their talents with others. Ask yourself what ways you would choose to express yourself.

MANUEL ACOSTA

Painter of *El Barrio*

Most people have their own special worlds of family, friends, and community. Your community may be a neighborhood in a big city. It may be a section of a suburb or a small town where you know everyone. It may be a farm or ranch community where houses are many miles apart. Your community is the place where you feel at home. It's your own special world.

Manuel Acosta is a painter and his own special world is his Mexican-American community, or *barrio,* in El Paso, Texas. His *barrio* is a warm and friendly place where people know each other well.

In some communities, people do not know their neighbors. In others, people move in and out every few years. In the *barrio,* it is different. Many people live in their *barrio* all their lives. They know their neighbors. Relatives and friends are always nearby. Theirs is a closely knit community.

Manuel Acosta and his family have a small plot of land on a street that has many homes. A stone wall surrounds the Acostas' house, their garden of flowers and trees, and Manuel Acosta's studio where he paints every day.

But the Acostas are not cut off from their surroundings. Friends and neighbors often come to visit. Manuel Acosta asks many of them to pose for portraits. He paints portraits of people whose faces and personalities impress him. He paints ordinary, everyday people and shows how unique each individual is.

Here is what Acosta has said about the people whom he paints: "I have such a wide selection of subject matter. There are many ways of life and of dress. Best of all, there are so many different kinds of faces — all shades of every color, all possible combinations of shapes and expressions. I can't wait to get to my easel each day and paint!"

The pictures on these pages show the faces of some of the people in Manuel Acosta's world. He calls them "my people, my village, my friends." In Spanish, he says, *"mi gente* [mee hen-tay], *mi pueblo* [mee pway-blo], *mis amigos* [mees ah-mee-gos]." Indeed, the *barrio* is like a *pueblo,* or village.

The children of the *barrio* are among Acosta's favorite subjects. He likes to paint them with another of his favorite subjects — flowers. Look at the picture of the young girl. Acosta calls this picture, "Flower Child." Can you see why?

Now look at the picture of two boys at play. This picture is called "Watermelon Boat." It shows children playing a game of make-believe. Imagination and creativity are qualities in children that Acosta admires and wishes to praise.

Many people have been able to see and enjoy Manuel Acosta's work. His paintings may be seen in the museums of Texas, New Mexico, California, and Arizona. He has also painted murals — paintings on walls — for schools, banks, and other public buildings in the Southwest.

Manuel Acosta's family is proud of his paintings. His mother treasures the portrait he did of her. In her face, you can see the strength of character and the determination that enabled her to leave the tiny town of Chihuahua, in northern Mexico, with her husband and son to find a new life in El Paso, Texas.

People all over the United States and, indeed, all over the world know of her son, Manuel. He painted the portrait of Cesar Chavez, a leader of the United Farm Workers of America, that appeared on a cover of *Time* magazine. Now, that portrait hangs in the National Portrait Gallery of the Smithsonian Institution in Washington, D.C. The paintings of this Mexican-American artist are among the great treasures of the United States.

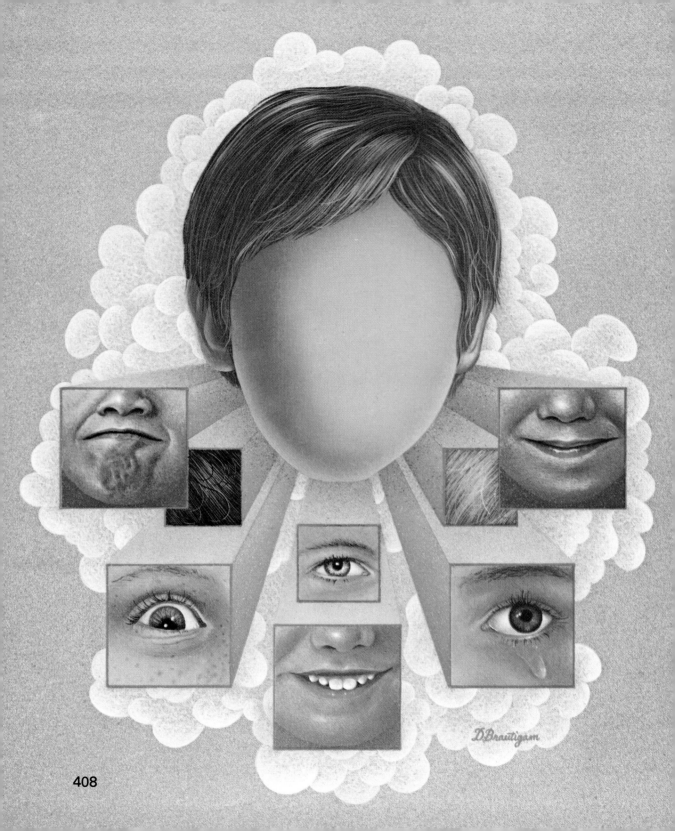

EXPRESSIONISM

DINA ANASTASIO

Pretend that next week is your friend's birthday, and you would like to give him or her something you've made. You might try to paint your friend's portrait. There are several ways to do this.

You can take a photograph of your friend and try to copy it exactly, making sure that the nose, eyes, and chin look just as they do in real life. But a portrait of this type will not express how you feel about your friend.

To do this, think about the "inside" of the person. Think about what you like about him or her. Look beyond the color of the person's eyes to what lies behind them. Do they express kindness, goodness, sadness? Try to find the soul of the person, not just the color of the person's hair or the shape of the person's nose.

When you have done this, you should have a painting of feeling, an expression of how you see your friend. You should have an expressionistic portrait.

This expressionistic portrait is titled *Auguste Forel.* It was painted by Oskar Kokoschka in 1910. The artist attempted to show the inside of this

Courtesy of Stadtische Kunsthalle Mannheim. © by Spadem Paris

man. And he was successful. Study the eyes and hands of the man. When you look at this portrait, you do not merely feel, "This is a nice-looking man." You feel, "This man has worked hard. He has thought hard, and he has lived hard. I like him."

Collection, The Museum of Modern Art, N.Y. Acquired through the Lillie P. Bliss Bequest.

This painting by Vincent Van Gogh, *The Starry Night,* was painted in 1889. It was one of the first expressionistic paintings. Before it was painted, most artists tried to portray the world realistically. They were not interested in emotions. When Van Gogh looked at the sky at night, it did not look this way to him. But this is how it made him feel.

Artists often change reality in order to express their emotions and feelings, as in this painting, *The Blue Window.* It was painted in 1911 by Henri Matisse.

Matisse wrote: "What I am after above all is expression . . . the whole arrangement of my picture is expressive."

Collection, The Museum of Modern Art, N.Y. Abby Aldrich Rockefeller Fund.

And he went on to say: "What I dream of is an art of balance, of purity . . . without any troubling subject matter . . . like a good armchair in which to rest."

Expressionistic paintings are often not realistic at all. Some artists do not paint objects and people at all. They paint only a mood—as in this picture by Kandinsky, painted in 1915.

This painting, *Guernica,* is one of the greatest expressionistic paintings. Pablo Picasso painted it in 1937 to show a town destroyed by war. In *Guernica,* Picasso expressed his horror and fury over a needless tragedy. If you study this painting, you will begin to feel the way Picasso felt when he painted it. This makes *Guernica* a truly expressionistic painting.

MODERN DANCE

People have expressed themselves through the movements, steps, and rhythms of dance since the beginning of time. They have prayed and celebrated their victories through dance. People have mourned their dead and healed their sick through dance, the language of the body.

Today there are many kinds of dancing. For example, there is folk dancing, ballet dancing, and modern dancing.

Modern dance, which began in the early 1900s, is a very expressionistic dance. Modern dancers follow no set pattern. Rather, they create their own movements to match the feelings they are trying to express. But modern dance means more than just self-expression.

Modern dancers must first master the science of movement and muscle control. Then the dancers must learn to use these skills in combination with their emotions.

Martha Graham is one of the pioneers of modern dance. As a young dancer, she studied with some of the founders of the modern dance. movement. Influenced by many different kinds of dancing, Martha Graham developed her own personal dance style. She later formed her own dance company and school in New York City. The following are some of her feelings about her art:

The modern dancer's costume is an important part of his or her dance. There is always some reason why a dance should be a certain color or why an outfit should be cut in a certain way. The reason comes out of the dance itself. Unlike a ballet costume, the modern dance costume is designed around each particular dance.

Martha Graham

The dancers' art lives only while they are dancing. When their dancing days are over, nothing is left of the dancers' art except the pictures and the memories.

Dances come from something deep within a person. That something cannot be expressed with words; it must be told through movement.

Because dance expresses emotions, it affects the mind and the body. Dance should not be taken apart and interpreted. Dance must be experienced.

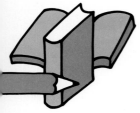

In a Nutshell

Sometimes you see friends at the end of the day. They ask you, "What happened in school?" You probably do not give every detail. For example, you would not mention that you got a drink of water or hung up your coat. Instead, you would report only the most exciting or important things that occurred. You might mention that your team won a basketball game or that you did well on a test.

A report of only the most important information or ideas is called a *summary*. You can give a summary of your daily activities. You can also give a summary of a selection you have read. A good summary is brief, but thorough and accurate.

When you make a summary of a selection, be sure you have read the material carefully. Skim the selection to find all the important ideas. Put the ideas in a logical order. When you write the ideas, be sure to use your own words. Do not copy sentences word for word from the selection. After you make a summary, read it over. The summary should be much shorter than the original selection. But the information in your summary should be accurate and complete.

Here is a summary of the selection about Manuel Acosta. Notice how brief, yet thorough and accurate, it is. All the important information about Manuel Acosta is included in the summary.

Manuel Acosta is a Mexican-American artist. He paints portraits of neighbors in his community in Texas. Acosta especially likes to paint pictures of children with flowers. His paintings are national treasures. They appear in many musems around the country.

ACTIVITY A   Read the selection below. Note the important ideas. On your paper, write a summary of the selection in your own words. Your summary should be about four or five sentences long.

Shell mounds are piles of garbage left from ancient times. They consist mainly of shells, bones, stones, and horns. Some of these mounds left by our ancestors are as high as twenty feet.

The mounds are usually found near waterside sites. Some mounds show that people only visited the area in warmer months. Other mounds give evidence that the areas were used throughout the year. In some places where there is no water now, the mounds show that the land has changed greatly over several thousand years. Whole areas once filled with water are now dry.

Scientists today continue to study the mounds. They have dug up jewelry, pottery, and other items from the past. The more they dig, the more they learn about our ancestors.

ACTIVITY B   Reread the selection "Modern Dance." Write a summary of the selection.

ACTIVITY C   Think of another selection you have read in this book. Read the selection again. Write a summary of the selection.

ISSA
HAIKU POET

RAY YEAGER

O little snail
Climb mighty Mt. Fuji
But slowly, slowly.

The poem on the opposite page and the poems found throughout this story were written by a Japanese poet who was born in 1763. His name was Issa. This type of poem, having three lines and about seventeen syllables, is called haiku. *It is usually on a subject from nature. People began writing haiku in Japan in the 1500's.*

In any art form, there is usually one person who stands above all others. This is often because that artist appeals to the common people. In Japan, Issa is probably the most beloved of all haiku poets.

His favorite subjects were children, insects, flowers, animals, and birds. He wrote of ordinary things and everyday happenings that many people overlook throughout their lives. But Issa did not overlook them.

Issa turned an ordinary happening, such as a bird singing or rain falling, into something to be shared.

The wren is singing,
But the evening grows dark
Just the same.

Winter seclusion;
Listening in the dark to the
Rain in the mountains.

In the two poems on the opposite page, a simple scene is described. In the first, you are told that it is evening and that a bird is singing. In the second, you are told that it is winter and that it is raining. In haiku, every detail is not spelled out. The readers are asked to use their imaginations to feel that moment Issa felt two hundred years ago.

The blazing heat of a summer day, a raging winter's storm, a flower in bloom, an insect crying in the night, an old man working in the fields— each is beautiful in its own way. Issa did not try to explain what he saw and felt; he only hinted.

Issa was most famous for his poetry about insects. He wrote about them as if they were close friends. And they might have been. He was very poor most of his life, and fleas, flies, and mosquitos were a part of his everyday life.

Mr. Grasshopper
Please do not disturb
    The bright pearls of dew.

The spider's children
Scatter in all directions
    To make their own way.

For you fleas too
The night must be long.
    It must be lonely.

With all the beauty Issa found around him, he also found sadness. And he wrote about the sad things, as well as the happy.

He never knew his mother. She died when he was two years old. It is said that he wrote this poem when he was nine years old.

Please come
Motherless sparrows
    And play with me.

To travel in Japan in Issa's time, you walked. Issa spent many nights on the road in his years wandering the countryside. His tent was a limb of a tree. His bed was a straw mat.

A single mat
Beneath an old pine tree
    Makes a summerhouse.

Issa married while in his forties. He and his wife had four children. All of them died when they were very young.

A little boy:
His laughter taken by—
    Autumn nightfall.

After ten years of marriage, his young wife also died.

Insects do not cry,
There are loves that have to part
    Even in the stars.

His many long days and nights were expressed in these poems.

The old owl
Does not change its expression
    In the spring rain.

On the steps of
An old mountain temple
    A deer is crying.

Issa died at the age of fifty-four. His house was destroyed by fire, and he was living in a storage shack with no windows. It was in the middle of winter. His last poem was said to have been found beneath his pillow.

Thanks are due.
This snow on the bed quilt
    Is also from heaven.

422

HAIKU

Haiku is a very old and beautiful form of verse or poetry. The Japanese have been writing haiku for centuries.

The purpose of haiku is to present one simple observation. The haiku poets do not express their own thoughts or feelings. Rather, they describe a scene. It is as though they were taking a picture of something — like a camera. They record only what they see. This is one reason why haiku verse is so short — three lines. There is also another reason. A haiku verse is meant to be spoken in one breath.

A haiku verse looks very simple, but it is not easy to write. The whole verse has just seventeen syllables. The first line has five syllables, the second has seven, and the last line has five. Usually, a haiku poem answers three questions for the reader: *what* is being talked about; *where* and *when* it is taking place.

Look at the haiku verses below. See if they meet the requirements of haiku. Which one doesn't? How could it be changed to make it haiku?

The ferry windows
Are picture frames for the sky,
Holding it in place.

In the leafy tree
Is a little robin's nest,
Hiding five blue eggs.

The birds take their places
On the frozen earth,
One by one by one.

Now try to write a haiku verse of your own. Choose one of the following subjects or use your own subject: the last leaf on a tree, a snowflake, or a grain of sand on a beach.

Birds of Summer

PITSEOLAK:
Pictures Out of My Life

from interviews by Dorothy Eber

My name is Pitseolak, the Eskimo word for the sea pigeon. When I see pitseolaks over the sea, I say, "There go those lovely birds—that's me, flying!"

I have lost the time when I was born, but I am old now—my sons say maybe I am seventy. When Ashoona, my husband, died, my sons were not even married. Now they are married and having their children.

I think I am a real artist. Even when they are out of papers at the Co-op, they find papers for me. I draw the things I have never seen, the monsters and spirits. And I draw the old ways, the things we did long ago when things were different. I don't know how many drawings I have done, but more than a thousand. There are many Pitseolaks now, for I have signed my name many times.

I was born on Nottingham Island in Hudson's Bay. My mother and father were on their way from the coast of northern Quebec, in Canada, northward into the Arctic to join relatives.

I had a happy childhood. I was always healthy and never sick. I had a large family, three brothers and a sister, and we were always happy to be together. We lived in the old Eskimo way. We would pick up and go to different camps. Sometimes they were near Cape Dorset, and sometimes they were far away. It depended whether a person wanted to go far or to be near a settlement. My father hunted in the old way, too—with a bow and arrow. He had a shotgun, but he didn't use it. Sometimes there were bad winters and we would go hungry, but there was no starvation.

Ashoona and I used to be little children together. He had told my brothers that he would marry me. After my father died, Ashoona's father came to get me on a dog team. We were married in the summer.

Sometimes in the winter it was boring in the igloo, but we never stayed inside much. We had warmer clothes in those days, and it used to be fun when it was windy. The fathers would make toy sleds for their sons and daughters to slide on. And when the children had their sleds and their toy whips, they would play outside most of the day. Now they are in school all day, and they have the habit of staying indoors.

Very often in those days, when we felt happy in camp, Ashoona and I would play the accordion. My favorite brother once gave me an accordion, and we both could play. The little children would come and dance. Ashoona used to like to juggle. He could keep three small stones in the air, and sometimes, just for two seconds, I could keep three stones up.

After Ashoona died, we were very poor, and
often we were hungry. We were poor until Jim and
the government houses came.

Before Jim Houston came to Cape Dorset, we had
people at the bay who were here for furs. And
we were grateful to have them and very pleased
to be able to get tea, sugar, and flour. But I
think Jim was the first person to help the Eskimos.
Ever since he came, the Eskimo people have been
able to find work. Here in Cape Dorset, they call
him "the man."

Two winters, two years, after Jim came to live in
Cape Dorset, he began to ask for drawings. Many
people had been doing the drawings before I
started. It was only just before Jim went away that
I heard people were drawing to make money. I
heard that Kiakshuk was drawing. He was my very
close relative—my mother's sister's son.

Kiakshuk was drawing a lot, and I wanted to do
drawings, too, to make some money. I bought some
paper myself, and I think I made four small drawings.
I think I drew little monsters. I meant the drawings
to be animals, but they turned out to be funny
looking because I had never done drawings before.
I took these drawings to Jim's office. I was scared
to go there at first, but he gave me money—I think
it was twenty dollars.

Jim Houston told me to draw the old ways, and
I've been drawing the old ways and the monsters
ever since. We heard that Jim told the people to
draw anything, in any shape, and to put a head
and a face on it. He told the people that this

type of drawing was very good. Some people saw the monsters, somewhere, someplace. But I have never seen the monsters I draw. But I keep on drawing these things. Sometimes, when I take Terry a monster drawing, I say, "Perhaps when I die, I'll see the monsters."

Terry Ryan came to Cape Dorset just before Jim went away. Terry, whom we call "the printer," came to run the Co-op. The Co-op sends the carvings and prints to the south, and it is owned by Eskimos. I don't know exactly how it works, but there is this board of directors who are Eskimo. Terry gives out the pens and the papers for drawing, and later when we bring him our work, he pays for the drawings and carvings. I don't do drawings when Terry has gone somewhere. When Terry's away, I get tired of waiting for him. A lot of people miss him when he's away.

The Woman With the Blue Fish Spear

Since the Co-op began, I have earned a lot of money with my drawings. I get clothes from the drawings, and I earn a living from them. And I am very grateful for these papers—papers we tear so easily. Whenever I am out of everything, I do some drawings, and I take them to Terry at the Co-op, and he gives me money with which I can buy clothes and tea and food for the family. He pays well. I am happy to have the money, and I am glad we have a Co-op.

The other day I drew an Eskimo woman with a blue fish spear. I did not want to leave the fish spear alone—that is why I put the bird on her head. There's a baby hidden inside the parka, too—you can tell by the shape of the parka!

*Sometimes, Just for Two Seconds,
I Could Keep Three Stones Up*

When I first started doing the drawings, I did all the work in black and brown, and I still like these two colors. But now we are using many colored pens. Jim said to draw the old ways in bright colors.

After Terry gets the drawings, some are put on the stone and made into prints. The drawings are carved into stone. After they are put on the stone, they are always better. Sometimes we make prints, too, with stencils and with copper plates. Now some of the drawings are also arranged on cloth, and when it is carefully done, it looks very good.

I know I have had an unusual life. I was born in a skin tent, and I have lived to hear on the radio that two men have landed on the moon. I think the new times started for Eskimos when the people from the south began to build houses in the Arctic. Eskimos began to move into the settlements, and then the southerners started helping us to get these houses. That's why my life changed. I don't think everybody was too fond of moving from the camps, but they still came anyway. Now they just stay here in Cape Dorset. Many of them are working for the southerners now.

I have heard that they like my drawings in the south, and I am grateful and happy about it. Nowadays, when very special people arrive on the plane to visit the Co-op, I am always invited. I am usually very shy, but often they shake hands. Last week a very important minister was here from Ottawa. They gave the minister the stone which was made from one of my drawings. It was a sealskin boat I did last winter.

To make prints is not easy. You must think first, and this is hard to do. But I am happy doing the prints. After my husband died, I felt very alone and unwanted. Making prints is what has made me happiest since he died. I am going to keep on doing them until they tell me to stop. If no one tells me to stop, I shall make them as long as I am well.

SEIJI
SAITO

The hot summer sun beats down in the work yard behind the city museum. Small chips of stone litter the ground as a sculptor chisels away at his unfinished statue. The artist, Seiji Saito, is carving a statue of a mother and child from a huge piece of granite.

Creating a statue out of granite takes a long time. First, Saito makes many sketches of the piece. Then he sculpts several small models. The piece of granite has to be ordered and delivered. As he works on the granite, it has to be moved about carefully with a large hoist.

Carving outside depends on the weather. Working under a burning summer sun can be very tiring. Working outside in the winter can be dangerous. Saito says that when his hands grow numb from the cold, he must be careful not to strike his fingers instead of the stone.

Seiji Saito was born in Utsunomiya, Japan, and studied art in Tokyo. He moved to the United States in 1961 and taught sculpture for a while at the Brooklyn Museum Art School. Now he spends all his time working on his own pieces. He has an indoor studio several blocks from the museum. A number of statues, all in different stages of completion, sit in the studio. Sometimes, Saito works on one piece all day without stopping. Other times, he sculpts for several hours and then rests or works on a different piece for a while.

When asked how he first became interested in art, Saito said, "That is very hard to say. When I was about three years old, I had already started drawing with pencils, crayons, and colored pencils."

As a young boy, Saito used to visit his father's baking factory. He would take pieces of cookie dough and model them into animals and other shapes. Today, Saito's own son sometimes visits his father's studio. He, too, can try making anything he wants.

Saito sculpts in more than one way. At one time, he may begin a statue by simply cutting into a piece of stone or wood. At another time, he will build up a statue by adding clay or plaster to a wooden frame. When asked why he uses several methods, Saito replies, "I am always thinking about studying and learning. Working in different ways sets up challenges."

Seiji Saito always likes to have new problems to solve and new techniques to master.

*This song was written by Mr. Oscar Hammerstein II
for* The Sound of Music.
*Music for this song was written by Mr. Richard Rodgers.
Although Mr. Rodgers' music helped make this
song unforgettable, the poetry of Mr. Hammerstein's
words can easily stand alone.*

MY FAVORITE THINGS

MR. OSCAR HAMMERSTEIN II

Raindrops on roses and whiskers on kittens,
Bright copper kettles and warm woolen mittens,
Brown paper packages tied up with strings,
These are a few of my favorite things.

Cream colored ponies and crisp apple strudels,
Doorbells and sleighbells and schnitzel with noodles,
Wild geese that fly with the moon on their wings,
These are a few of my favorite things.

Girls in white dresses with blue satin sashes,
Snowflakes that stay on my nose and eyelashes,
Silver white winters that melt into springs,
These are a few of my favorite things.

When the dog bites,
When the bee stings,
When I'm feeling sad,
I simply remember my favorite things,
And then I don't feel so bad.

Cameras and Courage

IRIS NOBLE

In the warm dusk of the New Jersey evening, Margaret's mother led her off the lighted porch down onto the front lawn. They were to play a game, she explained. Margaret was to run around the house one way, her mother would run the other way. They would meet and see who had run the faster.

"Run!" Mrs. White urged, picking up her ankle-length skirt–fashionable in 1912–and starting off to the left.

Margaret looked at her mother's back and then at the shadowy path to the right of the house. This was a dreadful

game; she did not want to play. At six years of age, Margaret was so timid that almost everything scared her.

She took a step back toward the safety of the lighted porch, but her mother called again—"Run!"

So she ran. Immediately around the corner of the house and away from the lighted porch, she was into deep shadow, with the path hardly visible ahead of her. Her heart began to pound. Something waved over her head and dipped toward her and brushed her forehead with damp fingers; Margaret's throat froze tight. She would have to turn back. She couldn't go on.

Then there was her mother's gentle laugh and her mother's arms tight around her. Margaret's throat unfroze. She could laugh, too, as they walked back the same way she had come. The fearful thing with the damp fingers turned out to be a lilac branch, wet with dew. "Didn't you know?" asked Mrs. White. "Really?"

Yes, of course she had known. Even in the worst of her terror, she had smelled the familiar lilac smell and seen the fireflies dancing in the bush. She had known.

Even at six she had learned something important—that fear could make her believe what she knew was not so.

"Face your fears," insisted Mrs. White, "and then do something." The doing-something was the important part of the theory.

The person who finally helped her overcome all fear was her father.

The first time Margaret's father told her to hold out her hand while he put a small, furry caterpillar onto her palm, she flung it off. Then her father came and sat beside her and held out his own hand with a caterpillar on it.

Gently he talked to her, while they both studied the tiny thing. He told Margaret how harmless it was and what it ate and of its whole life cycle.

After a while he brought her another. She touched the caterpillar with her finger. "It's so soft!" she exclaimed. Something as soft as that didn't seem to be so dangerous. Soon she let her father transfer the caterpillar to her fingers for just a second.

The third time Joe White brought her a caterpillar,

she accepted it and let it move on her palm. The next time she thought of nothing except how fascinating a creature it was.

The summer she was seven, she was beginning to hold and examine everything. When she was eight, she had to be warned that some snakes were dangerous, because she had become so fascinated by snakes. Margaret had found that they were not clammy to touch. And she was so proud of conquering her fears that she boasted: let others have birds or kittens as pets, she wanted snakes. When she grew up, she was going to work with all kinds of reptiles.

This was a little more than the family had bargained for; but her parents bought Margaret a baby boa constrictor, so young it had to live in a warm blanket for a while, and an old puff adder—harmless, but horrifying to look at. These two were added to the collection of local snakes she gathered herself. Her pets were supposed to live in cages, but they were usually found wandering about the house.

Margaret told everyone she would become a herpetologist, an expert on snakes. She would travel all over the world, she said, and collect rare snakes.

"Face your fears and then do something," Mrs. White had said. And she had been right.

In 1923 at the age of seventeen, Margaret entered Columbia University in New York. One of her first courses was in photography. When Mrs. White heard this, she sent her youngest daughter a present: a camera.

Margaret liked the camera, and she liked the course, although it was merely a side interest. The teacher was exceptionally good and had a way of making photography seem something more important than taking snapshots of

family picnics. She enjoyed it, but her real interest was still herpetology.

When Margaret needed one more year of college to become a professional herpetologist, she studied what various colleges had to offer and decided to transfer to Cornell, in upper New York State.

When she got there, Margaret had to find work. She had a little saved, but not enough to see her through the whole senior year. Margaret applied, through college channels, for a job. "Sorry, every job is taken," she was told.

What was she to do? It seemed as if she would not be able to stay beyond the first term.

It was a beautiful day in the town of Ithaca; the college campus was beautiful. She wandered about, looking at the lovely library tower and the other fine buildings and the green lawns. At last she came to a waterfall and sat and looked at it.

The sight was so beautiful. She remembered the camera that her mother had bought her three years ago. At least she could take pictures of the waterfall and the campus buildings. Even if she had to leave Cornell, she could take such pictures with her.

At that moment the idea came to her: why not make and sell such pictures? If she wanted to have the scenes on print, surely others might also want them. Would they want them enough to buy them?

It was a wild idea, and she knew it. There was no guarantee that she could take artistic pictures or that anyone would want to buy them if she did. Nevertheless, it was the only idea she had for making any money, and she determined to try it.

All that autumn, while Cornell and the surrounding countryside grew more and more beautiful with each changing month, Margaret took pictures.

It was not enough, she found, to point the camera at what she saw and hope to get a picture of it. She learned that it was just as important to leave out material from a picture as it was to get it in.

She began to compose her photographs. Sometimes, she found, a person at the base of a building would show, by comparison, the real height of the building. A tall structure alone might seem only ordinary. She began to realize that some of her pictures were lopsided or out of balance or too crowded. And when a picture pleased her, she studied it to find out why.

She could not afford to have experts clean and service her camera, and so she learned to take it apart and do everything herself. She could not afford to have her film processed by others, but she arranged with a photographer in Ithaca to allow her to use his darkroom to develop and enlarge her prints.

Just before Christmas, she carefully selected her best enlarged photographs. She placed them on a table in front of the dormitory dining room. With them was a hand-lettered price list announcing that she would take orders for any prints desired. To her surprise, the orders came in so quickly that she could not write fast enough.

The sum she earned was large. But she could not resist going on to make more and more pictures. Winter, when the ice formed on the waterfalls and snow covered the campus, blanketing trees and roofs of buildings, brought out an itch in her to photograph everything she saw.

Winter scene. Photo by M. Bourke-White. Courtesy of the Time-Life Picture Agency.

446

She was becoming fascinated by what the camera could do. She was finding drama and beauty in objects not ordinarily considered either dramatic or beautiful. Anyone could appreciate a waterfall, but Margaret could make a striking picture of an icicle hanging from the eave above a window.

The day came when she looked about the photographer's commercial studio and saw that, while her bad pictures were awful, her best were better than any of his. Also, hers were selling—so well, in fact, that she hired student salespeople to work for her.

What was even more thrilling was that the Alumni News bought a picture of a different campus building from her every single month for the cover, paying her five dollars for each. The five dollars was fine, but those cover pictures gave her an entirely new idea of her camera work.

The magazine was sent all over America to people who had been graduated from Cornell. Cornell graduate architects, working throughout the country, saw those pictures of buildings. They wrote to her, saying that she was a very talented architectural photographer and there were few good ones around. Was she going to take this up as a career?

An architectural photographer? She hadn't planned to be any kind of a photographer. It was now close to graduation, and she had been offered a job by the Curator of Herpetology at the Museum of Natural History in New York. For this she had studied and trained. Could she give this up for a career with a camera? Did she want to?

The answer was yes. Margaret had found that photography was more important to her than her other interests.

To get an expert's opinion of her work, she went to New York to the office of architect Benjamin Moskowitz. Margaret asked to see Mr. Moskowitz. No, she couldn't. She had no appointment. It was late. The offices were closing soon. But at that moment Mr. Moskowitz came walking past, with his coat on and his briefcase in hand. He was much annoyed to be interrupted by this young girl who kept getting in front of him to show him some pictures.

But the elevator was late arriving. Margaret moved around so that she could slide her opened portfolio between Mr. Moskowitz and the elevator door at which he was staring. He had to look. The first picture was of the library tower.

The elevator arrived. But Mr. Moskowitz ignored it. "Did you take those pictures?" he asked. When she said yes, he turned and said to her: "Bring those and come back to my office!"

Margaret did go back and was given a job. It was not long before her architectural photographs were discovered by the publishers of some of America's top magazines, who promptly hired her. Her interest in architectural photography soon grew into an interest in all forms of photography.

MARGARET BOURKE-WHITE

Special to The New York Times
August 28, 1971—Margaret Bourke-White went on to become one of the world's most famous photo-journalists. A photo-journalist is a person who tells a news story in pictures and also writes the text. She once said, "The camera is a remarkable instrument. If you know your subject, the camera will all but take you by the hand."

And indeed her camera took her through a life of high adventure that included wars, dust bowls, riots, death camps, floods, and several bombing raids. She was torpedoed off North Africa in World War II, and she was ambushed during the Korean War.

Aggressive and relentless in pursuit of pictures, Maggie, as Margaret Bourke-White was generally known, had the knack of being at the right place at the right time.

Many of the world's most famous leaders sat for her shutter.

For her meeting with the famous Russian leader Stalin, Margaret Bourke-White found a way to catch him off guard. Recalling the incident, she wrote:

"I made up my mind that I wouldn't leave without getting a picture of Stalin smiling. When I met him, his face looked as though it were carved out of stone. He wouldn't show any emotion at all. I went almost crazy trying to make that face come alive.

"I got down on my hands and knees on the floor and tried out all kinds of crazy postures, searching for a good camera angle. Stalin looked down at the way I was squirming and for a second he smiled —and I got my picture.

"I feel that utter truth is essential," Margaret Bourke-White said of her work, *"and to get that truth may take a lot of searching and long hours."*

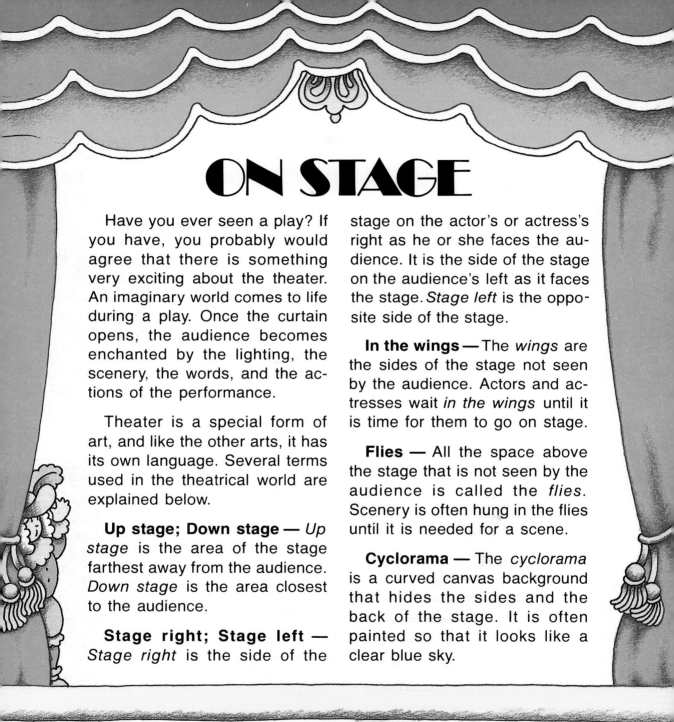

ON STAGE

Have you ever seen a play? If you have, you probably would agree that there is something very exciting about the theater. An imaginary world comes to life during a play. Once the curtain opens, the audience becomes enchanted by the lighting, the scenery, the words, and the actions of the performance.

Theater is a special form of art, and like the other arts, it has its own language. Several terms used in the theatrical world are explained below.

Up stage; Down stage — *Up stage* is the area of the stage farthest away from the audience. *Down stage* is the area closest to the audience.

Stage right; Stage left — *Stage right* is the side of the stage on the actor's or actress's right as he or she faces the audience. It is the side of the stage on the audience's left as it faces the stage. *Stage left* is the opposite side of the stage.

In the wings — The *wings* are the sides of the stage not seen by the audience. Actors and actresses wait *in the wings* until it is time for them to go on stage.

Flies — All the space above the stage that is not seen by the audience is called the *flies.* Scenery is often hung in the flies until it is needed for a scene.

Cyclorama — The *cyclorama* is a curved canvas background that hides the sides and the back of the stage. It is often painted so that it looks like a clear blue sky.

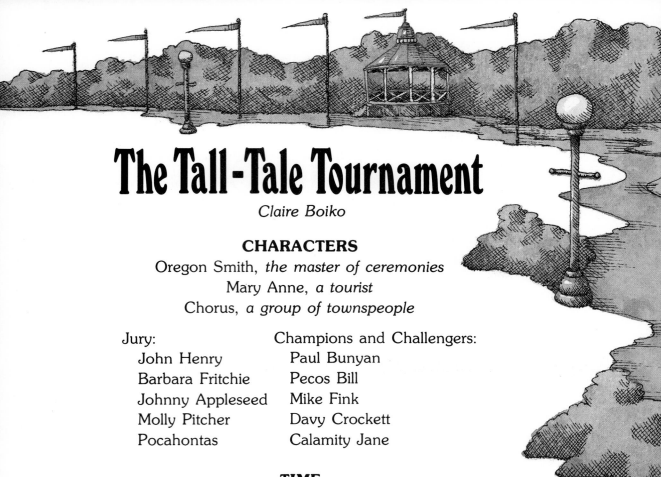

The Tall-Tale Tournament

Claire Boiko

CHARACTERS

Oregon Smith, *the master of ceremonies*
Mary Anne, *a tourist*
Chorus, *a group of townspeople*

Jury:	Champions and Challengers:
John Henry	Paul Bunyan
Barbara Fritchie	Pecos Bill
Johnny Appleseed	Mike Fink
Molly Pitcher	Davy Crockett
Pocahontas	Calamity Jane

TIME

The present, just before high noon

SETTING

A public square in Bloomington, Indiana

(At curtain rise, the square is decorated with gaily colored pennants. A banner across the back reads: "Welcome! Ninety-Ninth Annual Tall-Tale Tournament." A speaker's stand is down right; a bench for the jury is at center; and chairs for the Chorus are placed in a semicircle at the rear of the stage. Another bench is down left. Oregon Smith is chalking a large X down right center on the stage floor.)

OREGON: (*To himself*) There. X marks the spot for the tall-tale champion. (*He draws a circle on the floor, left of center.*) There's the magic circle for the challenger. (*Tipping his hat to the audience*) Howdy! Welcome to the Ninety-Ninth Grand and Glorious Tall-Tale Tournament. At high noon today, there's going to be a meeting of champions. You'll never again hear tales stretched so tall or fetched so far. (*Clock strikes.*) Listen . . . high noon. (Mary Anne, *holding booklet titled* Tourist Attractions, *enters right. On stroke of twelve, she sits on bench at left.*)

451

MARY ANNE: High noon. I have just fifteen minutes to explore the public square before my bus tour leaves town. Now let me see . . . (*She consults booklet.*) How interesting. The town square of Bloomington, Indiana, has a famous liar's bench. People used to sit on it for hours and swap stories. The famous storyteller, Oregon Smith, used to be a kind of master of ceremonies. The liar's bench. . .I wonder where it is. (*To Oregon*) I'm Mary Anne, a stranger in town. Would you direct me to the liar's bench?

452

OREGON: Land o'Goshen! The liar's bench? You've plunked yourself down on it. Now you're stuck good and proper.

MARY ANNE: Stuck? (*She tries to stand but cannot.*) I can't move — not an inch.

OREGON: You should never sit on the liar's bench at high noon on the day of the Tall-Tale Tournament. Why that old bench will just keep you sitting there for days, until you tell a tall tale.

MARY ANNE: Me? Tell a tall tale? But I'm only a tourist. I can't stay for your tournament. (*She tries to move.*)

OREGON: Now, now. You'll think of something.

MARY ANNE: You mean this bench really won't let me go until I think of a story to tell?

OREGON: That's about the size of it. But I won't call on you until the tag-end of the tournament. That'll give you time to think of something.

MARY ANNE: I don't even know how to begin.

OREGON: Begin small and build big, Mary Anne. (Oregon *takes place at speaker's stand, rapping gavel.*) Come on, folks! Welcome one and all to the Ninety-Ninth Grand and Glorious Tall-Tale Tournament! (*Cheers offstage. Chorus enters right and stands beside chairs.*) Ladies and gents, be seated! Let the members of the jury take their places. (*He raps the gavel once for each jury member.*) Big John Henry, from the state of West Virginia. (John Henry *enters, swinging hammer.*)

CHORUS: Here he comes, with his hammer in his hand.
Here he comes, with his hammer in his hand.

OREGON: Barbara Fritchie, from the state of Maryland. (Barbara Fritchie *enters, carrying flag.*)

CHORUS: "Shoot, if you must, this old gray head,
But spare your country's flag," she said.

OREGON: Johnny Appleseed, from the state of Ohio. (Johnny Appleseed *enters, scattering seed from knapsack.*)

OREGON: Molly Pitcher, from the state of New Jersey. (Molly *enters, pretending to pour water into hands of* Chorus.)

CHORUS: Come, Molly, bring us some water.
Bring your cool pitcher this way.
For Monmouth is dry as a desert,
And we're fighting for freedom today!

454

OREGON: And last but far from least, Pocahontas, from the state of Virginia. (Pocahontas *enters.*) And now, ladies and gentlemen of the jury, let the proceedings begin. (*Jury sits on bench at center.*) There will be three separate categories of fiction today. Each category will have a champion and challenger. I now call upon the champion of the Mighty Deeds and Doings category to appear and defend his title. (Paul Bunyan *strides on right, shouldering ax.*)

PAUL BUNYAN: Here I am. Champion — Paul Bunyan, giant of the north and lord of the lumberjacks! You ask me to tell you some mighty deeds. Well, mighty deeds are just everyday happenings with me. For instance, I raised some sawmills up north one time. I needed some ponds to float the logs around in, so I shoveled a few basins here and there. Do you know what they call those ponds today? The Great Lakes!

CHORUS: The Great Lakes! (Pecos Bill *enters.*)

PECOS BILL: I'll challenge that. I'm Pecos Bill, friend of the coyotes, rider of lightning streaks, and roper of railroad trains. Listen to me. I had this long, long cattle drive. 'Twas from Australia to the North Pole, and I needed a little old water trough. Just a simple, little trough to water about a million and a half head of cattle. So I scraped my fingernail along the south of Texas, and I made a watering trough. Do you know what they call that watering trough today? They call it the Rio Grande!

CHORUS: The Rio Grande! (Paul Bunyan *and* Pecos Bill *bow to each other.*)

OREGON: Enough. Shake hands with each other, gents, and sit down on the liar's bench yonder. (*They shake hands, raise their hats to* Mary Anne, *and sit next to her.*) Now we will hear from the champion of the second category, Boasters and Braggers. (Mike Fink, *pole in hand, enters with a wild yell.*)

MIKE FINK: That's me — a boaster and a bragger. I'm Mike Fink, king of the Ohio River. Why the Ohio River doesn't flow in the morning until it asks my permission. I can outrun, outdance, outjump, outdive, and outfight anything in the shape of a human for two thousand miles of the big Mississip'. (*He thumps chest. Davy Crockett swaggers on left.*)

DAVY CROCKETT: Is that so? Well, you've never met your challenger. Allow me to introduce my shining self, Davy Crockett. I rode an alligator up Niagara Falls when I was two. I have the roughest horse, the prettiest sister, the surest rifle, and the ugliest dog in the entire district.

MIKE FINK: Bet you can't jump like me, Davy. Why, I can jump clear across the Mississip' without even bending my knees. If I want to, I can change my mind in the middle of the air and jump right back to where I was before I started.

DAVY CROCKETT: Any rabbit can jump. Now, me—I can saddle the sun and ride around the world and get off where I please.

OREGON: Enough, fellers. Now shake hands like good sports. Go cool your heels yonder on the liar's bench. (*Calamity Jane enters right.*)

CALAMITY JANE: Yahoo!

OREGON: Well, here she is, Calamity Jane, right on time for the next category: Whoppers.

CALAMITY JANE: Whoppers, you say? Why, I'll take on the whole kit and caboodle of you. I'm the fastest Pony Express rider there *ever* was. I can ride over mountains so steep my pony gallops upside down.

JOHN HENRY: You call that steep? Why, I come from West Virginia where the mountains are so steep they have to tie the pumpkins down so they won't roll away.

OREGON: Now, just a minute here. You have to have a proper challenger, Calamity Jane.

CALAMITY JANE: A proper challenger? Well, I don't *see* one.

OREGON: (*Pointing to* Mary Anne): There she is. She's small but mighty. Whip out a whopper, Mary Anne. (Mary Anne *shakes her head.*) Where are you from, anyway?

MARY ANNE: New York City. I'm afraid that's not as exciting as the Mississippi or the Rio Grande.

JOHNNY APPLESEED: New York City. A quiet little village. I planted some nice trees there once.

MARY ANNE: Oh, New York isn't a quiet little village. It's a big city. More than thirteen million people live there. The buildings are so tall they reach to the clouds. We call them "skyscrapers."

ALL: Skyscrapers! (*They nudge each other and wink.*) Oh, sure, sure.

MARY ANNE: It's true! Honestly! (*She stands.*) Why, I'm free. I can move away from the bench.

OREGON: Of course. You just told your first tall tale.

MARY ANNE: (*crossing to circle*): But it's the truth. I came from New York City on a big bus.

MOLLY PITCHER: What is a big bus?

MARY ANNE: It's a vehicle. People sit inside it, and it takes them where they want to go.

POCAHONTAS: You tell good whoppers. How many horses pull this big bus?

MARY ANNE: Horses don't pull the bus. It runs by itself, with an engine that uses gasoline and oil.

ALL: Ha, ha, ha! That's a real knee-slapper. (*They all slap their knees.*)

CALAMITY JANE: Shucks, I can tell one as good as that. I know a feller who trained a swarm of mosquitoes to hunt for him. Every time he wanted a juicy jackrabbit, he'd send out a mosquito to spear it with his stinger. Can you top that, gal?

MARY ANNE: I don't think so. I don't know anything about mosquitoes. Where I come from, we just have things like rockets.

BARBARA FRITCHIE: Fourth of July rockets?

MARY ANNE: Much bigger rockets than that. Why, we had a rocket over thirty stories high that went to the moon. I watched it on television.

MOLLY PITCHER: What is television?

MARY ANNE: That's kind of hard to explain. Television is a moving picture of something that happens. Everybody can watch the picture on a little box.

CHORUS: (*Slapping knees and clapping*): Yahoo!

OREGON: Ladies and gents of the jury, have you come to a decision? (*Members of jury talk together.*)

JOHN HENRY: We have. As spokesperson for this jury, I am pleased as punch to announce our decision. For the mightiest deed, the biggest boast, and the wildest whopper, we elect Mary Anne. (*All cheer. Chorus sings to tune of "She'll Be Comin' Round the Mountain."*)

CHORUS: She's the grand and glorious champion of all.
Yes, she is.
She's the grand and glorious champion of all.
Yes, she is.
She is quick and she is able
To confabulate a fable.
She's the grand and glorious champion of all.
Yes, she is.

OREGON: Well, I do declare! A dark horse has won the derby. Yes, siree! I reckon we ought to celebrate the event. Let's all have a picnic on Pike's Peak. Last one up the mountain is a knock-kneed nanny goat. (*He waves his hat and exits right. Others shake Mary Anne's hand.*)

CALAMITY JANE: Come on, gal. You won — fair and square. Last one up the mountain is a knock-kneed nanny goat! (*She exits and others follow.*)

MARY ANNE: (*Trying unsuccessfully to move her feet*) But my bus tour doesn't go as far as Pike's Peak, and my feet seem to be stuck. (*Horn sounds off-stage.*) The bus! It didn't leave without me, after all. (*She raises her feet.*) There, I can move my feet again. (*She crosses down center, addressing audience, a little puzzled.*) Now, did it all really happen, or did I imagine it all? There's only one way to find out. I'll come back for the One-Hundredth Tall-Tale Tournament. I can't wait to tell them all about things like elevators and submarines. Won't their eyes pop? Why — isn't it funny? The whole twentieth century is one big unbelievable whopper! (*Horn sounds again.*) I'm coming! (*As she runs off*) Last one on the bus is a knock-kneed nanny goat!
(*Curtain falls.*)

461

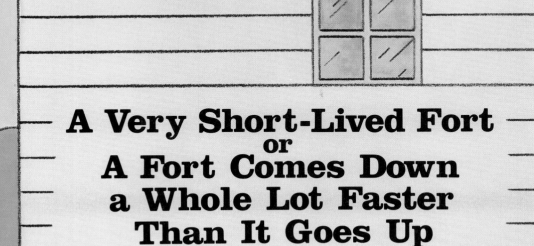

A Very Short-Lived Fort
or
A Fort Comes Down a Whole Lot Faster Than It Goes Up

Fritz Karch, Age 15

Ever since I was a little boy, I've wanted to build a fort of some kind. I had two reasons for wanting a fort. First, I like to build things. Second, I wanted a place to get away from it all. So one summer when the time seemed right, my brothers, some friends, and I went to work.

Our best time to get materials was during junk week. It takes place every spring and fall in our town. This is the time when everyone cleans out the cellar, attic, and garage. Junk is put on the curb to be taken away by garbage collectors or anyone else who wants it. We could also get materials from neighbors who wanted to save themselves a trip to the dump and from junk thrown out in the woods.

Our tools included hammers, saws, a crowbar, screwdrivers, and a shovel. Nails became a problem, and we really did have to hunt for them. Big spike nails were the ones we needed and used the most, and they were also the hardest to find. All our relatives and friends gave us some. Windows were a great addition to the fort and really helped to light the place.

1. We dug four holes about two and a half feet deep. Then we placed four strong, thick posts in the holes. We then filled the holes with rocks and dirt, wet them, and stamped the ground down hard.

2. We nailed two-by-fours between the posts at the top and the bottom.

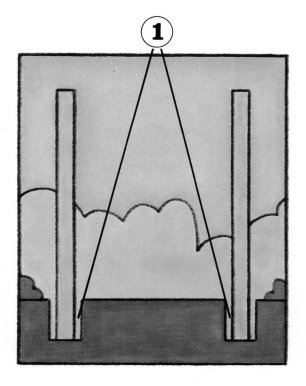
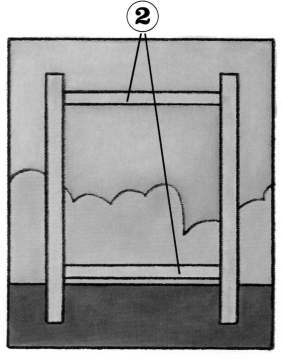

3. For the walls, we fitted wood from the top beam to the bottom beam and nailed the wood to the beams.

4. When we wanted to put in a window, we added a horizontal beam and nailed the window to the beam.

5. To make the roof of the first floor, we nailed strong boards, such as two-by-fours or two-by-sixes, to the tops of the wallboards. We did the same things to make the other floors.

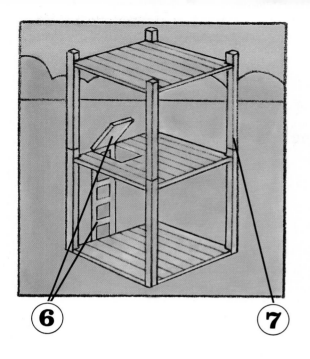

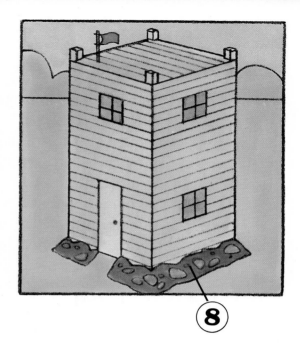

6. To get from one floor of the fort to another, we used trapdoors and ladders. To build a trapdoor, we ran a little beam from the top of the lower wall in a corner to where we stopped the floor boards. Then we just cut a board to fit and secured it with hinges. For a ladder, we ran two strong boards from the floor to the two corners of the trapdoor and nailed on thick pieces of wood for the rungs.

7. To make our fort more than one story high, we let the four posts from the first level stick up above the roof. We continued these posts by nailing four new beams to the first ones. We then used the same procedure we used on the first level.

8. To stop the rain from seeping in the bottom, we piled big rocks and dirt into a mound about a foot up the outside wall of the fort.

The trouble started one day in October. My father told me that the building inspector had looked at the fort and said that someone had complained about it. From that moment on, we just about wore our brains out trying to figure out which of our neighbors didn't like the fort. The building inspector came back and told us that the fort was illegal, and we had to tear it down. He wouldn't tell us who complained. When we asked him what made it so illegal, he said just about everything in the building code. He gave us a copy of the building code, but we didn't understand it at all.

Before he left, he said that there were two ways that we might be able to keep the fort. We could file for a building permit or, if that didn't work, a zoning variance. A building permit is a piece of paper saying that what you are going to build is legal under the building code. It costs one dollar for every two hundred and fifty dollars you spend on the building. This cost would have been great for us, for we had only spent two dollars. But we couldn't get a building permit because our fort was too high and too close to the property lines.

We then tried to get a zoning variance. This is a piece of paper that says you can build even though your building breaks the building code. To get this, we had to go to court and plead our case in front of the zoning board.

The zoning board is a group of people who decide whether or not a particular building can be built. In our case, they had to decide whether we could keep our building up or if we had to tear it down. We filled out forms at the building inspector's office until they were coming out of our ears. The inspector then explained that we must sign up for the zoning board's monthly meeting.

We managed to stay calm and think about other things until our night to meet with the zoning board. In the back of all our minds, we knew we had very little chance to win. But we decided to try. On the night of the meeting, all our friends and supporters turned out to root for us. Our neighbors who didn't like the fort showed up with a lawyer. I had to stand up and answer several questions about the fort. We then went home to await the zoning board's decision.

At about midnight, the word came that we had lost. We had forty days to tear the fort down. If it wasn't down in that time, our parents would be fined. Of course, it didn't take anywhere near forty days to dismantle it. It is always much easier to destroy something than it is to build it.

A BIT OF MAGIC

DINA ANASTASIO

When my mother was seventeen, her boyfriend gave her a bottle. Now it wasn't just an ordinary bottle, for inside it was a lovely ship. The ship was tiny and delicate, with three white sails rising from its hull.

When I was little, my mother would hold the bottle gently in her hands and say, "You know, Kim, this is not just any old bottle. This is a very special bottle with a very special ship. At one time this tiny little ship was a great sailing vessel that sailed the seas from New York to Bombay. And then, one sad, dreary day, as the great ship was rounding Cape Horn, a terrible catastrophe occurred. An enormous, sleepy, blue whale yawned, and before you could say, 'Kimberly King,' the great ship was inside the whale's stomach."

"You're kidding!" I'd say. "There's no such thing as a whale that big!"

"Oh, yes there is," she'd insist. "There certainly is!"

"And then what happened to the ship?" I would ask, breathlessly.

"Well, the great blue whale took a nap. When it awoke, it yawned again. And guess what?"

"What?"

"The great sailing vessel came sliding out of the whale's mouth."

"You're kidding!"

"Nope! But the funny thing was, the great sailing vessel was now a tiny little ship in a tiny little bottle!"

"No!"

"Yes!"

"How did that happen?"

"Well—who know's what goes on in the belly of a great blue whale?" she would whisper. And then we would both sit silently for a long time as we considered this incredible event.

"Tell me how you got it!" I would cry time after time. And she would say, "Well, one day when my boyfriend was diving for pearls off the coast of Africa, what should he see but this tiny little bit of magic. And then he sent it to me."

Then my father, who was usually listening to this fantastic story, would sigh and say, "Oh boy! I wish I had a ship with a story like that!" And I think he really meant it; maybe because my mother's boyfriend had given her the ship, and maybe because he just liked the story. But, most likely it was a little of both.

As silly as this may sound, when I was a little girl I believed every single word of that story.

But then I grew up, and I began to realize that, although blue whales were indeed very large, they just weren't large enough to swallow up a great sailing vessel.

Now although I didn't believe the great whale theory any more, I couldn't figure out how that tiny little ship ever did get into that bottle.

And then one day when I was eleven, I found out.

It was the day before my father's birthday, and I was trying to think of something to give him. I thought for a long time, and then I remembered. The one thing that my father had ever really said he wanted was a ship in a bottle that he could call his own.

And so I set to work to make him one. The first thing to do, I decided, was to find a bottle just the right size. I searched through the garbage for a long time before I came upon a bottle with a neck large enough for a tiny ship to fit through. I cleaned it thoroughly and set it aside.

Next I built the ship. I used a small, narrow piece of wood and some toothpicks. I attached the toothpicks to the piece of wood with glue, taped some typing paper to the toothpicks for the sails, and tried to push the whole thing into the bottle. But of course it didn't fit, for the sails were much too high for the neck of the bottle.

"How," I wondered, "did my mother's old boyfriend ever get that ship into that bottle?" I sat there for a long, long time before I gave it up and headed for the library. There I found a book on ships in bottles. I took it home and read it carefully from cover to cover. By the time I was through, I had just about made up my mind to give my father a nice scarf for his birthday. Putting ships into bottles was not an easy task, to say the least.

And then I read the book once more.

"Although I certainly can't make one of the fancy ships in this book," I decided, "I have at least figured out the ship-in-the-bottle secret."

And so I gritted my teeth and set to work once more. After many failures, I finally decided that this was the best way to proceed.

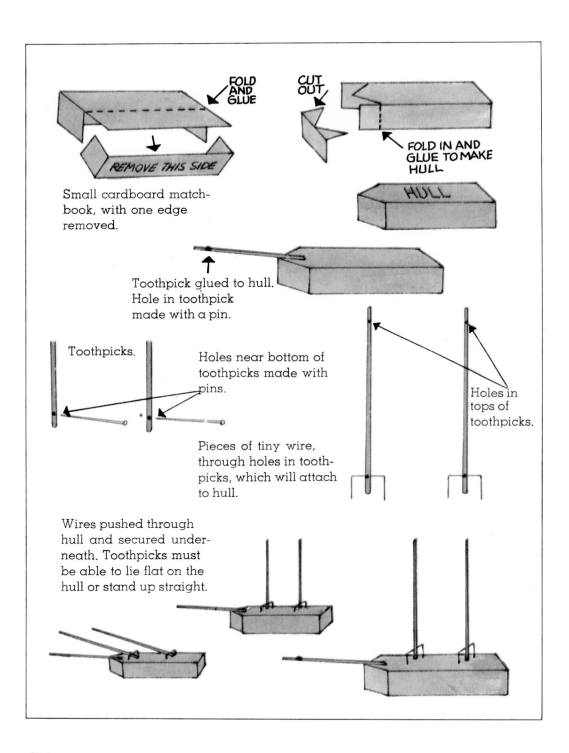

FOLD AND GLUE

REMOVE THIS SIDE

Small cardboard matchbook, with one edge removed.

CUT OUT

FOLD IN AND GLUE TO MAKE HULL

HULL

Toothpick glued to hull. Hole in toothpick made with a pin.

Toothpicks.

Holes near bottom of toothpicks made with pins.

Holes in tops of toothpicks.

Pieces of tiny wire, through holes in toothpicks, which will attach to hull.

Wires pushed through hull and secured underneath. Toothpicks must be able to lie flat on the hull or stand up straight.

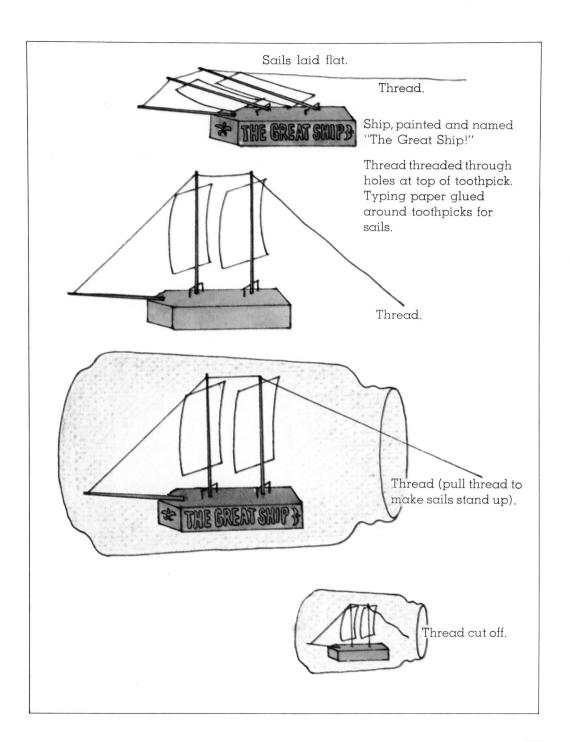

Sails laid flat.

Thread.

Ship, painted and named "The Great Ship!"

Thread threaded through holes at top of toothpick. Typing paper glued around toothpicks for sails.

Thread.

Thread (pull thread to make sails stand up).

Thread cut off.

When at last the ship rested snugly in its bottle, I sat back and studied my work. The sails were crooked, the hull was a little bent, and it didn't look like any ship I'd ever seen. But still it was a ship, and it was in a bottle—and that was my primary aim.

I wrapped it carefully, and then I wrote this note.

Daddy—

You may think that this ship is just an ordinary ship, but it isn't. At one time this was a large sailing vessel that sailed the seven seas. But then one day it sailed into a murky, polluted harbor that was cluttered with garbage, bottles, and a strange, oily substance. Now, who knows what goes on in murky, oily harbors? But whatever it is, before you could say "David John King," the ship had shrunk to the size of a matchbox and floated into this bottle.

One fine day not long after this strange occurrence, when I was seated on a big rock fishing peacefully in the harbor, what should I catch but this tiny bit of magic.

Love, Kim

The next morning when my father opened his present, he was very pleased. He was more than pleased. He was delighted. And the first thing he did with his sailing vessel was to place it on the shelf beside my mother's.

When my mother saw the ship up there on the shelf, she sighed and said, "I wish I had a ship with a story like that." And I think she really meant it.

Now two great vessels gaze down on the King family—one created by a large blue whale and one created by a murky, oily harbor—bringing a little bit of magic into our home.

All in All

When you read or do research, you often make generalizations about the information you read and gather. A *generalization* is a conclusion drawn from this information. Generalizations can be true or false. Read the following paragraph about dinosaurs.

> Dinosaurs roamed the earth millions of years ago. The largest plant-eating dinosaurs were about ninety feet long and weighed eighty-five tons. The *Brontosaurus* was about eighty feet long. The largest meat-eating dinosaurs often stood twenty feet tall. Their skulls were four feet long. The famous *Tyrannosaurus* measured forty-five feet from head to tail.

Generalization 1: All dinosaurs were gigantic.
Generalization 2: Some dinosaurs were very large.

The first generalization is false. Another fact is that the smallest common dinosaur was only two and a half feet long. The second generalization is true.

You have read only one paragraph about dinosaurs. No single paragraph can possibly tell you all about dinosaurs. When you make generalizations, avoid using words such as *everyone, always, all,* and *no,* because most generalizations have some exceptions.

Sometimes a generalization is made about a group of people. An example is, "All cooks eat too much." This is a false or undependable generalization. Some cooks may eat too much, but others do not. Unless you have met all cooks, you cannot say that all cooks eat too much.

ACTIVITY A   Read this paragraph and the two generalizations that follow it. Write the true, or dependable, generalization on your paper.

Jogging has become a popular sport in the U.S. No matter what the weather, streets and parks are full of joggers. You can find people of all ages jogging on weekdays and weekends. The sport is enjoyed in all fifty states.

Generalization 1: Many people in the U.S. enjoy jogging.
Generalization 2: Everyone in the U.S. jogs.

ACTIVITY B   Read the paragraphs below. Write whether the generalization drawn from each paragraph is true or false. If the generalization is true, explain why. If the generalization is false, write a generalization that is true.

1. In the last twenty years, television has become very popular. There are special shows for children and adults. Television can entertain, amuse, and educate. Some people watch television for many hours each day.

   Generalization: Everybody enjoys television.

2. Teenagers listen to many kinds of music. They play records, radios, and tapes many hours of the day. They carry portable radios and tape recorders with them wherever they go. You can often tell that teenagers are around because you can hear their music.

   Generalization: Many teenagers enjoy music.

I MAKE MANY THINGS

JEAN CRAIGHEAD GEORGE

Twelve-year-old Sam Gribley runs away from his New York City home to live on his great-grand-father's land in the Catskill Mountains. He plans to live off the land for one year. His house is the inside of an old tree. His food is plants, fish caught in a nearby stream, and meat caught by his pet falcon, Frightful. Sam's friends are The Baron, a wild weasel; Jessie Coon James, a skinny, young raccoon; and Frightful.

One day in the middle of summer, Sam comes upon a teacher who has been hiking in the woods. Sam nicknames the teacher Bando. Bando becomes Sam's friend, and together they build a raft and do many other things. On scraps of wrapping paper or bark, Sam keeps notes about his life on the mountain.

One day Bando went to town and came back with five pounds of sugar.

"I want to make blueberry jam," he said. "All those excellent berries and no jam."

He worked for two days at this. He knew how to make the jam. He had watched his pa make it in Mississippi, but he got stuck on what to put it in.

I wrote this one night:

August 29

"The raft is almost done. Bando has promised to stay until we can sail out into the deep fishing holes.

"Bando and I found some clay along the stream bank. It was as slick as ice. Bando thought it would make good pottery. He shaped some jars and lids. They look good. We dried them on a rock, and later Bando made a clay oven and baked them in it. He thinks they might hold the blueberry jam he has been making.

"Bando got the fire hot by blowing on it with some homemade bellows that he fashioned from one of my skins that he tied together like a balloon. A reed is the nozzle."

August 30

"It was a terribly hot day for Bando to be firing clay jars, but he stuck with it. They look jamworthy, as he says, and he filled three of them tonight. The jam is good, the pots remind me of flower pots without the hole in the bottom. Some of the lids don't fit. Bando says he will go home and read more about pottery making. Then he can do a better job next time.

"We like the jam. We eat it on hard acorn pancakes.

"Later. Bando met The Baron Weasel today for the first time. I don't know where The Baron has been this past week, but suddenly he appeared and nearly jumped down Bando's shirt collar. Bando said he liked The Baron best when he was in his hole."

September 3

"Bando taught me how to make willow whistles today. He and I went to the stream and cut two whistles about eight inches long. He slipped the bark on them. That means he pulled the wood out of the bark, leaving a tube. He made a mouthpiece at one end, cut a hole beneath it, and used the wood to slide up and down like a trombone.

"We played music until the moon came up. Bando could even play jazz on the willow whistles. They are wonderful instruments, sounding much like the wind in the top of the tree."

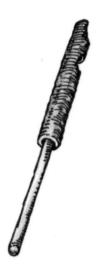

There were no more notes for many days. Bando had left me saying, "Good-bye, I'll see you at Christmas." I was so lonely that I kept sewing on my moccasins to keep myself busy. I sewed every free minute for four days. And when they were finished, I began a glove to protect my hand from Frightful's sharp talons.

One day when I was thinking very hard about being alone, Frightful gave a gentle call. I looked up.

"Bird," I said. "I had almost forgotten how we used to talk." She made tiny movements with her beak and fluffed her feathers. This was a language I had forgotten since Bando came. It meant she was glad to see me and hear me, that she was well-fed and happy. I picked her up and squeaked into her neck feathers. She moved her beak, turned her bright head, and bit my nose very gently.

Jessie Coon James came down from the trees for the first time in ten days. He finished my fish dinner. Then, just before dusk, The Baron came up on a boulder and scratched and cleaned and played with a leaf.

I had the feeling we were all back together again.

Soon September cut a trail into the mountains. First she burned the grasses and turned leaves yellow.

Then she sent the squirrels and chipmunks running boldly through the forest, collecting and hiding nuts.

Then she gathered the birds together in flocks, and the mountaintop was full of songs and flashing wings. The birds were ready to move to the south.

And I, Sam Gribley, felt just wonderful.

I pushed the raft down the stream and gathered bulbs and roots.

And then the crop of crickets appeared. Frightful hopped all over the meadow catching them in her great talons and eating them. I tried them, because I had heard they are good. I think it was another kind of cricket that was meant. I think the field cricket would taste excellent if you were starving. I was not starving, so I preferred to listen to them. I left the crickets and went back to the goodness of the earth.

I smoked fish and rabbit, dug wild onions, and raced September for her crop.

October 15

"Today The Baron Weasel looked moldy. I couldn't get near enough to see what was the matter with him, but he might be changing his summer fur for his white winter coat. If he is, it is an itchy process. He scratches a lot."

Seeing The Baron changing his coat for winter awoke the first fears in me. I wrote that note on a little birch bark, curled up on my bed, and shivered.

The snow and the cold and the long lifeless months are ahead, I thought. The wind was blowing hard and cool across the mountain. I lit my candle, took out the rabbit and squirrel hides I had been saving, and began rubbing them to softness.

The Baron was getting a new suit for winter. I must have one, too. Some fur underwear, some mittens, fur-lined socks.

Frightful, who was sitting on the foot post of the bed, yawned, fluffed, and thrust her head into the gray feathers of her back. She slept. I worked for several hours.

I must say here that I was beginning to wonder if I should not go home for the winter and come back again in the spring. Everything in the forest was getting prepared for the hard months. Jessie Coon James was very fat. He came down the tree slowly, his fat falling in a roll over his shoulders. The squirrels were working and storing food. They were building leaf nests. The skunks dug holes and plugged themselves in at dawn with bunches of leaves. No wind could reach them.

As I thought of the skunks and all the animals preparing themselves against the winter, I realized suddenly that my tree would be as cold as the air if I did not somehow find a way to heat it.

A few days later, I rafted out into the deep pools of the creek to fish. It was a lazy sort of autumn day, the sky clear, the leaves beginning to brighten, the air warm. I stretched out on my back, because the fish weren't biting, and I hummed.

My line jerked, and I sat up to pull but was too late. However, I was not too late to notice that I had drifted into the bank—the very bank where Bando had dug the clay for the jam pots.

At that moment I knew what I was going to do. I was going to build a fireplace of clay, even make a little chimney of clay. It would be small, but enough to warm the tree during the long winter.

The next day I dragged the clay up the mountain to my tree in my second-best pair of city pants. I tied the bottoms of the legs, stuffed them full, and as I looked down on my strange cargo, I thought of scarecrows and Halloween. Suddenly I was terribly lonely. The air smelled of leaves, and the cool wind from the stream hugged me. The birds in the trees above me seemed excited about their trip

south. I stopped halfway up the mountain and dropped my head. I was lonely and close to tears. Suddenly there was a flash, a pricking sensation on my leg. I looked down in time to see The Baron leap from my pants to the cover of fern.

He scared the loneliness right out of me. I ran after him and chased him up the mountain, losing him from time to time in the ferns and crowfeet. We stormed into camp an awful sight, The Baron bouncing and screaming ahead of me, and me dragging that half scarecrow of clay.

It took three days to get the fireplace worked out so that it didn't smoke me out of the tree like a bee. It was a huge problem. In the first place, the chimney sagged because the clay was too heavy to hold itself up. I had to get some dry grasses to work into it so it could hold its own weight.

I dug out one of the old knotholes to let the smoke out, and built the chimney down from this. Of course when the clay dried, it pulled away from the tree, and all the smoke poured back in on me.

So I tried sealing the leak with pine pitch, and that worked all right. But then the funnel over the fire bed cracked, and I had to put wooden props under that.

The wooden props burned, and I could see that this wasn't going to work either; so I went down the mountain to the site of the old Gribley farmhouse and looked around for some iron spikes or some sort of metal.

I took the wooden shovel that I had carved from the board and dug around what I thought must have been the back door or possibly the woodhouse.

I found a hinge, old handmade nails that would come in handy, and finally, treasure of treasures, the axle of an old wagon. It was much too big. I had no saw to cut it into smaller pieces, and I was not strong enough to heat it and hammer it apart. Besides, I didn't have anything but a small wooden hammer I had made.

I carried my trophies home and sat down before my tree to fix dinner and feed Frightful. The evening was cooling down for a frost. I looked at Frightful's warm feathers. I didn't even have a deer hide for a blanket. I had used the two I had for a door and a pair of pants. I wished that I might grow feathers.

I tossed Frightful off my fist, and she flashed through the trees and out over the meadow. She went with determination. "She is going to leave," I cried. "I have never seen her fly so wildly." I pushed the smoked fish aside and ran to the meadow. I whistled and whistled and whistled until my mouth was dry and no more whistle came.

I ran onto a big boulder. I could not see her. I licked my lips and whistled again. The sun was a cold, steely color as it dipped below the mountain. The air was now brisk, and Frightful was gone. I was sure that she had suddenly gone south. My heart was sore and pounding. I had enough food, I was sure. Frightful was not absolutely necessary for my survival; but I was now so fond of her. She was more than a bird. I knew I must have her back to talk to and play with if I was going to make it through the winter.

I whistled. Then I heard a cry in the grasses up near the white birches.

In the gathering darkness, I saw movement. I think I flew to the spot. And there she was; she had caught herself a bird. I rolled into the grass beside her and clutched her. She didn't intend to leave, but I was going to make sure that she didn't. I grabbed her so swiftly that my hand hit a rock and I hurt my knuckles.

The rock was flat and narrow and long; it was the answer to my fireplace. I picked up Frightful in

one hand and the stone in the other. I laughed at the cold, steely sun as it slipped out of sight, because I knew I was going to be warm. This flat stone was what I needed to hold up the funnel and finish my fireplace.

And that's what I did with it. I broke it into two pieces, set one on each side under the funnel, lit the fire, closed the flap of the door, and listened to the wind bring the first frost to the mountain. I was warm.

Then I noticed something dreadful. Frightful was sitting on the bedpost, her head under her wings. She jerked her head out of her feathers. Her eyes looked glassy. She seemed to be sick. I picked her up and stroked her, and we both might have died there if I had not opened the tent flap to get her some water. The cold night air revived her. "Air," I said. "The fireplace used up all the oxygen. I've got to get more air into this place."

We sat out in the cold for a long time because I was more than a little afraid of what our end might have been.

I put out the fire, took the door down and wrapped up in it. Frightful and I slept with the good frost nipping our faces.

Notes:

"I cut out several more knotholes to let air in and out of the tree room. I tried it today. I have Frightful on my fist watching her. It's been about two hours, and she hasn't fainted. And I haven't gone numb. I can still write and see clearly.

"Test: Frightful's healthy face."

The Piper

WILLIAM BLAKE

Piping down the valleys wild,
  Piping songs of pleasant glee,
On a cloud I saw a child,
  And he laughing said to me:

"Pipe a song about a lamb!"
  So I piped with merry cheer.
"Piper, pipe that song again";
  So I piped: he wept to hear.

"Drop thy pipe, thy happy pipe;
  Sing thy songs of happy cheer!"
So I sung the same again,
  While he wept with joy to hear.

"Piper, sit thee down and write
  In a book that all may read."
So he vanished from my sight;
  And I plucked a hollow reed,

And I made a rural pen,
  And I stained the water clear,
And I wrote my happy songs
  Every child may joy to hear.

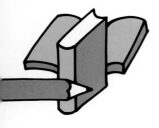

Shades of Meaning

Did you know that the Eskimo language has twenty-six words for *snow*? Each word names a different kind of snow. The language has many words for snow because snow is important in Eskimo life.

Words are important in everyone's life. We use words to communicate with others. In order to make ourselves clear, we must always choose the best possible words.

Some words have similar meanings. These words are called *synonyms*. For example, the words *look, stare, peek, gaze, glance*, and *gape* are all synonyms.

Here are two sentences using two of the above synonyms.

> The busy worker <u>looked</u> at the newspaper.
> The busy worker <u>glanced</u> at the newspaper.

The above sentences have similar meanings. Yet they create slightly different pictures in the mind of the reader. Someone who looks at a newspaper may look for five seconds or five hours. The word *look* doesn't indicate any amount of time. The word *glance*, on the other hand, is more exact. It means "to look for a very brief period of time."

When you choose among synonyms in your writing, select the one with the most exact meaning. Use a thesaurus or a dictionary to find the best possible synonym. The most exact word creates the clearest picture for the reader.

494

ACTIVITY A Read each sentence. Choose the word in parentheses that you think offers the more exact meaning. Write the word on your paper.

1. The hard hit ball _____ over the fence. (went, sailed)
2. The active dog _____ through the park. (loped, ran)
3. The astronomer _____ at the star. (gazed, looked)
4. The neighbors _____ for hours. (spoke, chatted)
5. A duck _____ near the pond. (walked, waddled)
6. The _____ horses raced home. (swift, fast)
7. Linda prepared a _____ dinner. (good, tasty)
8. The _____ elephant escaped today. (big, enormous)

ACTIVITY B Read each sentence. Think of a more exact synonym for the underlined word. You may use a thesaurus or a dictionary. On your paper, write the sentence with your new word. Do not change the meaning of the sentence.

1. The happy fans cheered throughout the game.
2. The eager players ran onto the field.
3. A family relaxed by going through the park.
4. The driver stepped on the brakes quickly.
5. We talked for hours about our vacations.
6. A lonely cat looked for food in the dark.
7. The warm sun gave everyone a sunburn.
8. A large crowd watched the parade.
9. Thousands of people filled the auditorium.

ACTIVITY C On your paper, write a different sentence using each of these synonyms: *smart, clever, sharp, keen*.

EXPRESSIONS

People's talents and the expressions of these talents add richness and variety to life. These creative expressions often reflect the artists' backgrounds and experiences, as well as their talents. In "Expressions," you read about many people—poets, painters, photographers—who created things that reflected their feelings and experiences. We can all express ourselves in some way, and each expression is a way of saying, "This is what I can do and what I want to share with you."

Thinking About "Expressions"

1. What similar theme did Manuel Acosta, the painter, and Issa, the poet, use in their work?
2. In what ways were Pitseolak's art and Margaret White's photography important to them?
3. How did Mary Anne win the Tall-Tale Tournament by telling the truth?
4. "A Bit of Magic" and "I Make Many Things" are both fictional selections. How do the characters in each story find very unusual ways of expressing themselves?
5. Which of the methods of self-expression that you read about most appeals to you?
6. In "The Tall-Tale Tournament," Mary Anne won a contest by telling a tall tale. Write a tall tale of your own.

A HORSE CAME RUNNING

In life, the things that happen to you—your experiences—influence what you do, how you feel, and how you relate to the people around you. The events in your life help make you who you are. In literature, a writer often takes an event, sometimes an extraordinary one, and shows how story characters react to it. The writer shows how the event influences the attitudes, feelings, and actions of the characters.

In "A Horse Came Running," you will see how an author develops an unforgettable adventure. With a young boy, you will watch in amazement as a violent tornado twists and turns its way through the farmland that is his home. You will share the boy's reaction to the disappearance of his beloved old horse, Colonel. You will watch as he forms a friendship with a neighbor and helps the neighbor save his injured wife. You will see how the friendship between the boy and the man deepens as the two depend on each other for survival.

As you read, think about how each character behaves in each new situation. Think about what you learn about the characters as they react to events over which they have no control. Ask yourself what you can learn about people from their reactions to different situations.

497

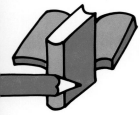

A Turning Point

Many people plan their vacations carefully. They decide in advance what they want to see on the trip. Advance planning increases their enjoyment of the trip.

Reading a novel is like taking a long trip. You read about many people, places, and events in the story. Knowing what to look for as you read helps you enjoy the the novel more.

The novel you are about to read is called *A Horse Came Running*. This novel, like other novels, has many aspects. One aspect is the *setting*. The setting is the time and place of the story. In a novel, the time could be the past, present, or future. The time may also be more specific. It may be a particular date or a time of day. The very first sentence in *A Horse Came Running* states that the time is dusk. The next sentence states that the place is a pasture. After reading the first two sentences, you know that the setting for Chapter One is a pasture at dusk.

Since a novel is a long story, the setting may change many times. Sometimes, the setting moves from one period of time to an earlier period of time. This backward movement in time is called a *flashback*. The author tells you about an event that occurred at an earlier time. Be prepared for the flashback in *A Horse Came Running*. Chapter One starts at dusk. Chapter Two, however, skips back to noon of the same day. Soon, however, the action returns to the original time.

Another important aspect of a novel is the *plot*. The plot is the action that takes place in the story. Everything that characters do is part of the plot. A plot has a beginning, a middle, and an end.

The plot usually focuses on a problem which one or more characters face. In *A Horse Came Running,* you will discover that the character named Mark has a problem to solve. Other characters have problems, too. As the story unfolds, their problems take shape and develop.

When you read a good story, you become interested in how the problems of the plot will be solved. The events in a story build to a *climax,* or dramatic highpoint. After the climax, you discover how the problem will be solved. This aspect of the novel is called the *resolution* and comes at the end of the story.

The plot and setting help create a *mood* in a novel. The mood is the novel's general feeling or atmosphere. Ghost stories, for example, create a scary mood. Comedies, on the other hand, create a happy mood. In the opening scene of *A Horse Came Running,* a dark, frightening feeling is created by the occurrence of a tornado.

As you read *A Horse Came Running,* pay attention to the setting, plot, and mood of the story. Ask yourself these questions:

1. What changes in setting take place?
2. What are the problems in the plot? How do these problems develop and become greater as the story continues?
3. What is the climax of the story? What is its resolution?
4. How does the mood change as the story develops?

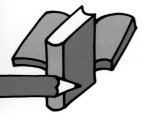

Role Playing

You have already learned that a novel has many aspects. These aspects include the setting, plot, and mood. Another important aspect of a novel is the *characters*. Characters are the people in a story. Characters may include animals as well as people. In *A Horse Came Running,* you will discover that two horses, Colonel and Creek, are important characters.

A novel has two types of characters: *major characters* and *minor characters*. The major characters are the most important characters in the story. You learn the most about these characters. In *A Horse Came Running,* the major characters are Mark, Mr. Sayers, Creek, and Colonel.

The minor characters are less important than the major characters. Minor characters in this novel include Mrs. Sayers and Mark's parents. You do not learn a great deal about them, but they play an important part in the story.

There are three important ways to learn about a character:

1. The first way to learn is through the character's own words and actions. In *A Horse Came Running,* you will learn about Mark from the things he says and does. He is a boy with a vivid imagination. He also has a great love for horses. He shows his love in the way he looks after Creek and Colonel.

2. The second way to learn about a character is through the words and actions of other characters. For example, Mr. Sayers' comments to his wife indicate that Mark is a likable and mature young man.

3. The third way to learn about a character is through the author's description. For example, one sentence says, "Mark stood, wavering, anxious to run to Colonel, but needing to quiet the new horse." You learn from the author's description that the character named Mark is aware of his responsibilities to both Colonel and the new horse.

Characters face problems in a story. Often the problems involve other people. For example, in *A Horse Came Running,* Mark and the Sayers face a problem with looters at one point. Sometimes, the characters must battle nature. For example, when the tornado strikes, Mark and the other characters must face this problem. A third kind of problem involves only one character. For example, Mark must overcome his fears about life.

Often, the characters in a novel develop and change during the course of the novel. Their experiences teach them something new about themselves or about life. In *A Horse Came Running,* notice how Mark has changed by the end of the novel.

As you read the novel, ask yourself these questions:

1. Why do the characters act as they do in each situation?
2. What is special about the relationship between Mark and Mr. Sayers? Between Mark and Colonel? Between Mark and Creek?
3. What does Mark learn about himself and about others as a result of his experiences?
4. How do you feel about each character? Do your feelings about any of the characters change as you read more about each of them?

502

1

It was dusk. Two horses were standing at their pasture fence. The old horse was waiting, the young horse, new to the place, was merely staying close. The old horse seemed to be looking toward the big white house that rose at the end of the pasture, but he was really looking beyond, toward a hill around which the evening train must come. He stood stamping, tail switching, impatient to begin his twice-daily game of racing the twice-daily train the length of the pasture.

The new horse came closer. She stared across the railroad tracks at a grove of big trees but saw nothing. She was only waiting to take her cue from the old horse. Then, like this morning and yesterday—her first day—she would run easily alongside the pounding, old horse and the pounding, loaded train.

She knew that they would bring themselves up just short of crashing into the fence at the end of the pasture. Then the train would roll on relentlessly, and they would return to their grazing, side by side—that was all the new horse needed or wanted in her homesick heaviness.

At that quiet moment, train sounds came to the ears of the old horse. But the sounds were too far and too thin to begin his first move.

Then came a roar—the roar as of a hundred rushing trains. But no train came. Instead, over the top of the distant hill rose a black, whipping, funnel-shaped cloud. On it came, swinging, slinging its great evil snout— reaching out to devour everything in the helpless country-side. In white-eyed terror the horses raced ahead of it.

Far behind the horses the door of the big white house was thrown open, and a man came running down the steps. He called back to the house, "Lin, come help me get that new horse of yours. She's scared and if the tornado *does* come this way we'll . . ." A young girl rushed out on the porch. "Daddy!" she called, "the radio says it's headed this way! We won't have time to . . ." She whirled at the roar behind her. "It's here, it's here!" she screamed, and pointed, then dashed back into the house.

The man turned and saw the black funnel dipping toward the house. He cleared the steps in one jump, ran in the house, grabbed the girl by one hand and came out with her. "It's safer in the stable," he yelled as they ran. "Lie flat on the floor," he gasped as he pushed her inside and slammed the door of the stable.

The whirling funnel came down, enveloped the big white house, sucked it up and rose with it high in the air. The splintering house within the black maw added its own scream to the shriek and the horror.

The tornado had taken the house off its basement walls, but the stable stood untouched back of the house under a clump of trees.

Now, as the tornado lifted, it was as if it saw the plunging horses at the pasture's end. Down it dipped again, flinging a roof beam, a twisted stove, beds, tables, and a white refrigerator from its snout. The dropped things smashed or speared into the ground, helter-skelter the length of the pasture.

On it came, and the horses could only plunge madly back and forth as they tried to escape. The old horse whinnied and tried to break through the fence, but the heavy wire threw him back and he fell to the ground dead. The new horse turned and ran in frantic fear as the tornado sucked the old horse up into itself. Behind her, sections of fence pulled into the air. She tore ahead of the disappearing fence, snorting her terror. Suddenly her feet were not on the ground. She, too, was in the air, hoofs pawing, legs pistoning, caught in the outer edge of the funnel. Then the tornado shifted, dropped her back to the ground, and turned out of the pasture toward the grove of trees across the tracks.

The new horse landed on all four legs, stuttered a few wooden steps, then stood in dazed shock as the tornado whipped the lash of its tail among the trees of the little birds.

Before her eyes the great trees began to scream and twist out of the ground. They whined up, tossed for a moment, then smashed down on their branches in a tangled heap. Just beyond them the tornado dropped the old horse. He, too, lay upside down and horribly still.

Then, as if she had just found she could move, the new horse backed away from the spooking horror of the dead horse and the giant roots clawing whitely up into the sky. Further on, the tornado dipped into a gully and thrashed there unseen like a roaring, idiot giant. After long moments it rose high into the air and moved away.

With a snort the horse came out of her shock, whirled, and charged toward the stable. Somehow she avoided the debris the tornado had scattered in the pasture, but the basement walls of the gone, white house brought her up short and quivering. She stared at the naked, strange walls, and, instead of turning toward the safety of the stable, she wheeled away.

In her sudden turning she leaped a white refrigerator that lay smashed in her path. She cleared it, but she cut her ankle on a chisel-sharp piece of metal pointing up from the outflung door. In new, hurt madness she plowed through a bush in the front yard. A woman's dress was caught in its branches. The filmy stuff wrapped itself around her leg, pasted and stuck there in the thick, guttering blood from the cut. The hem of the dress fluttering under her made her plunge and sunfish wildly.

Unable to get away from the fluttering cloth she broke into a blind run. Accidentally she took the path the tornado had come—a mowed, swept path of destruction. Finally she crossed an asphalt road and was about to run down it, when a farmyard water trough slid out of the top of a tree and clanged down in front of her.

Eyes rolling, nostrils gaping, she fled once more up the path of the tornado. On and on she ran, not aware of exhaustion until she came to a steep hill. But then, suddenly, as if only now aware of her hurt leg, she stopped a moment and then limped slowly up the hill. There she stopped again and looked around. Far across the fields she saw an unwrecked barn whose great hay doors stood open. She started toward them.

As she crossed into the field she came to a gully at the end of a small wood. There in the gully lay more twisted trees—and there, too, was a horse. An old, white horse. But this horse was not dead. This horse was on his feet, imprisoned in the tangle of trees.

Slow step by slow step she backed away from the white horse and the white roots pointing in the air. At last she was able to turn away, but, instead of going to the barn with its wide-open doors, she angled off at an uneasy jog around the gully, and she ended up in the small woodlot.

The little wood was still, everything was upright and untouched. She went in among the quiet trees. The old horse in the gully whinnied after her pathetically, but she did not answer him—she did not seem to hear. She jogged away into the darkness under the safe, strong trees.

She came to a small creek and walked into it, unseeing. The sudden coldness of the water shocked her to a stop. She stood trembling. The horse in the gully whinnied once more, but she did not answer. She stood in safe darkness—the creek gurgled soft, babyish sounds up at her.

The horse in the gully was silent now. The horse in the creek stood still—a frozen statue. The creek gurgled its safe little sounds and cool water curled around her four rigid feet.

2

It was noon of the day of the tornado. Mark was down in the barnyard feeding potato peelings to old Colonel. Of course, Mark did not know that this was going to be the day of the tornado. Nobody knew that late in the afternoon a tornado would come rising in a black roar over the hills and fall on the helpless countryside.

No, this noon when Mark was with Colonel, it was a day like any other day except that Colonel still lay in the gateway between the barnyard and the pasture. The old horse had lain there all night and all the day before.

This morning when Mark had watched his mother peel potatoes, he had thought that if he fed the peelings to Colonel maybe it would give the old horse strength to get up again. If he could get up he could eat grass and get stronger. Then they'd go across the pasture to the high bank of catalpa trees. There was a water pipe sticking out of the bank that came from a spring. He would hold a pail under the end of the pipe and when it filled, Colonel could drink. Then he'd eat more grass and maybe stay up on his feet.

But this noon Colonel couldn't even lift his head to nibble the parings from the flat pan. Mark sat discouraged until he tried rubbing a piece of peeling into the side of Colonel's mouth. It worked! Colonel opened his big, yellow teeth, chewed and swallowed!

Mark was so busy feeding the peelings into Colonel's mouth that he didn't hear his dad drive up to the barn, but his father saw him and called out, "Mark, what the blazes are you doing?"

"Just feeding Colonel," Mark yelled. "He can't get up to eat grass."

Dad studied Colonel and shook his head. "Guess I've been so busy finishing that new store in Stanton that I haven't paid much attention to what's going on around here. I didn't realize it had got this bad with the old horse." Dad pressed his lips together. At last he said, "Mark, this oughtn't to come as a surprise to you—you were with me when I bought this farm. All I wanted was the wonderful old house, but the farmer wouldn't sell it. No, I had to take the farm and the old horse with it. Remember, the old man told us Colonel was on his last legs? He *is* on his last legs now, Mark, and you've got to face it."

Mark got up and stood stiff and straight. Dad kept talking.

"Can't you understand that to keep Colonel like this is cruel? We promised the old man that we'd give the horse the best of care. This isn't the best, it's the worst—lying here hungry and thirsty and too weak to get up. Mark, the vet will put Colonel out of his misery, and it'll be quick and easy—it'll be a mercy for the poor old fellow."

Mark looked up at Dad. He couldn't believe it. How could grown-ups make themselves believe things just by saying them?

How could Dad say it?

How could he believe it?

Why would it be a mercy—Colonel'd be dead, wouldn't he?

510

"Mark, tomorrow's your birthday, isn't it?"

Mark nodded. He didn't dare to speak, or he'd cry.

"Well, then, how'd you like a pony?" Dad looked around the pasture. "What an ocean of grass! Maybe we ought to get a whale—still, whales don't swim so good in grass. Well, how *about* a pony?"

It was hard to keep the tears back with Dad making unfunny jokes. He didn't want a pony. He had Colonel and Colonel was his friend. Why couldn't Dad understand? He shook his head.

"Well . . . maybe your mother can explain it better." Dad started toward the house.

Now there was nothing to do but crouch down and start feeding Colonel again.

Finally Dad came out of the house and went to the barn. He called down, "Okay, Mark. Your mother says to give Colonel a little longer. She says maybe he'll get up for your birthday tomorrow. If I find time this afternoon I might be able to look for a young horse or a pony. Maybe with a young horse on the place Colonel will want to be young again. Who knows . . ."

"Dad! Dad!" Mark shouted, "If it made Colonel stay on his feet, then I'd have two horses and then . . ."

But Dad had started the truck and the whole barn roared with the noise. Colonel lifted his head at the sudden roar. Then Mark couldn't just stand there yelling—Colonel had his head up, Colonel could drink.

Mark stormed across the pasture to fill a pail from the spring. When he got back Colonel still had his head up enough to drink out of the tipped-down pail. It was sloshy, but Colonel did drink. After that Mark got busy. He found an old rusty sickle in the barn and a bushel basket. He went behind the house where the grass grew the greenest and the juiciest in the shade from the cellarway's propped-up door. He cut a whole basketful and carried it to Colonel.

Then he folded it into little bundles, and he shoved the bundles between Colonel's teeth and down into his mouth. Colonel's yellow old teeth got green-juicy from the tender grass. Oh, it must be full of strength and goodness. It had to get Colonel back on his feet—if not today then tomorrow.

At lunch time, Colonel still wasn't up. He'd had two bushels of grass and the potato peelings, but he hadn't even tried to get up. Maybe he was saving his strength so he could get up tomorrow, but it wasn't easy to make yourself believe it. So it wasn't easy to eat lunch with Mother in the quiet kitchen. Mother made a little joke, too. She asked, "What do you want for your birthday—a bushel of oats for Colonel?"

He didn't feel like joking—but a bushel of oats! There ought to be all kinds of strength in a bushel of oats. So he said, "Yes, if you're not joking, I would like that." He had to say it slowly or he'd start to cry.

But Mother said, "Okay then, it'll be one of your presents, but I'll get it today. Now that your dad came home to get the truck and left the car here, I'm going to go into the city, but on the way home I'll stop at the feed mill for the oats and maybe a tonic—if they have a tonic for horses. But look, whose birthday is this, yours or Colonel's? Anyhow, I've got a present right now for your horse. When I was peeling potatoes for the salad, I cut up all the small ones I found into tiny pieces so they won't choke Colonel. You can give them to him after lunch."

Suddenly Mark was afraid. He wanted to ask, Mother, why are you giving Colonel presents? Do you know he is going to die?

But he couldn't ask it. That would make it real. "May I go out and feed him now?" he asked instead.

"Yes, but don't spend the whole afternoon with Colonel. Play a little and let Colonel rest."

He was almost at the door when he put down the pail and rushed back to kiss Mother hard. Then he promised, "I'll play in the tunnels I made in the hay pile in the barn. I'll play a long time."

He was going to do it, too. It would be a kind of bargain. He'd feed Colonel, maybe give him another drink, and then he wouldn't even go near him. He wouldn't cheat by watching through the cracks of the barn up in the haymow to see if Colonel *had* got up on his feet. He'd play almost the whole afternoon. That would be *his* part of the bargain. Then if he kept his part Colonel would live. It had to be.

"Mark," Mother called from the kitchen door, "feed Colonel the potatoes, but don't expect them to change into strength just like that—it takes a while. You play and let Colonel rest after the potatoes. Then maybe by the time your dad comes home, Colonel will have strength enough so that Dad and I can help you get him on his feet."

That was a wonderful thought. Mark stopped and looked back, but he was too taken up with it to answer.

"And Mark, your dad wants to go out to that pony farm to see just what they have. He doesn't know what they cost, but he'd feel better if you had a pony. You think about it while you play."

Mark nodded. He didn't answer because he didn't know— he didn't want anything but Colonel. He'd think about it, but later.

"See you, Mom, see you," he yelled as he ran toward the barnyard.

3

Mark lay stretched out in his new, partly dug tunnel under the hay pile up in the barn. He'd had to stop digging because the fine hay dust was making him sneeze. He had his face in his arms waiting for the last sneeze when the question jumped into his mind—would it be nice to have a pony? A pony would be his size. He could ride a pony. He wouldn't have to claw himself up the way he did with Colonel. He only got up on Colonel when the old horse wasn't lame and stumbly, but he was always sorry when he did. Colonel was a big old work horse, bony and wide. He had to sit spraddled, legs sticking out straight, and it hurt. Riding Colonel was like riding a bony earthquake. Mark laughed—Colonel a bony earthquake!

It was easier and more fun just to walk with Colonel. By now he had shown Colonel all the spots that he knew over the whole farm—even small bird nests hidden down in the grass. That was important so that during school when Colonel was grazing alone he wouldn't crush the nests with his big, flat, squashed-out feet.

But Colonel knew all kinds of places, too. Colonel had been born on this farm. He knew. He was the one who had shown Mark the little whispering creek that ran through the gully and on through the woodlot. When you stood still under the trees, it was hushed and important. It was almost like being in church except that the little creek always whispered. It was so narrow they couldn't wade together, so Mark had to come splashing on behind Colonel. But often Colonel just wanted to stand with the creek water washing and whispering around his feet. What if Colonel had got up from all the strength of the pail full of potatoes—what if he was up right now! Then they could go to the cool-water creek in the woodlot under the trees.

Mark began tunneling again—it was hot and dusty and sneezy under the hay, but it was the only way he knew of keeping himself from sneaking looks at Colonel. Then suddenly he broke through into the main tunnel that he'd made long ago. He'd done it. He'd played, and he'd broken through.

He'd played just as he'd promised, and he'd kept his part of the bargain. But a pony wouldn't be any good.

Mark lay panting after crawling into the main tunnel. There was light at the end of this tunnel, dim barn light, and there was air. It was even a little cooler here—but not much.

What time was it? The light looked sort of dim. It could be late. He'd played and played and thought and thought, and it had taken a long time to feed the potatoes to Colonel. What if right now Dad and Mother were on their way home? And Colonel still down because he needed water. He'd run to the house and look at the clock, and if there was time, he'd get a pail of water for Colonel.

Mark scrambled down the haymow ladder and stopped startled in the open doorway of the barn. It wasn't only the barn that was dim! Everything everywhere was dim and mean and threatening. Everything was waiting. Had he really played so long under the hay that it was late? But Mother and Dad still weren't home. Mark flew to the house to look at the clock.

Oh, it *was* late, way late—ten to six. Much later than Dad usually came home. There wouldn't be time to run to the spring. He looked out of the window and saw that Colonel was still down—flat down. He'd looked, but it was late—he'd kept his part of the bargain!

Mark ran to the living room where he could see far down the road, but there was no car coming. Mark fretted at the window. Maybe they were so late because they'd gone to get a pony. What could he do if they came with a pony? You couldn't tell your parents, "No, I don't want it for my birthday." Not if it was here.

Mark moved along the windows until at the dining room window he could look across the single field that separated their farm from the Sayers farm. As Mark stood there Mr. and Mrs. Sayers came running out of their house. Mr. Sayers was carrying a radio, but Mrs. Sayers stood looking toward their house as if looking straight at him.

Then they looked up at the sky, and Mr. Sayers ran back and grabbed Mrs. Sayers' arm and started tugging her out toward their barn. But, as if she had seen Mark at the window, she pulled away from her husband and seemed to be shouting. Mark couldn't hear because there came a great roaring. He ran out of the house and into the field, but Mr. Sayers motioned him back with the waving radio. Mrs. Sayers screamed and screamed at him, but he couldn't make out a word for the awfulness of the roaring.

Then Mr. Sayers pointed and Mark looked up. Over the hill came a great black cloud, swinging and threatening. Then Mrs. Sayers' scream pierced through the noise. "Mark, get into the basement—it's a tornado!"

Mark ran toward the barn. "Not in your barn, not in your barn!" Mrs. Sayers yelled. But now the two old people were running to their barn—funny, he wasn't to run to his!

"Colonel is down, I've got to . . ." Mark screamed down the field. But the old people couldn't hear; they kept running. Already the tornado was there behind them. It twisted and whirled in the sky and then it dipped down on their house. Immediately it rose again, but now there was no roof on the house. Only the roofless walls were left under the screaming blackness.

Confused, scared, threatened, Mark started to run to Colonel, but suddenly there was such a wrenching, screeching noise, Mark turned and stood rooted. It was the Sayers' barn! The tornado had the barn and now it rose up with it, and there were only the bare basement walls left. The tornado had the barn and Mr. and Mrs. Sayers must be up in the tornado.

Now the tornado turned toward the single field that was between their houses—now it was coming for him and he couldn't move! He couldn't move and there lay Colonel!

He heard himself screeching, "Run, Colonel. Run!" Colonel couldn't run, but somehow it helped him to move. Then Mark was at the cellarway with the open trap door. There was nothing he could do for Colonel now. He hurled himself down the steps.

Now the tornado would get Colonel. Mark rushed up the steps again—if he could get Colonel up and in the basement of the barn with him. . . .

There wasn't time. The tornado had already crossed the field. It was in the yard, and the cellar door was still open. Mark unhooked the door and tried to pull it down

over him, but the tornado was so close the suction
flapped the door up and flapped the door down like
a great wooden wing. There Mark hung, unable to let
go. There he hung watching Colonel, listening to
Colonel's screaming. The old horse's scream was so
scared and so shrill that it cut through the roar of the
tornado.

Then Colonel flung his head back so far that Mark
saw Colonel's head upside down, his screaming mouth
open and his big teeth showing. In a mighty lunge he
rolled over, gathered his legs under him and was up. He
staggered only a moment, then with great stiff plunges he
tore into the pasture ahead of the tornado. Colonel was
up! The next moment the slinging cloud of blackness
closed in behind him, and Mark could see him no more.

The suction suddenly was gone. The trap door fell
shut with a slap like thunder. It smashed Mark down the
steps. He rolled limply among the scattered potatoes.
Everything went black and still.

4

It was as if by inches Mark came back to consciousness. His cheek and nose were against something soft and cushiony that had a musty, earthy smell. He took it in his hand—it was a potato, it squashed. "Mom! Dad!" he screamed. No one answered, everything was still. Mark scrambled to his feet. He was dizzy, but now he knew where he was, now he remembered. But everything was still, too still.

He was in the cellar. He'd been lying among the potatoes where the trap door had flung him when it had crashed down. There had been a tornado, and from the cellar door he had seen Colonel get to his feet and gallop into the pasture ahead of the tornado.

Now in one mighty slam the stillness was broken. Rain thundered on the closed trap door and found cracks in the splintered, rotted wood. Big drops smacked against Mark's neck and crawled coldly down his back. With one hand Mark felt the top of his head where the door had hit and where the slow blood throbbed. His head was wet, but rain-wet, not blood-wet—blood would be warm and sticky. This was cold and crawly with crumbles and splinters of wood. He wiped off his neck with the flat of his hand, and staggered up the cellar steps. He had to get outside and see what had happened to Colonel.

Mark braced himself, both hands around the edge of the top step, and with bent back up against the soaked, warped door he tried to force it out of its framework. He heaved himself up against it, but it did not yield. The rain was coming harder now. It soaked his head, ran down inside his shirt, divided, and ran down both legs into his socks and his shoes. It was cold, but it stopped the throbbing in his head. He stepped down to the middle step and let the rain water run over his head and wash down his face.

Suddenly he felt foolish. Here he was heaving away at a stuck door with his head pounding when all he had to do was to feel his way across the cellar and up the inside stairway to the dining room. He shuffled through the scattered potatoes so as not to fall again. Heck, he was a dirty, wet mess anyway! He dropped to his hands and knees and crawled up the inside stairway.

When Mark opened the door to the dining room, he was startled to see that it was almost as dark up here as it had been in the windowless cellar. The whole house was enclosed in a dark curtain of rain. The gutters could not hold the smash of rain that thundered on the roof; they overflowed and the water spilled down in thick, dark sheets over the windows. Inside the house was empty and silent, except for him. Was it night-dark or rain-dark? How long had he lain in the cellar?

Mark ran to see the kitchen clock. The hands still stood at ten to six—right where they'd stood just before the tornado. That must have been when the electric wires had gone down between here and Stanton.

He turned to snap on the light. There was no light. He lifted the receiver on the wall telephone above the kitchen table. The phone was as silent as the clock.

Nobody would call—nobody could. And in a rain like this no one could come. Only night was coming—night and dark and rain. In such a rain not even Mr. Sayers could walk across the field that separated their houses, and he couldn't get out to the neighbors. Oh! He'd forgotten! The neighbors were gone—gone with their barn. Colonel was gone. There was no one.

The thought of Colonel made Mark race to the storeroom that had its window above the cellar door. But he could only see as far as the barn, and it was just a dull red lump inside the sheets of rain roaring off its roof. The barnyard sloping to the pasture was a boiling, racing river. Mark shivered. If Colonel hadn't gotten up, he would have drowned where he had lain. If it hadn't been for the tornado coming so close, Colonel wouldn't have gotten up.

If Colonel had fallen again, if he lay with his head to the ground, he could die in the pasture. Mark couldn't see, he couldn't go out there, could he? If he fell in the dark, he'd drown too, wouldn't he? And a lantern wouldn't stay lit.

Lantern! Mark tore back to the kitchen, jerked open the cabinet door under the sink and, as he'd remembered, there was the lantern. He shook it. Oil rattled. He lit the lantern and set it in the sink for safety.

When he'd done that, there was nothing more to do but stand listening to the rain that closed everything out but closed him in. If Colonel was alive, the rain was beating down on him, even if he was up on his feet. It must hurt, it must feel like hail or sharp, beating sticks. But even that would be better than Colonel lying flat on the ground.

He would wait for the rain to slow down, but he'd get his boots and raincoat and have them ready. He ran to his room.

Back in the kitchen he pulled on his boots, then he thought of something else. Leaving his raincoat and hat on a chair, he went gallumping in his clumsy boots to the storeroom where he'd seen a big carton. He jumped on it and smashed it to flatness. The rain must be slowing, for his stamping had seemed noisier than the rain.

With the flattened carton Mark went back to the kitchen. He laid it on the table and hunted a carpenter's flat pencil out of the drawer—that would write thick and black.

He listened while he thought about what he should write. The rain must be slowing. Quickly he wrote: "Mom, Dad. The tornado came and Colonel got up and ran into the pasture. I couldn't help him then, but now I have to find him. If I'm not here when you come, I'm out looking for Colonel."

He'd made the writing good and big. He set the carton on the sink. The moment they opened the door they'd see it by lantern light. There was still a space at the bottom of the carton. He'd write small. "Mr. and Mrs. Sayers went up in the tornado with their barn." He put the carton back. Small as he'd written these last words, they seemed the biggest of all, they were so scary. He picked up the pencil and added: "I think." It was a little better, but not much. He set the coffee pot against the carton so it couldn't fall down on the lantern. Then he pulled the window curtain to one side to see if the rain was stopping.

It had slowed. The water wasn't gushing over the edge of the gutter anymore, and across the field a queer evening light had come into the sky. It showed the white walls of the Sayers' house standing open to the rain.

The rain fell dark inside the white walls. Their barn was gone, the old people were gone, and suddenly Mark noticed that the old white car that had seldom run had also gone up in the tornado.

The strange light glistened on something in the road in front of the Sayers' house. It was a great roll and tangle of twisted, gleaming wires—the telephone and the electric wires rolled together, and the dark wooden telephone poles rolled inside the wires.

There was no road to Stanton anymore. Beyond the wires the road ran dead into a mass of upended, uprooted trees. The roadside trees were smashed down in the road from both sides, and other trees rose out of them as if planted upside down, their great stark roots upstanding. Under the trees the streaming road lay like a river.

Then the rain stopped. Now nothing but the water moved, and the queer, glassy light faded from the sky. Night darkness came to take the place of the rain darkness. There was no sound except the drip, drip, drip.

Mark moved away from the window to his rain clothes. If he looked outside any longer, he'd be too scared to move. Mother and Dad couldn't come. There wasn't any road. If they walked, it would take them hours. But the pasture would be dark. Mark reached for the lantern. No, if he took it and Mother and Dad did come, they wouldn't be able to read his note. And if he didn't find Colonel and had to come back alone, there wouldn't be any light in the window.

It was scary to go out and it was scary here. Mark pulled the rain hat down hard over his head. He was *going* to find Colonel! He'd bring him to the house, get the lantern, and then be with Colonel and the lantern in the big, safe barn.

Mark threw the back door open and ran out, letting it slam shut behind him. It sounded like a shot as he raced away.

It wasn't raining anymore, and he didn't need his raincoat. He was wet anyway. He ripped it off as he ran and flung it toward the open doors. It'd be hard enough to climb the fence in his clumsy boots without having the raincoat in his way.

Without the raincoat Mark felt freed and speedy. He must hurry. Suddenly he realized he was in the pasture. There had been no fence to climb. It was gone—ripped away from where it had been nailed to the corner of the barn!

Mark started. The tornado had come around the barn that close! It had ripped the fence away as if the quicker to get at Colonel. It had been that low to the ground. But when he'd seen it beyond the barn, it had been high enough that he'd seen Colonel plunge out ahead of it. If it had been low, he couldn't have seen Colonel. That meant the tornado had been lifting up into the sky. It couldn't have sucked Colonel up, could it?

It was only when the tornado came down over things like it did over the Sayers' barn that it whirled them up into itself. If it was already high in the sky, Colonel would have been safe. So he must be somewhere in the pasture.

Mark felt easier. He yelled Colonel's name out ahead of him as he ran. Now his eyes were more accustomed to the faint light, and he could run faster. But suddenly in the midst of a running step Mark stopped cold. He backed away a little and couldn't force himself on. Colonel wasn't safe at all. He couldn't be! The middle pasture was full of big, heavy things. The tornado had dumped stuff everywhere. The pasture was crazy with things that belonged in people's houses—not in a field!

There was a white enamel stove in the grass with a mirror smashed into it. Far away small starlight trembled in the broken slivers. There were beds and tables and a smashed dresser and doors driven into the ground among big beams from barns speared down into the grass. And there lay a kitchen sink. Some of it must have hit Colonel.

And there beyond the clutter of mixed-up things was a roof—a whole roof in their pasture. It was the roof of the Sayers' house! It was the scariest of all, the roof of a house you *knew* in your pasture. Suppose that roof had come down on Colonel! The tornado hadn't sucked Colonel up, but it must have hurled everything at the galloping horse. Maybe right now Colonel lay smashed under the roof, maybe he was hurt, maybe Colonel was needing him.

A whimper in his throat, Mark raced down the pasture to the roof. Halfway there his legs bounced up from under him and he was thrown flat. He'd run across a soggy mattress in the grass. Lying flat, Mark saw just beyond him a big roll of money with a rubber band around it. He crawled over and picked it up. Working the wet money into his pocket, looking down at it, made it easier to get to the roof. Colonel wasn't there. In his relief Mark all but danced up the slant of the roof, over the shingles to the ridge. From there he could pick out details in the pasture clear to the deep gully that separated it from the woodlot beyond. There were more stars now, with more light. Why, everything was clear and clean at the pasture's end.

The smashed-down junk was only in the middle pasture. Nowhere lay the white of Colonel, but neither was Colonel standing in the clean end of the pasture. Then it must be that Colonel had gone to stand in the creek with his sore feet. He always did.

Mark yelled, "Colonel," and ran down the steep slope of the roof. And with that start he galloped to the pasture's end by the gully.

The tornado had been in the gully! Down there lay twisted trees in a tangle of ghost-white roots.

But something whiter than the roots was among the tangle of leaves and branches. In the gully under the torn-up trees was the white of Colonel.

Then suddenly he knew—it couldn't be the white of Colonel. He knew it was the chalky white of Mr. Sayers' old-fashioned car. That's what it was. Why, Colonel couldn't even get down the steep side of the gully. He'd been so worried about Colonel that he'd thought everything white must be Colonel.

Mark turned and ran along the gully's high bank, down the long slope to the woodlot. That's where Colonel would be—cooling his feet in the creek water.

And as he ran in under the dark trees of the woodlot, there *was* a horse in the creek. But it was a dark horse. Uneasily Mark inched forward. In the hushed darkness under the big trees the little creek went on whispering. Mark had a strange thought. This morning Dad had talked about another horse. Could this be the birthday horse? Could Dad have brought this horse to the woodlot to keep it secret until tomorrow, his birthday? It was so solemn and quiet here with the drip of the trees and the creek's whispering that it was easy to believe anything. The horse did not look up.

Mark edged forward to look at the horse. She was a beauty. She was sleek and lean and brown. She was slim and young. "I'm going to call you 'Creek,'" he told her, "because you are here in Colonel's creek. I'm going to take you home and call you Creek while I have you."

Mark's soft whispering made the new horse look up at him, and just then, just as Creek looked up, a horse neighed. The neighing came from the gully. Colonel *was* in the gully. Colonel was alive!

"Colonel! Colonel!" Mark screamed, "I'm coming, I'm coming!"

His yelling made the new horse rear and tremble. "Aw, I scared you," Mark said. "That's from being in the tornado, isn't it?" He stood wavering, anxious to rush to Colonel, but needing to quiet the new horse. She shook and put her head down. Mark saw the piece of dress wrapped around her ankle. A loose end of the stuff floated in the creek's current. That was what was making her nervous. He'd take it off before he ran to Colonel. He slid down the bank into the creek and rapped on the horse's leg to indicate she was to lift her hoof. He began to unwrap the flimsy cloth.

Oh, but it wasn't just a piece of dress—it was a bandage. There was blood. The bandage mustn't come off. Mark wrapped it around the ankle again and puzzled how to keep it in place in the running water. The horse looked down at him. Mark wrenched the roll of bills out of his pocket and stripped off the rubber band. "Golly, I just remembered this money. Look, it's got a rubber band. That'll hold your bandage, that'll fix it."

The horse seemed to understand. It was simple to secure the bandage with the rubber band. Far simpler than getting the wet money back in his pocket. In his impatience to get to Colonel, Mark dropped the money. He pounced and grabbed most of the bills before they floated away in the current, shoved them in his pocket, and clambered up out of the creek. "I'm going to get Colonel," he told the new horse. "You just wait here. We'll be right back."

Mark kept looking back over his shoulder to be sure the new horse was all right as he hurried away. Then the new horse threw up her head and whinnied after him.

It was marvelous how Colonel had done it. He must have run down the steep side of the gully into the snarl of trees right after they'd been turned upside down by the tornado. He'd run into the great V crotch of the biggest tree of all. The man-thick branches of the big crotch had squeezed Colonel in, and held him up on his stiff old legs. Then the small branches had snapped back in place under him. There he stood in a prison of branches that kept him on his feet.

"Oh, you," he praised Colonel. "Oh, you were smart." But Colonel didn't like his prison. He whinnied over Mark's head toward the creek. Then he looked down and his long underlip quivered and flopped. He didn't have a bit of patience with Mark being so slow in freeing him. Well, of course not. Colonel wanted to see the new horse who would be his mate—if she stayed, if he could keep her. It was a wonderful thought.

"She's a she," Mark told Colonel while he tugged and bent back the thicker branches. With them out of the way, Colonel backed out of the crotch and just waded down the smaller branches. He crushed them.

Once out of the crotch, Colonel wheeled and made straight for the woodlot. Mark had to run to catch the rope on Colonel's halter. Colonel went straight for the new horse.

The two horses didn't neigh, didn't nuzzle, but they crowded so close together that their whole sides touched. They must be sending messages through their skins, because slowly all the shakes and shivers went out of Creek. She stood quiet and slim beside old Colonel.

Everything was so still that Mark could hear the creek making its soft whisperings. Now he had Colonel back, and now he knew how to keep him up on his feet. All Colonel needed was something under him so he couldn't lie down on his stiff, sore legs.

Would that be a big surprise for Dad! If he could fix up Colonel's stall in the barn to show Dad how Colonel could be kept on his feet, then the old horse could stay on the farm. And now—at least for a while—there would be Creek. Colonel and Creek! Creek and Colonel! Mark's tongue fondled the names. And suppose things turned out that Creek could stay. Oh, it would be wonderful.

Mark couldn't wait to try out his plan. He grabbed the rope of Colonel's halter and led him through the water to the end of the woodlot. The new horse followed sweetly down the narrow, winding creek.

532

5

As Mark walked down the lane between his two horses and the big barn loomed near, he couldn't make up his mind. He did so want his parents to be home when he came with the horses, yet he wanted to have Colonel all fixed in his stall so Dad could see how Colonel could be kept on his feet. Colonel walked fine now, just as fast as Creek. And after lying all that time in the barnyard. It must be that the hard, fast run to get away from the tornado had unlimbered his stiff old legs. He'd even plunged down the steep sides of the gully.

Mark glanced down at the dress wrapped around Creek's leg. In a way it made Creek more Colonel's wife—she with one bad leg and Colonel with four—it made them belong together.

Mark felt that since such wonderful things had happened—Colonel alive and Creek coming—another wonderful thing should happen, too. Just as soon as he came around the barn the headlights of Dad's truck should shine on him and his two horses. Mother and Dad would look down through the big windshield and hardly believe what they saw.

What if it would happen? It could! Maybe Dad's truck could have come through the fields even though the roads were blocked. Now in a minute they'd be around the barn!

If the truck was there, he'd stand right in the glare of the headlights and the minute Dad jumped down he'd say, "Dad, see my family of horses? Colonel got up on his feet and Creek came. You did get her for my birthday, didn't you? But if you didn't, can we still keep her here?"

But no truck was there and nothing was coming—no headlights, no rumble of a truck. Mark was disappointed but he stood there thinking. Mr. and Mrs. Sayers had gone up with *their* barn in the tornado—maybe the owners of Creek had gone in the tornado, too. Then there'd be no one but him to take care of Creek—feed her, fix her ankle, and be her friend. Oh, if Creek could stay.

Mark looked toward the house. It rose dark against the faint sky light with only a dim gleam from the lantern in the kitchen sink. There was no truck behind the house. He looked in the doors of the upper barn. There was only his raincoat where he'd flung it on the ramp. He looked across the dark field where the Sayers' house stood roofless, without any light, without any people. Even their big barn was gone. He shivered. The long, black night was here. He moved closer to Colonel.

"Come," he said, "I'm going to get the lantern and fix your stall for you." The two horses followed him to the kitchen door. He gave Colonel a pat on the shoulder, "Keep Creek with you," he said. He ran in, grabbed the lantern, ran back to the horses; and they followed him willingly to the barn.

Inside, Mark puzzled where to keep the horses while he worked on Colonel's stall. Colonel mustn't lie down or he wouldn't be able to get up again. Then in the far corner Mark saw the little old-fashioned milk wagon that had belonged to the old man who had owned the farm. He tied Creek and Colonel side by side to one of the wheels. Now Colonel would be safe.

Now what to use to hold Colonel up? There had to be something, there was so much stuff the old man had left. Then as Mark searched he spied it. Up on a cross beam lay a thick roll of something that looked heavy enough. He poked it down with a stick. It unrolled over the floor, broad and thick and webbed. It would be just right. It was long enough that he could cut it in sections and have two or three heavy pieces to go under Colonel's thick old body to keep him up. If he nailed the ends of the belts to the wall above Colonel's stall, put Colonel in the stall, looped the belts under him and then up and over the other side of the wall, and nailed them with big spikes, Colonel couldn't possibly weigh them down. He'd just rest on them—even sleep, sleep without lying down.

Mark stormed to the tool box, found spikes and a hammer and a sickle knife. Then he took a barrel, rolled it into Colonel's stall, set it up. He cut the belt in three pieces, climbed on the barrel, and nailed the belt to the wall. He hung from it to test it—it was strong and the three spikes held it secure. He jumped down hanging on to the belt. The mighty jerk almost pulled his arms from their sockets, but the broad belt held tight.

Mark took the other two lengths and nailed them beside the first one. Then he had to lead Colonel away from Creek. "It's just for a few moments," he told her, "then I'll tie you to Colonel's crib and even though you'll be on the other side of the partition you can see each other and you can eat hay out of the crib with Colonel . . . and Mother is going to bring oats," he promised. Creek needed to be near Colonel after what the tornado had done to her. Alone she was shaky.

It wasn't as easy and fast as he'd promised himself and Creek. He had to hang from the first belt to draw it snug and tight under Colonel's body and hold it that way, and at the same time push a spike into the webbing of the belt and hammer it down. The first nail spat across the barn and tinkled away over the concrete floor. Creek jumped and tugged at her rope until the little milk wagon wheels screaked.

It was such a high, squealy noise that Mark twisted around on top of the barrel. But there had also been a sound—as if someone was pounding on the ramp of the upper barn, as if someone had come running through the doorway above and then had run right down the ramp again. Mark stared up at the rafters—he didn't know, he'd been so intent on his job and on Creek that it was as if he hadn't heard the pounding until it was over. It must have been the wagon Creek had dragged across the floor.

He nailed two more spikes in the belt and then he stopped. Could it have been Dad? What if it had been and there lay his raincoat? Dad wouldn't know what to make of it.

"Colonel," Mark begged, "don't lie down." He jumped down. "I'll be right back, maybe with Dad."

But when Mark ran out of the basement and around to the upper barn, he could see that the house was dark. There was no sound. There seemed to be no one. But when he dashed up the ramp, there was no raincoat lying there. Someone or something had taken his raincoat!

Mark stood staring at the house, and as he stared a ray from a flashlight ranged through the kitchen.

"Dad!" Mark screamed. "Dad! Mother!"

The light stabbed out of the kitchen door and picked him out as he came running.

"Mark, boy!" a voice yelled. "Mark! Thank goodness you're alive."

But it wasn't Dad. It was Mr. Sayers.

"Mr. Sayers! I saw your barn go up—how did you get away from the tornado?"

"We didn't. It took the whole barn—and left nothing but us and the grain bin."

Mr. Sayers opened the screen door to let Mark in. They stood looking at each other, and then the old man said, "Son, I've got to sit down—let's sit down together." They went into the living room by the light of the flashlight and sat on the sofa. But for a while Mr. Sayers did not talk, then he said slowly, "This flashlight's all I've got. We'd best talk in the dark."

"I've got a lantern in the barn, but it's almost out of oil." Mark said.

Then the old man roused himself. "Mark, your mother talked over the radio. There's no way for her to get out here. So she asked anybody that could—especially me—to come and look after you."

"But Mother was coming home with Dad from Stanton, and maybe he was bringing a pony on his truck."

"Listen, Mark. Stanton is nearly all gone in the tornado. It went right through the village and your dad got hurt—how, I don't know. All I know is that they got him into the hospital in the city and your mother's with him."

"Is he hurt bad?" Mark's voice was shaky.

"All I know is what I've told you, son. He's alive and in the hospital. That's something this night. Mama's hurt bad, and she's lying in our dusty old oat bin. It's all that's left of our barn. If that danged old tornado hadn't taken my old car, too, I'd have tried to get her into the hospital in it—but the roads are blocked."

Mark jumped up. "Look, Mr. Sayers. There's an old milk wagon in our barn and a new horse that came in the tornado. Her leg is cut, but maybe she could pull the milk wagon. And there's the road behind our farm that Dad sometimes comes down with the truck—maybe we could go to the hospital that way, and maybe there'd be a house with a telephone, and we could call the hospital for Mrs. Sayers and talk to Mother.''

"Boy, boy! It just could be—it's got to be! Help me get a mattress from one of your beds to put in the back of the wagon.'' He shoved the flashlight at Mark. "Show me the way.''

"Creek's leg is bad—that's the horse that came here—so I don't know for sure she can pull a wagon.''

"Everything's hurt tonight,'' Mr. Sayers said. "And if she could run here . . . well, anyhow what's least hurt has got to help what's really hurt. I'll look at the leg.''

They ripped the bedding off Mark's bed and let it heap on the floor. "You can run back for that while I look at the horse,'' the old man said.

They set the mattress straight up. Mr. Sayers draped the mattress cover over the edge. "We'll take it, too. I can rip it up for bandages—it's as thick as canvas. It'll hold the cut together.''

They slid the mattress down the stairs, then hoisted it under their arms. In the barn the lantern was still burning. They shoved the mattress into the milk cart. It fit.

The old man was amazed at the broad belts under Colonel. Mark explained and the old man muttered, "An old threshing-machine belt! Who but a kid would think of that?''

"But won't it work?'' Mark asked anxiously.

"No reason why not. I'll help you nail up the other belts the moment we get the new horse fixed up. Now you run and get that bedding so we can tuck Mama in on the mattress. You take the flash. I can work on the horse by the lantern light.''

When Mark got back with the bedding, Creek's leg was bound up tight with a strip of the mattress cover. "It's a deep, bad cut, and I suspect only a tornado kept her running on it—the dress wrapped around it helped. It may get worse if we use her on the wagon . . . we might ruin this horse, Mark. But it's got to be. Mama's got to get to the hospital, and you've got to know about your dad. You understand?"

"Yes," Mark said with tight lips.

6

Colonel was in his stall. Mr. Sayers had nailed both the other belts snug under him, and at the far end of the barn Creek stood harnessed to the milk wagon.

The old milk wagon had stood unused so long that its wooden wheels had shrunken and the rims around them were loose—so loose they'd wobble off. If they did, the wheels would fall apart and the wagon would come down with Mama and hurt her still more. So now each of the wagon wheels stood in a puddle of water. Mr. Sayers hoped the water would make the wheels expand. But he had gone out to find wire to tie the wheels in case the water didn't work.

Colonel was sleeping on the belts. The partition groaned with the old horse's breathing.

Suddenly Mark heard a voice. Mr. Sayers must be talking to himself. Mark grinned. But then there was a yell, an angry yell, and a sound of glass smashing. Mark snapped on his light as he ran out to the pasture.

With the beam of his light things went still. Then Mr. Sayers yelled out, "Mark, come here fast and bring the shotgun. Load it as you come."

Mark took a moment to locate the rusty old shotgun up on a beam. He poked it down, rubbed off the cobwebs, and started out of the barn on a run. Mr. Sayers had said, "Load it." Load it how? With what? He couldn't take time now to wonder.

"I'm coming," he yelled. "Where are you?"

"Over here by my roof. Hurry up, boy."

Mark came running. He gave the gun to Mr. Sayers.

"I've got four of them under the roof," he told Mark. "All right," he called out, "All of you come out with your hands up."

It was hard to see them against the black of the roof, but then Mr. Sayers took the flashlight and shone it on them. But Mark looked down at a big girl lying in a sprawl right at Mr. Sayers' feet.

Mr. Sayers shook his head, "Shouldn't have done that—didn't mean to hit her that hard. The base of the lantern must have caught her just right. Looters! That's all I need this night yet—looters."

Mr. Sayers now said in a steadier voice. "They sent the girl to make sure what I was after. Know what she said? 'How you doing? We've got a whole pailful of stuff, besides our pockets full.' That's when I let her have it—" The old man's voice went screechy. He kicked over the pail that stood beside the girl on the ground. Watches, rings, and bracelets spilled out.

Mr. Sayers didn't even look at the jewelry. "Grab the pail," he ordered Mark, "while I hold them here with the gun. Find a puddle . . . the muddier the better, then come back and throw it over her to bring her to."

Mark ran to the first water puddle. He wanted to hand the pail to Mr. Sayers, but the old man shook his head. "No, you throw it over her. I've the gun on them."

Mark had to throw the water. The girl came up sputtering, choking, and thrashing her arms.

"We didn't come out to loot," she told him. "But there it lay and we started."

Mr. Sayers did not answer her. "Go around them," he ordered Mark. "Don't get between them and the gun, keep behind them but pull everything out of their pockets —everything. We'll give them a taste of how it feels to be robbed."

Mark queasily started with the man. He pulled a billfold from the man's back pocket. "That's my own billfold," the man said.

"Good," Mr. Sayers said. "Then you know how it feels. Throw it in the pail, Mark. Now feel in his other pockets and around his waist."

It was miserable to have to feel around people and dig in their pockets.

"Can't we just throw it all on the ground ourselves?" one of the men asked. "We're not armed. We're not going to try anything in front of a gun. We'll go straight home, and I can tell you we're going to stay there."

"All right, toss it in the pail and then the faster you disappear the less I'll be tempted to give you a spray of buckshot."

Things pinged against the metal pail as the five tossed away their loot. Then they whirled and were gone in the darkness. With the shotgun to his shoulder Mr. Sayers stood watching them. Mark picked up the pail and brought it to him. Suddenly the old man broke the gun to see if there were shells inside and accidentally struck it against the pail. The sharp bang sounded loud, and the dark, running figures scuttled. "Shine the flash on them," Mr. Sayers said.

"It's almost gone, it won't shine that far," Mark told him.

"They won't know. Let each of them worry about being picked out for a load of buckshot."

But the running figures were gone. There wasn't a sound, and the old man dismissed them as if they had never been. He threw down the gun, picked up the pail, and started for the barn. "Come on. Those five looters couldn't have picked a worse time, but I guess the wagon wheels had to have time to soak and swell." He set a great pace across the pasture, but he didn't forget the wire. "See if you can find a length of wire—your eyes are young and we must save the flashlight for when we'll need it for Mama."

There was wire everywhere. Mark dragged a great snaking length of it as he trotted to keep up with the old man.

In the barn he had to find his dad's tool box for Mr. Sayers. "I'm going to have to take time to clip wire and twist it around the rims—hand me a pair of pliers." Mr. Sayers wrenched with both hands at one of the wobbly wheels. "Great Jehoshaphat! This old wagon standing here all these years is ready to fall apart and oughtn't to be used at all, but we've got to use it for an ambulance. It's like your Creek—they've got to be used whatever happens to them."

Mr. Sayers worked rapidly, cutting and twisting wires. He suddenly spoke up. "Looters. I don't think those five will be back, but there'll be more and my house wide open to the sky. Can you lock yours? Well, never mind, we'll nail it shut."

They didn't waste further words. They worked. Then it was done, the best it could be done. "Throw the extra wire and your dad's tool box in the wagon, Mark." Mr. Sayers didn't test anything, he just backed Creek and the wagon out of the barn. They stopped to drive three nails in the kitchen door, and then they set off across the field.

Outside the blown-away barn Mr. Sayers yelled out, "Mama, we're here with a wagon."

"I'm ready," Mama called back, "I'm as ready as I ever will be."

The old man backed the wagon almost up to the grain bin door; then he grabbed a hammer and pliers and pulled the hinges off the door.

When it was down, he and Mark used the door as a ramp from the top of the grain bin to the back of the wagon. Mama, on hands and knees, pulled herself up on it and crawled painfully to the wagon. She made dreadful sounds at every move. Then as she saw Mark's scared face, she tried to laugh.

"You'd think I was being loaded for market. Mark, if you ever tell anyone, even your mother, about this, when I get home I'll take you over my knee and whale you."

"Oh, I wouldn't tell," Mark promised. He wanted to say something to make all this seem better. "Mama, the tornado was bad, but it did bring Creek, and now she can take you to the hospital."

Mama knew just how he meant it. She looked up at him. "Sure, honey, sure. But what a night like this makes a boy like you go through."

Mark nodded.

Mr. Sayers put the tailgate of the wagon up. "Mama, the mattress is softer than oats, but it's a long ride and it won't be over smooth roads. Can you take it—it's likely to be a long night of pain?"

"What have I got here but no hope and all pain? Up on that seat, old man, and get the horse going. Mark, you hold my hand."

7

The wobbly-wheeled milk wagon rolled smoothly over the bare barn floor, but jolted sharply down the squared sill no matter how carefully Mr. Sayers eased it through the doorway. Mama clenched her teeth, but chittered with pain; she flung both arms out, grabbed the sides of the wagon. They cracked; the old woman in her pain tore the top edges away.

"Give me something to grab when the jolts come," she exclaimed. "I think I've got broken ribs."

Mark scrambled up from beside her. He grabbed his father's heavy tool box and wedged it between the mattress and the side of the wagon. He placed Mama's hand on the handle. He looked around for something else, saw the pail of the looters, and wedged it down on the other side of Mama. She clutched the rim of the pail. "That'll help," she gritted. "Something to fight and to cling to. On with it, old man."

But the barnyard was flooded, and Mr. Sayers couldn't see what was under the muddy spread of puddles. The wagon bounced over a sunken pig trough, now visible as the muddy water stirred.

The heavy tool box held as Mama fought it, but she lifted the whole pail with loot and in her wrenching spilled it out over her. "What is that?" the old woman demanded, startled by the glitter and rattle.

Mr. Sayers explained as Mark scrabbled up the scattered loot.

"Looters!" Mama exclaimed. "And our house wide open to the sky."

"There ain't much left to loot—at least, nothing upstairs," the old man said bitterly. "Even the closets are sucked out and bare."

"Look," Mark yelped, scrabbling watches and rings, bracelets and lavalieres out of the bottom of the wagon. "Look, flashlights. Three of them—little ones. They threw their flashlights in the pail, too."

"Give me one, and save the others so I can use each one in turn to pick out the bad spots ahead of the horse. I won't go through puddles any more. We'll have to depend on the wet grass to keep the wheels soaked and swelling. Flashlights!" he said grimly. "So they didn't come to loot; it was just lying there, and they innocently started. And I had no buckshot for them!"

"Never mind that, just drive," Mama said sharply. Then she looked startled. "Up in my closet inside a hatbox I kept a two-gallon jar with dimes. It was almost full. I saved dimes all my life and kept them hid in the hatbox, because robbers never look in hatboxes—but in it were the dimes from all my life."

"Mama," the old man said, "you're not out of your head? Your mind ain't wandering? Dimes? Whatever for?"

"For this, you old fool, for a tornado and a hospital and to put a roof back on our house, and so as not to go to the poor house."

The old man sat twisted, marveling at his wife. Mark leaped from the wagon and stormed to the house.

He found the hatbox on the shelf, but couldn't reach high enough to look into it, and he couldn't move it. "It's here, it's still here," he yelled up to the night sky out of the open closet.

In moments Mr. Sayers came up the stairs. He carried the pail with the loot still in it. "Let's pour the dimes in it, too. In a pail we can carry it down together, I hope—who's to know how much two gallons of dimes weigh?"

They stumbled with the effort to get the pail of dimes back to the wagon. It took the two of them to set the pail beside Mama. "With my dimes to hang on to, I can go through anything. Mark, talk to me, tell me everything that happened to you."

Mark told Mama everything while the wagon zigzagged and meandered down the length of the farm with the old man sitting bent over, picking out the best paths by occasional flicks of the flashlight. Now and then Mama rocked the heavy pail in her pain, but she listened, nodded and listened to make Mark talk on. Suddenly Mark remembered the bills stuffed in his pocket and dug them out and put them in Mama's shaking hand. She clenched her fingers around them as the jolting wagon fell into the ruts of an old wagon track.

"Found the old track we used to use to get firewood from the woodlot," the old man exclaimed. "Now if the wheels will stay together, it'll go better with them fitted in ruts."

Mama made Mark shine his flashlight. She looked at the squeezed bills. "Mark! Hundred-dollar bills—a half dozen at least!"

"Oh, there were more," Mark explained, "but I dropped them, and they went down the creek."

Mama wound the wadded bills around the tool box handle and closed her hand over them. "Dimes on the one hand, hundred-dollar bills on the other. Right now it's medicine, it's hope and everything. But somebody lost all their money and we'll turn it in—with the pail of loot —as soon as we can. The tornado let us keep our dimes, and a wagon besides—we've been lucky."

"Creek, too," Mark added eagerly. "The tornado brought Creek and Creek's bringing us to the hospital. If my dad really got Creek for me, and she didn't just come running—then I'll have Colonel, and now Creek, too."

"If he didn't, he should have, and if he didn't, I will with my dimes. If they'll sell Creek, I'll buy her for you. We've got to keep her for what she's doing for us. But, Mark, her name ought to be Hope."

Mark stoutly disagreed. "No. It's Creek, because she was in Colonel's creek, and Colonel was still alive."

"Do I have to referee a fight back there?" the old man suddenly spoke up. "What talk, you two—arguing over the name of a horse that neither one of you owns. Be quiet, I thought I heard voices." He stopped the wagon.

"Oh, the blessedness of this thing standing still," Mama whispered to Mark.

Mr. Sayers shushed her. He was sitting up straight and rigid. Creek's ears stood alert.

Mark leaned out over the side of the wagon. It wasn't voices—it seemed a single voice like over a radio or through a telephone.

"Looters?" the old man whispered. "And we ditched that gun."

Mark didn't answer. The faraway, strange mechanical voice had started again, stopped, and now there wasn't a sound in the dark fields anywhere.

"Mark, if it's looters," Mama whispered. Mark bent to her.

"If they come, sit on the pail, sit on the dimes, and don't you stir or say anything. I'll tell them you broke your leg—old women can lie much straighter-faced than children. Sit on the dimes right now.'' Mama peeled the hundred-dollar bills from around the handle of the tool box and, under the sheet, stuffed them down the front of her corset. "Now let them come,'' she decided.

Mr. Sayers up on the seat said, "Mark, crawl over and dig in that tool box for the biggest and longest wrench you can find and hand it up to me.''

"Give me one, too,'' Mama ordered.

Mark kept the claw hammer for himself.

Each clutching his weapon, they waited, but the strange mechanical voice did not sound, and no figures eased out of the woods anywhere. At last the old man clucked to Creek and they moved on into the woodlot.

It was so grim and silent that Mama had to joke. "Maybe sitting warm on those dimes will hatch out more.'' She nudged Mark with her wrench. "But not too many, hear, I can't hold anything more down my corset.''

The wagon moved on into the darkness under the trees, bumped over the uneven ground and exposed roots and fallen branches, for the old man did not dare use the flashlight to light his way. Nothing happened; nowhere was there a sound. Then they came to the little creek that ran shallow here with hardly any banks.

Mr. Sayers drove the wheels of the wagon into the creek. "There's no way for a wagon like this to be quiet, we're just like so many squealing pigs,'' he said. "I figured they've heard us anyway and are watching, waiting for us to come to them. Well, let's wait for them to come to us—at least, the creek water will do the wheels some good.''

They waited and waited, and the silence under the trees closed down on them. "I'm counting up to seven thousand, five hundred and seventy-five to keep myself from screaming,'' Mama whispered to Mark.

As if in answer a voice close by spoke out of the waiting darkness. "All right, if you're going to play 'possum, too, then stay right there. Don't make a move; we're coming to you."

"And who are you to order me around on my own farm?" Mr. Sayers answered angrily. "Any ordering here, I'll do. Now get off this farm, or I'll shoot." He actually raised the long-handled pipe wrench to his shoulder as if it were a gun.

Somebody laughed in the darkness. In moments they were surrounded. From everywhere dark figures stepped from behind shielding trunks of the big trees and came at the wagon.

"All right, sir, put that loaded pipe wrench down, you're scaring us to death," a laughing voice ordered.

The old man grunted disgustedly and laid the pipe wrench down on the seat in easy reach. "If you're looking for loot, there's nothing here but my badly hurt wife. I'm trying to get her to the hospital," he explained grudgingly. Then he yelled out: "Soldiers! Mama, Mark! Soldiers in uniform—not looters. Somebody at last come to help."

Mama did not answer. She was crying, and Mark let his hammer slide down the side of the pail. It was as if the whole wagon sagged with him.

"Hurt bad, hunh? That's right, we're here to help. Let's have a look. But you ain't going to get far in this chariot."

The old man chuckled dryly. "You got something better? A tornado doesn't leave you too much to pick and choose. This old milk wagon's not been used for years, but it's used tonight, and we had the horse, so we started out."

The soldier slung a walkie-talkie on his chest around to his back, shone a big flashlight up into Mr. Sayers' face, then walked around to the back of the wagon and lowered the tailgate. Mama blinked and stared into his powerful flashlight. Mark leaned down to her. "It's a walkie-talkie. That was the telephone kind of voice we heard. He's got a walkie-talkie."

Mama didn't know what a walkie-talkie was. She looked confused and blinded. The other soldiers under the trees did not come up—it must be they were covering the big man with the walkie-talkie in case anything went wrong.

The soldier took a big step from the edge of the creek into the wagon. The whole wagon tilted and tipped. The soldier jumped back. "Better drive your ark out of this water," he ordered the old man, "or if I add my weight, we'll all go over."

"Need it to keep the wheels together—the wires aren't going to last too long once we get on a road—if there is a clear road."

"Got more wire?" the man asked.

"Brought all kinds of it for when we'd need more."

The big soldier—he must be the sergeant—spoke up to his men. "Let's get more wire on all these wheels, every few inches. Use it until it's gone," he ordered.

Four more soldiers came up. Mark with his foot slid the tool box along the mattress toward the sergeant. "There's all kinds of tools in here."

The wagon ground up out of the creek. At every wheel a man got busy winding and twisting and cutting wire. "We're proud of you," the big sergeant said. "At least the three of you are trying to help yourselves. Most of them can't—so many dead and hurt, and the others act confused. But I guess you can't prepare and set yourself for a tornado."

He stepped into the wagon, looked down at Mama under her sheet, and grinned at the wrench in her hand.

"You may be down, but you weren't going to take it lying down, were you? Okay, sonny, you better get out of here while I have a look at your grandma."

Mark looked at Mama, he did not stir.

"Kid, that's an order," the sergeant barked. But he did not wait. He whipped the sheet off Mama. As he ripped the sheet away some of the looters' rings and things, caught in the folds, rolled over the wagon floor, glittered and gleamed in the beam of the big flashlight standing on the floor of the wagon. At once everything changed, everything became ugly.

"Now up from that pail!" the sergeant yelled. At the same time he reached across and tore Mama's wrench out of her hand. The flashlight shone on the pailful of dimes. The four men at the wheels stared.

"So the horse is bandaged and supposed to be crippled, the old woman is laid out on a mattress, but the kid sits on a pail of dimes and loot!"

"Pretty darn fancy riding horse, too, sergeant. Hardly a horse you'd hitch to a rig like this. This horse looks like quality."

"And they used to hang horse thieves from the nearest tree," the sergeant said grimly. He towered in the wagon, stood looking down on Mama and Mark. Two soldiers stood beside Mr. Sayers.

It was such a surprisingly sudden turn the two old people were speechless, but Mark was suddenly hotly indignant at what they'd said about Creek. "It's my horse," he yelled up at the big man. "And she is, too, hurt, she's badly cut, but we had to use her, even though my dad just gave her to me for my birthday. My dad's in the hospital, and Mrs. Sayers has got to get there, too. This stuff was the loot we took away from the looters that came to loot our farm—that's all it is and we're going to turn it in—with the money I found. But

554

the dimes are Mama's from all her life. I sat on them because we thought you were looters, too."

"Well, I'll be darned," the big sergeant said. "Kid, that's so crazy, I believe you."

"We held up the looters on our farm with an empty shotgun," Mark said, indignant still. "We took all the loot away, and made them put it in the pail—we even took their own billfolds away." He slapped his hand to his mouth, but it was too late. "Was that wrong? To take their own billfolds."

"Wrong? Kid, that's rich! Loot the looters. That's the only good thing I've heard all night—loot the looters."

He stood spraddle-legged in the little wagon, threw his head back and laughed. The men on the ground laughed. Then they all laughed. Mark sagged with relief.

"Put it down as our one good laugh tonight," the sergeant said as he dropped to one knee beside Mama's mattress. "Now let's look you over good." He flashed his light over the bruised legs. "Gosh, Grandma," he said. "And you took it on a bouncing wagon! I'll give you a hypo so you won't know anything the rest of the trip, won't feel a thing, and the next thing you'll know, you'll wake up in bed in the hospital."

Mama grabbed the wrench. "You leave me be. I'm all right—I think there's broken ribs, but the corset will hold them together. And you don't stick no hypo or nothing into me!"

But before Mama knew what was happening, the sergeant jabbed in his hypodermic needle. "Now just lie quiet there and go to sleep."

Mama muttered, but the soldier turned to Mr. Sayers. "You know the Mason Road? It's the third one over from this farm. It's gravel, and the old road winds like a river, but it's clear all the way into town. We've got your rims wired, but take the wagon through the fields till you get to Mason Road—I doubt the wires will last otherwise. But our ambulances are using the road, too. So when you get there, put your wagon square across the road, flash your light, and force an ambulance to stop. Otherwise they'll go right by."

"Would there be a phone anywhere?" Mr. Sayers asked. "We ought to call the hospital—Mark's mother's there."

The sergeant shook his head. "Hail an ambulance, Dad. You go with it. Mark here can take the horse and wagon back—they won't let him in the hospital anyway. Mark, you won't be scared to come back alone?"

"I won't be scared," Mark assured him. "If I can't see my dad anyway . . . I'll wait back home for Mr. Sayers to come."

"Sergeant, what about the loot and the dimes?" one of the men spoke up from beside the wagon. "The kid alone would be fair game for looters."

"We'll bury it right here," the sergeant decided. "And mark the spot."

"No need for that," Mr. Sayers said. "I know every inch of this farm. I'll dig it up and turn the loot and money over to the police when everything is settled down."

One of the soldiers unslung a short spade strapped to his pack. They dug a hole in the soft ground beside the creek.

"What if it rains and the creek goes up again?" Mark said. "Those billfolds of the looters and all the watches will get all wet."

"Sad, isn't it?" the sergeant said. But he picked up Mark's raincoat from the wagon, and they wrapped the pail in it.

"Now, Mama," the sergeant joked, "if we could strap your corset around the pail, too, nobody could get at it."

Mama did not answer. "Good," the sergeant said. "She's out like a light. Get as far as you can, Dad, before she comes to again. We'll get on, too. There's no end to this night's work. There seems almost nowhere that tornado didn't go, and it sure didn't leave any good behind."

"Thank you for everything," Mr. Sayers said. "You and your men."

"Good luck then," the sergeant said and jumped off the wagon. With his four men he melted from sight.

The wagon squealed on through the woodlot.

8

They were hardly started when the wagon hit a rain-bared root; the front wheels stuttered over it, but the whole body of the wagon screaked and groaned. Mr. Sayers stopped Creek before the hind wheels could bounce over the same root. He looked back, shook his head. "It isn't hurting Mama now, but a few more jolts like that and this whole thing could fall apart, and then where would we be? Mark, she doesn't need you now. Come up on the seat with me. My old eyes aren't any good for this, and this silly little flashlight is no good at all."

Mark clambered up to sit beside the old man, but Mr. Sayers in the meanwhile must have had another thought. He turned the wagon around and they went back the way they'd come. "I've got to find the sergeant," the old man was muttering, "see if I can beg that big flashlight away from him."

The man wasn't hard to find. He stood alone in the field beyond the woodlot, talking orders and directions into his walkie-talkie. The four soldiers had scattered far afield.

At the sound of the wagon the man turned and shone his big flash.

"Sergeant," Mr. Sayers called out, "I bounced this wagon over a tree root, and it all but came apart. Could we have your flashlight? The little ones we've got don't pick out the holes and bumps for me. And I got to thinking. . . . Wouldn't it be something if we made it to Mason Road and they wouldn't see our little toy flashlights and we'd get run down by an ambulance? That's all we'd need tonight."

The sergeant laughed. "Shrewd thinking to get my flashlight away from me." He came over to the wagon, holding out the light.

"It's really Mark I'm thinking of. He's got to come back alone to an empty house."

"I'm not scared," Mark protested. "Not with Creek— and not when we're going back to Colonel. If I'm scared in the house, I'll stay in the barn with Creek and Colonel. I'll be fine."

"Good boy!" the sergeant said. "Just don't take them into the *living* room with you." Laughing, he handed up his flashlight and took Mr. Sayers' tiny one. "No good to me either, but I'll take it until I find another one. You can find about anything on a night like this, even a pailful of dimes."

"Don't go making fun of Mama's dimes. They're going to put the roof back on our house, maybe buy us a bed— and if the dimes aren't enough, we'll sleep in the oats in the grain bin."

"Don't worry, you'll get help," the sergeant assured him. "The Red Cross is already in Stanton. Things will soon straighten out. Now on your way lest Mama comes to before you get to the Mason Road. She's quite a woman, that wife of yours. She didn't whimper, but she must have had a very rough time until I gave her that shot. Almost tempted to give her a booster, but I'd better not. I'm not hep enough on that kind of stuff, so make it fast to an ambulance."

"Sergeant," Mark spoke up, "could you give Creek a hypo in her leg? She's limping bad."

The big man shook his head. "All I could do would be to put her to sleep so she'd lie down. You ask the men on the ambulance, they're interns. They may have something to ease the pain. They'll do it for you if they can. I'll give out the word on my walkie-talkie my first contact."

"But suppose because of this poor Creek gets crippled forever?"

The big man smiled at him. "And suppose Mama doesn't get to the hospital, suppose Mr. Sayers doesn't find out about your dad, suppose he doesn't get to see your mother, 'suppose.' . . ."

Mark grinned sheepishly. "All right, I get it. Giddap, Creek."

The old man handed him the flashlight. "You shine the way and pick out the best way across the field. When I get back we'll spend the rest of the night doctoring Creek. I'm an old horseman, raised horses all my life, doctored 'em, too—that's what the oats in the grain bin were from."

Oats! Mother had been going to bring some for Colonel, but instead the tornado had come. Now there were oats in the bin. They'd make Colonel strong and maybe help heal Creek's cut.

They zigzagged through the fields. Now they'd soon come to the Mason Road. Mama was still sleeping, and the milk wagon moved smoothly through the grass. The tornado hadn't touched down here at all. Then the flash beam picked a gray line far out ahead. "The Mason Road," Mark yelled.

"About time," the old man said.

And then they were on the gravel road. Creek rested and Mark jumped down to look at her bandaged leg. Mr. Sayers came down stiffly from the wagon and studied it, too. The bandage was still in place, but above it the flesh was puffed out and swollen. "That's from the tight bandage—but it's got to be. The moment I get to your house we'll loosen the bandage, but while you're there alone don't you touch it no matter how badly it swells. If she's hurting, Creek'll kick like a mule. Do you understand?"

Mark nodded. He hated for Creek to be hurting like this.

They stood and stood and nothing moved along the road. Nothing came. "The sergeant said it might be a long wait—we're not the only ones," Mr. Sayers cautioned Mark. But finally he became impatient himself. Suddenly he could stand no more. "What if no ambulance comes for hours, and Mama comes to, and then still we have to go all the miles into the hospital? You get in the back with the light. Keep shining it from wheel to wheel and watch the wires. We'll stop before the last one wears through, but we'll at least be doing something instead of standing here. The sergeant said this road was clear so I won't need any light ahead. You keep it on the wheels and watch like a hawk."

"But what'll I do going back without any wires on the wheels?"

"Mark, boy, have you ever ridden a real riding horse bareback?"

Mark gave him a startled look. "Yes, yes I have. I never told anyone, but on the way to school there's a house with a yard for their riding horse. I used to feed him sugar. Once I climbed the fence and got on his back. He threw me. I fell under him, and he stepped right over me, and he came back and nuzzled me until I remembered and reached a cube of sugar up to him. Then he let me get on again and we rode and rode. I was late to school but it was worth it."

"Threw you and you got on again! You'll be all right with horses! Look, if you ride Creek back, it'll be a lot easier on her than dragging the wagon. This wagon isn't important. We'll leave it at the side of the road when the ambulance comes."

"What'll we do with Dad's tool box?"

"We'll hide it back of bushes in a ditch. Now hop in and watch the rims."

As Mr. Sayers said the words there was a roar. An ambulance came hurtling out of the night, and they hadn't put the wagon across the road to block it. Mark waved the flashlight, but the ambulance shot by. Mr. Sayers groaned and said, "Kick me for being such a wise guy and knowing better than the sergeant."

They went on down the road at a slow careful pace because of Creek's bad limp. Mark stood in the box of the wagon shining the flash from wheel to wheel and then on Creek's awful limp. It scared him, but it scared him to look at Mama lying there so dead-looking. He knew they had to get to the hospital.

The steel-rimmed wheels dug into the gravel. Then came the first sharp ping as the tightly wound wire snapped and sprang away. After the first one they all seemed to go. At last Mark said sadly, "We'll have to stop now."

The old man looked around. One of the rims was riding off the wheel. He stopped Creek. There was no sound anywhere; nothing moved. The few stars of the evening had gone away. The old man clucked to Creek and turned the wagon crosswise in the road. They waited for an ambulance.

It seemed hours before there was a roaring far down the road. "Now wave the flashlight in circles and up and down. It's got to see us long before it gets here if it's going to stop in time. Be ready to jump if I have to drive down in the ditch."

Then there was time for nothing. The ambulance roared down on them, squealed to a stop, and slowed in the gravel. It was scary for a moment, then two men jumped down.

They had the tailgate down by the time Mr. Sayers struggled down from the seat.

"Good," one of the men said, "she's on a mattress. We'll take mattress and all, because all the room left is on the floor."

"Your wife?" the other man asked. "Then you sit on the floor with her and hold her steady. Do the best you can. We've got a man in there hurt bad—whole church caved down on the poor guy. What about this kid? Is he hurt, too?"

"He's going back. Mark, once you get to a level spot, unhitch the wagon and let it stand. Keep Creek's harness on—if her leg gives out and she goes down, you'll have something to hang on to. . . . My wife's had a hypo a while back. The sergeant thought maybe she'd need a booster."

The intern shook his head. "No, better wait. Don't want to interfere with what the docs might give her. We'll be in the hospital in a few minutes."

"Please, mister," Mark said. "Couldn't you give Creek the hypo you're not going to give Mama? It's a long way back home and she's limping bad."

"Creek? Oh, the horse."

"Could you?" Mr. Sayers said urgently. "Mark's never ridden her and if she went wild with pain . . . wouldn't it slow her down?"

The man shrugged. "I'm no horse doctor. Still it probably would make the horse calmer and more manageable."

Mark held Creek's head while the man jabbed the needle into her leg. He jabbed it in a circle around the puffing. "Ought to make her more comfortable. Lots of luck, son. This is the kind of crazy thing you do on a night like this—horse doctor!"

He jumped back in the ambulance. Mr. Sayers was already inside by Mama. The ambulance roared away. It was gone in a second, and Mark was all alone with Creek.

He walked her on the grassy edge of the road. When they came to a brush pile, he stopped, pulled the tool box out, and hid it back of the bushes. Then he led Creek away from the brush pile so the abandoned wagon wouldn't give the location of the tool box away. But the boy and the horse didn't go far. Creek's slow weary limp worried him. He unhitched her and put the flashlight on the wagon seat so he could reach out for it after he had mounted.

They went along the grassy side of the road until at last there were the wagon tracks leading out of the field. Now he wouldn't get lost. He could find his way back by the crushed tracks the wagon wheels had made in the grass.

It was so still, so alone. But he had a flashlight, and there would be Colonel when they got home, and all three of them would stay together in the barn until Mr. Sayers came. It was better to think about that than to think about who might be in the silent fields. Now only one more road to cross, then through the Sayers' farm and across the single field, and then Colonel would neigh a welcome from the barn because he would hear Creek.

It seemed that this whole night—everything they'd gone through together—had made Creek his. Why, he'd told the sergeant that his dad had given her to him for his birthday and the big man hadn't questioned it. It had to be so.

Oh, what if in the hospital the first thing Dad said to Mother was: "Did you find that horse I got for Mark? I left her in the woodlot."

And then faintly across the dark fields there was the walkie-talkie voice. He listened closely but he must have imagined it. There was nothing but silence.

Suddenly Mark was uneasy. Suppose the big sergeant was at some farm down the road, and a man there was saying, "I lost my horse. She ran away from my farm in the tornado. She's a brown riding horse. Have you seen her?"

And the sergeant would say, "A brown horse, with a star on her forehead?"

"That's her," the man would say.

"Funny, we saw a horse like that pulling a crazy, little wagon. Didn't seem to go together—horse was too fine. But the boy said he'd just got her for his birthday. Well, if she's your horse, she won't be hard to find. It's a farm on the Stanton road. The man said it hadn't been touched by the tornado—it'll be one of the few that wasn't. Give it a try. It might be your horse."

Mark shuddered and was glad he'd left the wagon on the road. He stared ahead. Maybe the man was out looking for Creek right now.

He'd made it all up from imagining the walkie-talkie, but now it was as real as the night. He wouldn't take Creek home to the barn. He'd go to the woodlot—that's what he'd do. He'd lead Creek down in the gully to the same crotch that had held Colonel. Nobody'd see her down there in the dark—she was dark, too. But he'd stay with her. He'd stay until Mr. Sayers came. Mr. Sayers wouldn't let anybody take Creek away from him. Maybe by that time he'd find out from Dad that Dad had bought her.

Mark lay over Creek and whispered in her ear. Together they went quietly through the deep dark to their own woodlot trees on their own farm.

9

They came into their own woodlot, and it was dream-like silent under the stately trees, with only the little creek susurrusing its tiny baby talk. Mark walked Creek into the water to let her drink before marching her up the gully and imprisoning her in the crotch of the fallen tree. He was pleased at her slow, dreamy amble without any limp at all. The good doctor in the ambulance must have really cured Creek with the shots he had put around her leg—a ring block he had called it. The leg was still miserably puffed out, but Mr. Sayers had said not to touch the bandage, not to loosen it.

It must be way after midnight. Why, then it was his birthday right now! It was the morning of his very own birthday, but here it felt as if it were Creek's and Colonel's birthday, too—all of them together, everything had worked out so well for them all.

At the beginning of the deep gully, Mark halted Creek and slid down. He took down the rolled-up driving lines and led her over the tornado-roughed-up ground into the tangle of upside-down trees. Nothing was scary now, just tired and sleepy and dreamy. Mark yawned a stretching great yawn. Creek jerked up her head and stared wide-eyed at him. He led her on carefully around every tangle, and they slow-stepped over tree trunks.

Now Creek was suddenly dreamy no more. She acted alarmed, her hide began to shiver as it had done when he'd first found her in the creek. Mark talked to her softly as he eased her into the crotch of the great tree— the crotch narrowed down to nothing and would keep her, as it had Colonel, from putting her weight down on her hurt leg.

Mark had to pull branches aside that had sprung back into place after Colonel had walked them down in backing out. Now there was only the thickest branch left. If he pushed it back in place behind Creek and across the V of the crotch, it would lock her in as if she were in a stall.

The branch was springy and tough and slippery from its wet, pasted leaves. It was so stout Mark could hardly keep both hands gripped around it. Suddenly it sprang out of his grasp like coiled steel, slashed like a bullwhip across Creek's leg, across the bandage, across the cut. Creek gave a scream that tore through the gully and split the silence of the night. She screamed again and reared straight up in her scare, her forefeet pawed at the crotch, then her hind legs slipped from under her in the wet muck and she went down, all four legs madly kicking out against the small branches of the crotch. Then she slid down and lay on her side under the tree, but still she thrashed on. The hurt leg got caught in the tangle of branches and her too wide, too loose harness. The bandage came loose, unrolled and unfurled.

Mark crawled under the thick branch of the crotch to get to her head, to hold her and talk her out of thrashing. She mustn't hurt herself still more. For a moment

Creek lay still, wild eyes watching him, but as Mark came close she flung her head away from him. She was afraid of him! She showed her teeth and screamed at him. Mark, feeling sick and gaggy in his horror, crawled away so as not to make her kick out more with the cut leg, caught and doubled-up in the harness.

It was him Creek was scared of. Creek thought he had hit her with the branch. Mark started to crawl back as if to tell her it had been an accident. Creek wouldn't allow it. She began thrashing; she kicked the leaves down on the ground into a horrible storm. He couldn't do anything for her—she hated him; she thought he had done it on purpose.

At last there seemed nothing to do but to go away. Maybe if he went away, Creek could somehow get up— the branch had hit her, she wasn't locked into the crotch by it now. Maybe she'd want to come to the barn to Colonel. In darkness, without light to help him, he forced himself to go away from Creek.

At last in the barn Mark snapped on the flashlight. Colonel was awake and up on his feet. The old horse whipped his head sharply around and neighed a great welcome out at Mark. Maybe Creek would hear and want to come. At least Colonel still liked him—of course, Colonel didn't know what he'd done to Creek. Mark tried to tell Colonel friendly fond things, but his voice wouldn't come out of his throat.

Colonel nosed around in his empty crib and looked back at Mark again. Colonel needed something to eat. It lifted Mark's spirits. After what he had done to Creek, he needed to do something good for Colonel. He thought of the potatoes in the cellar, but the kitchen door was nailed shut, and the tornado had driven the trap door so tight into its frame he doubted he could tug it out again. Mark dreaded going by way of the musty cellar up into the empty house where no one was and no one would come. Maybe even Mr. Sayers wouldn't be able to come all this night.

Mark thought of his play-pile hay in the loft of the barn. It was old hay, short and stubbly and dry and dusty, but it would be better than nothing. Maybe Colonel could munch on it some.

Up in the hay barn Mark stood amazed as he flashed his light all around the barn floor. The tornado in passing by the barn doors had sucked all the hay and dust, even the cobwebs, out of the barn. The floor lay sucked out and clean as if it had been vacuumed. He could shine the flashlight through the cracks in the floor and see Colonel down in his stall. The play-pile hay must have gone in the tornado, too. He felt too tired and forlorn to climb the ladder. Huh, Mother had promised him oats and tonic for his birthday! It was his birthday!

A thought leaped at him. In the kitchen was a whole bottle of vitamins. Wouldn't a whole bottle—no, half of it—help Colonel just like a tonic? He'd give Colonel half and keep the other half for Creek—in case she came. It would mean he'd have to go down through the cellar. The claw hammer was in the tool box in the ditch, so he couldn't open the nailed kitchen door. But half of a bottle for Colonel! And the half-bottle waiting for Creek would make it seem as if Creek must come.

Mark found a spade. Then, with the big flashlight shining, he marched himself resolutely to the cellar trap door. It took a lot of prying and straining with the flat spade, but finally he forced the door up out of its frame. He looked down into the yawning dark cellarway. Then he grabbed up the flashlight and rushed headlong down the steps and on up the stairway to the dining room. In the kitchen he snatched the bottle of vitamins and flew back over the rolling potatoes and out of the quiet place.

Once out, he flashed the light back of him down the cellarway and saw the potatoes. He shuddered. No, he couldn't sit down there and cut potatoes for the horses. But he had oats—why, he did have oats!

"Oats! Oats!" he said happily. There were oats in the Sayers' grain bin! He'd screen and sift the dust and dirt out of them. Mark dashed up the slant of the open trap door and yanked the half-screen down from the storeroom window. With the screen and the flashlight he galloped across the single field to sift oats in the Sayers' wide-open barn.

It seemed to have taken tired hours and hours to sift the oats, but now Mark was back in his own barn. Creek had not come. There was no Creek with Colonel, and nothing moved anywhere in the pasture.

Mark showed Colonel his spilling-full pail of oats, but did not give any to him. He first rubbed the half-bottle of vitamin capsules into Colonel's mouth, then spilled half of the pail of oats into Colonel's crib. Mark kept the biggest half for Creek and planted the half-bottle of vitamins in the oats as if it were a candle, waiting for Creek. Colonel munched on oats, and it was a comforting, homey sound, except that Mark felt too tired to appreciate anything. Oh, he was tired, his jaws kept cracking out big wretching yawns, then almost wouldn't go back in their sockets again. It hurt, and he was so tired.

Still there was one thing he ought to do—he ought to go back to the gully, maybe now after all this time Creek wouldn't be scared of him anymore. But what if she struggled again when she saw him, and hurt herself worse, hurt herself so she'd be a cripple forever?

Mark did not dare take the chance. But one thing he could do if Creek should free herself and still come to the barn. There was no room for her in Colonel's stall—not with the threshing machine belts holding Colonel up—but Creek would want to be close to the old horse. The upper barn was all sucked out, what if there should be something left of the packed-down hay pile in the haymow? The hay would make a fine bed for Creek to lie down in right close next to Colonel's stall.

With a long sigh, followed by an endless yawn, Mark wearily climbed to the haymow. Amazingly his play pile still was in its corner—the only thing left in the upper barn by the passing tornado.

The night's stillness stood as heavy as its darkness, but he seemed too tired to turn the flashlight on. He was too tired to move, and Mr. Sayers would never come, and Mother had to stay with Dad in the hospital. There was nobody to come and help him, and he couldn't help Creek because she was afraid of him—Creek hated him.

Mark found himself staring into the opening of the little tunnel he had made—it seemed years ago, but it had been just before the tornado. Oh, but the little tunnel looked safe and good. Safe to sleep and hide in. He'd take the flashlight with him for company and sleep under the hay. If he set the lit flashlight shining on him, his body would block out the light from the mouth of the tunnel so nobody coming to search for Creek would find her. He needed light, even if he fell asleep with it shining full in his face. It was so lonely here, and he felt so awful about Creek that it made everything awful; it was worse than being scared of the dark.

He wouldn't sleep really anyway. Mr. Sayers when he came would call his name, and he'd hear, and together they'd go down to Creek.

Mark sighed at the thought as he lay stretched in his tunnel, cradled his head in his arms, and fell asleep with his cheek pillowed on the hard casing of the rectangular flashlight.

Down in the basement Colonel munched oats with tired, slow, worn old teeth.

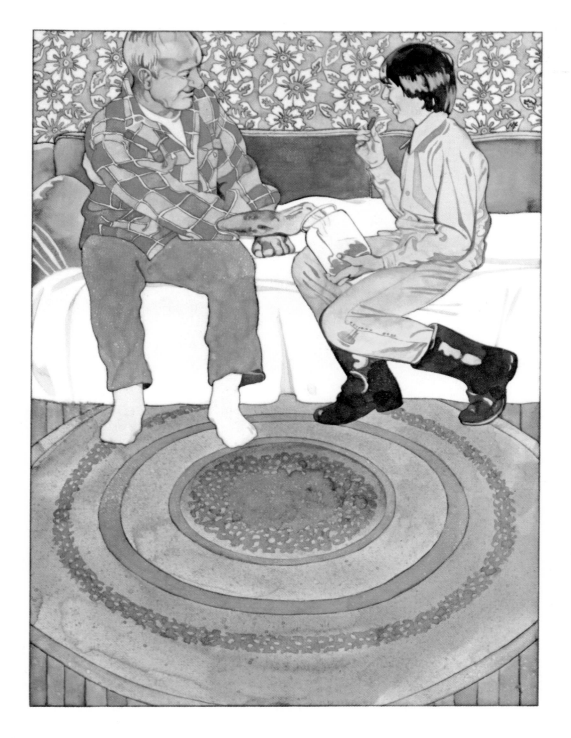

576

10

Mark woke in his stuffy, hot tunnel under the hay pile and lifted his numb cheek off the flashlight. He looked at the sharp daylight standing at the mouth of the tunnel. The sun was shining! Mr. Sayers hadn't come and it was day.

Shaking the warm sleep feeling out of his head, Mark climbed down the hayloft ladder to the basement of the barn. Creek wasn't there. Only Colonel neighed out at him and then went on munching oats. Colonel was still eating. He'd take the half-pail of oats and the half-bottle of vitamins out to Creek and maybe in the sunlight she wouldn't be afraid of him. He'd bring water to her from the creek.

The pail stood empty beside Colonel's stall and the vitamins were gone. Somebody had been in the barn while he slept and had fed Colonel the rest of the oats. It must have been Mr. Sayers, but where had he gone? Creek must still be in the gully—maybe dead, maybe bleeding to death with her cut kicked open, and here he'd slept right through the whole night!

He'd run to the gully with the pail and a knife and the mattress cover. He'd make bandages and bandage her leg. Then he'd lead her up to the barn to be with Colonel, and then he'd go back to the grain bin and get her oats.

Mark looked around for the mattress cover—it was gone, and they'd only cut one strip from it for a bandage. Had Mr. Sayers found Creek and gone to bandage her?

Mark's thoughts raced but they raced in circles. . . . He was so hungry! He hadn't had any supper—the tornado had come before supper, and afterward. . . . Now he knew—he'd quickly run to the house and get the cookie jar. No, he ought to run to the grain bin to see if Mr. Sayers was there. No, he couldn't run; he was too hungry to run there. His stomach leaped in a ravenous greed at the thought of cookies—handfuls! He raced toward the house, but he felt shamed—guilty to have hunger while maybe Creek lay in the gully.

The kitchen door was still nailed shut, but the trap door was open. He tore up the cellar steps and snatched the cookie jar from its shelf in the kitchen, popped it in the pail and started for the cellar stairs. He wouldn't eat a single cookie until he got to Creek.

Heck, he could eat as he ran. He unscrewed the top of the jar, and then out of the stillness came a harsh rasping sound that filled the house. Mark dropped the handful of cookies and stood rigid as his hair rose like hackles on the back of his neck. Then the sound came again and he giggled sheepishly. It was a snore! He ran through the kitchen into the dining room and around to the living room, the cookie jar banging in the tin pail.

On the sofa lay Mr. Sayers in all his clothes—even his shoes. He'd spread the mattress cover under him to keep the sofa clean. "What?" He sat up. "What is it? I'm coming, Mama."

Then he sat and stared. "Mark!" he finally said. "Boy, where were you, where've you been? I searched all over both our farms half the night. Where were you?"

"Under the hay pile in my tunnel," Mark said guiltily. Then it burst out. "I fell asleep. I was only going to sleep a little while until I could go back to Creek or if you came we could both go. . . . I never heard you—and Creek is still in the gully and she's probably dead. She's kicked herself to pieces. The bandage came off and she hates me, and she wouldn't let me help her, and I did it all because I tried to hide her from the man that was coming to claim her. . . . I couldn't stand it and I went to sleep, I did it and all I could do was lie there and sleep!" Mark was crying and choking out words at the same time.

Mr. Sayers said, "Now tell it over. Tell it slowly and in order, but don't you stand there crying because you fell asleep. I fell asleep, too. There comes a time when your wornout carcass calls a halt. Then you sleep as if someone'd hit you with an ax. Now blow your nose and stop that crying. Even if Creek's dead—and I doubt it— she saved Mama's life last night. All right, now we'll go and see to her, but only if you give me a handful of those cookies." Mr. Sayers made a face. "Cookies! In all my seventy-some years I've never had a breakfast of cookies—what a tornado doesn't do to you! I didn't have any supper—guess you didn't either, so we'll chew on cookies instead of getting breakfast right now. Don't worry, we'll save a few for Creek, she must be hungry."

Mr. Sayers seemed sure that Creek would be alive. They walked out through the cellarway. Then Mr. Sayers stopped. "Don't you want to know about your dad?"

Mark set down the pail and stared aghast. He hadn't even thought about his dad or his mother—just about Creek. He hadn't thought once!

Mr. Sayers grinned. "Don't look so spanked, boy. We've been through too much. . . . They can't say much about your dad yet. It's a concussion. He's out like a light, but the doctors think he'll be all right. Your mother's going to stay with him and Mama. There just aren't enough nurses—so many people hurt in the tornado. But she says to tell you she'll come flying home the moment she can get away. And Mama had three broken ribs and a broken leg. Think of it, she crawled into the wagon like that!"

Mr. Sayers sighed, "Now we'll go to Creek. But first another handful of those gooey cookies, and on the strength of them we'll carry that horse of yours home if we have to."

Mr. Sayers talked all the length of the pasture. There wasn't time to think for all the listening Mark had to do. "I got a ride back in an empty ambulance as far as where you left the wagon," Mr. Sayers said. "And I followed your tracks down to the middle of my woodlot— there I lost them. And when I got here you were nowhere. I yelled like crazy and I went all over both our farms. And then it was morning so I fed Colonel and fell down on the couch in your living room like a poled ox."

"I slept like a poled ox in my tunnel," Mark said. "What's a poled ox?"

"That's you and me, and now we're full of cookies," Mr. Sayers joked. "I've got your bottle of vitamins in my pocket, and my leg is sore from sleeping on them. I suppose they're for Creek."

They were going to Creek and Mr. Sayers was telling him everything about the hospital. Mark stumbled on beside him too absorbed to watch where he was going. Mr. Sayers talked to him just as if he were a grown-up. Now that he didn't have his wife to talk to he talked to him, Mark, as if he were as big as Mama.

Oh, Mr. Sayers was wonderful. Now he'd suddenly found a friend—a wonderful talking friend. Wasn't it strange that before the tornado Mr. Sayers had just talked to Dad or to Mother, except that now and then he'd toss a joke to him like you tossed a cookie to a little dog?

"Mr. Sayers, I like you!" Mark burst out.

"Well, if that's so, then don't keep calling me 'Mr. Sayers' so polite, as if I were a stranger. Call me Grandpa."

Mark tried it: "I like you, Grandpa."

"I like you, too, because, you know, I never had a son. Just four girls."

Mark jumped up and down at his sudden thought. "It's too late for me to be your son, isn't it? But, Grandpa, I could be your grandson, couldn't I? Even late?"

"It's a deal," Grandpa answered promptly. "Late, but high time, I'd say."

They shook hands on it, standing solemnly before each other in the middle of the pasture.

Grandpa walked on to get Creek, but Mark stood there. You got to a spot—like now in the middle of a field—and on that spot you became a grandson, and on your birthday. Mark let his grandpa walk on, but he stayed long enough to thrust a stick into the soggy ground in the exact spot where he'd become Grandpa's grandson. Then he galloped after his grandfather. Later he'd put up a better marker, but now he couldn't bear to be separated from his new grandpa. Now he was Mark, with a grandpa and two horses.

They went into the gully by way of the woodlot, because Grandpa was old like Colonel and couldn't get down the steep side of the gully, except maybe in a tornado. But as they neared the tree of the big crotch and saw Creek lying there motionless, Mark dropped behind. When Grandpa waited for him, Mark explained, "I'd better stay here. Creek thinks I did it and she hates me. She might start kicking again if she sees me."

"I doubt it," Grandpa said. "I doubt that very much. You just come right along with me and bring that jar of cookies, and then we'll see who hates whom. She won't get alarmed. See, in her struggles she worked her collar up over her head and the padding under the collar slipped down over her eyes. You know what? I think that saved her from any more struggling. And you know something else? I don't think it was you that scared her into panic when that branch slashed across her leg. I think it was the upside-down trees with those white roots sticking up. I think when she got caught in the tornado she must have seen trees go up and come down like that. And now roots sticking up like that spook her. We'll see. We'll leave the padding over her eyes, and you feed cookies to her while I work her out of that tangle."

Breathing his hope, Mark squatted noiselessly down before Creek's head and pushed a cookie between her lips that had begun trembling. Grandpa talked soothing things to her while he pulled away branches and stripped away the harness, but all the time he kept away from her hoofs.

Creek ate cookies and lay still. Then Grandpa said, "Now I think you'd better run to the creek and get her a pailful of water. It isn't easy for her to swallow lying down, and with a throat as long as hers the poor girl must be cookie crumbs all the way down. First give me your shirt—that ought to be just about the right length to tie over her eyes. The collar pad will fall off as soon as I strip off the harness."

Mark took off his shirt. Grandpa looked at him and saw him shaking, but he said nothing about it. Instead he took the shirt and studied it. "What a dirty shirt—where you been—in a tornado?"

Grandpa seemed to know just when to say a goofy thing. It kept you from going all heavy and scared down in your stomach.

When Mark returned with the sloshing pail, Grandpa had Creek up on her feet so she could drink properly. She sucked the whole pail empty, and she wasn't scared of him at all, but, of course, Grandpa had tied the shirt over her eyes. "Just 'till we get her away from this mess of roots. Then you'll see, I'll let you pull the shirt off her eyes, and you'll find out it was the trees and not anything you did. How could Creek hate you?"

Mark marveled at all Grandpa knew about horses. "How is her cut?" he asked.

Grandpa shrugged. "Worse, of course. Gone deeper, but that was from pulling the wagon because the wound didn't bleed at all here, not after she kicked the bandage off. So you didn't even harm her that way. In fact it was good; with the bandage gone her leg isn't puffed up anymore. There's only one thing—flies. I didn't want to, but I had to put the bandage back on so the flies couldn't get into the wound. Just so they haven't already laid their eggs. I'd hate to have to pour anything strong enough to prevent their eggs from hatching in that raw gash. She'd kick like a steer and rip the gash even deeper."

Mark was rigid with horror. Sour water washed around his teeth. He gagged. "But you said the bandage shouldn't be tight."

"We'll see. It'll be hard to keep flies out of the wound except with tight bandages, but I really think that exercise—just walking around in the air and sun—would heal her better than anything. But how to keep the danged flies out?"

"Feed sacks," Mark yelled. "There's a stack of them in the barn. Couldn't we put her leg in a sack and tie it shut on top? It'd be like a stocking."

"Mark," Grandpa said, "when they put you in the world, they didn't forget to screw your head on, did they?"

Grandpa led Creek out of the woodlot and Mark walked proudly behind.

Then they were in the lane that led to the barn, and Grandpa stopped Creek. He handed Mark the bridle. "Now you lead her. I'll walk behind. Pull that shirt away from her eyes, and you'll see it was the trees that panicked her—not anything you did. Then you march fast so I can cook us some breakfast—bacon and eggs, and eggs and bacon, and some coffee and a little bacon for dessert —but not one gooey cookie."

Mark hardly listened as he pulled the shirt from Creek's eyes. She blinked and stared, then threw back her head and neighed out over the field. From the barn Colonel neighed an echo. And then Creek reached down and nuzzled Mark's hair with soft, nibbling lips. Mark walked with his face straight forward on account of Grandpa behind and because he didn't want Grandpa to see him cry. Oh, it was wonderful.

"Now bacon and eggs," Grandpa said. "Now you'll enjoy them."

"Can you cook, too?" Mark asked.

"As a cook, Mark, I can tell you, I should be lined up against a wall and shot with burned bacon," Grandpa said. "But seeing for the next few days I've got to keep us alive, I'll only cook if you promise not to shoot me for my cooking. We'll fix Creek up with a feed sack and throw some hay down for a soft bed for her. Then you and I will begin batching it with bacon and eggs—and the first one that can't swallow them is an old maid."

Mark couldn't answer. Creek was hobbling and crippling almost like a dog on three legs, but she was going to the barn—his barn—and Colonel was there to comfort her.

11

They both wiped their mouths with the backs of their hands—Mark did it right after Grandpa. Then he did it again with the back of his other hand. They'd had breakfast and they'd finished every last crumb. It had been enormous. Bacon and eggs and fried potatoes—a farmer's breakfast, enough for any person. Then coffee— he'd even had coffee, black without cream, just like Grandpa's. Well, his had had some sugar in it, but he hadn't stirred up the sugar.

"Now do I have to find the shotgun and shoot you with burnt bacon up against the barn wall?" Mark asked. He rubbed his stomach and purred with contentment to show Grandpa it was all a big joke.

Grandpa grinned. "Nope, don't think I deserve that. Cooked everything just fine, even surprised myself."

Grandpa seemed to purr with contentment, too, and gave himself a second cup of coffee. "Ah," he said, "good solid food and coffee to float it down sure beats your cookies. But that's what a person needs after missing supper. We sure were hollowed-out, and we've got work to do. But that's good. Work cures about everything except a sore back—it takes away worries and helps waiting. And that's what we're going to have to do—wait. By now they must have started to clear the highway between Stanton and town, and then the buses will ride again. And linemen are no doubt swarming all over the telephone poles and the light wires. Then in a day or two you can talk to your mother by telephone. Meanwhile it's best you and I clear the pasture, so that tractors can get at my roof and cranes can lift it back on the house walls again."

"What's a concussion?" Mark abruptly demanded.

"Thinking about your dad? Well, that's the idea of all this pasture-clearing work—it's to keep us from thinking and worrying, and to help us wait. A concussion! Remember how you and I fell asleep last night, me here, you under the hay pile? I said then it was as if we'd been hit with an ax. Well, it's something like that with a concussion. It knocks you out. You go to sleep and lie there sleeping for days. But when you come to, you're usually in pretty good shape again."

"But then Dad can't tell Mother whether he got Creek for my birthday, and then I won't know. And what if somebody comes and claims her and takes her away? And how will Dad eat? And if he doesn't eat, won't he be too weak to talk?"

"How that mind of yours works! Now what do I answer from all that ruck of questions? Don't worry, your dad will sleep and they'll feed him right while he sleeps —right through his veins."

Mark sighed his relief. "But couldn't Mother come home, if Dad just sleeps? Does she need to watch him sleep?"

Grandpa hesitated. "Remember, there's Mama, too, for your mother to watch. And it—it's a different kind of sleep, more like being unconscious, only a little bit different from that, too. But meanwhile they'll be feeding him and giving him medicine through his veins. And all the time he lies there without wasting his strength talking, he'll heal like mad."

"Then shouldn't I go to Mother, if she can't leave Dad?"

"Of course you should, and of course you will as soon as the highway is cleared and the buses run. But it's too far to walk; it'd take us all day, and Creek here needing tending to, and Colonel, too. But I've got it all figured out. Your mother needs to see you and you need to see her, so we'll give her a free hour away from that hospital room. I think I might be able to persuade her to go out with you for an hour or two, while I watch instead. Then you two can sit over an ice cream soda, or two, or three, and talk yourselves out."

Mark sat wriggling with delight. Then he jumped up. "Let's go to work—let's clear the whole pasture."

"Well, maybe," Grandpa said. "But first let's just clear a path to my roof for the tractors; it isn't going to go as fast as all that."

"There's an old stoneboat lying in the grass up against the end of the barn," Mark told him excitedly. "If we could hitch Colonel and Creek to that, we could clear the pasture just like nothing."

"With Creek's cut leg?"

"Oh, no," Mark said regretfully. "But you said exercise would heal the cut faster," he argued.

"Exercise, but not strain. We'll just use Colonel, and Creek can hobble along but not work. Work would be good for Colonel, though. It ought to limber up his stiff old legs even better than this liniment I brought."

Mark jumped at the word. Unable to wait, he raced away to the barn. They let the belt straps down from under Colonel and backed him out of the stall.

They rubbed all Colonel's four legs with the liniment. It stained his white hide brown, and it stung and smarted in Mark's eyes and throat, but he rubbed on and on. "Oh, this is strong! It ought to make Colonel's legs all strong and better. Shall we use it on Creek, too?"

"No, hardly," the old man said. "At least, not on her sore leg. And I doubt how strong it's going to make Colonel, but at least he smells good and strong." He coughed and had to hurry to the doorway to get some air and blow his nose. Mark still rubbed Colonel a little more, but then he stormed to free the stoneboat from the weeds and grass while the old man harnessed Colonel.

They hitched Colonel to the stoneboat, and Creek of her own accord came limping out of the barn and hobbled along with them toward the middle pasture where the welter of tornado junk rose queerly and desperately out of the rain-beaten grass. Creek looked odd in her long sock made out of folded-over, lapped-over feed sack. But she did not seem to mind the odd thing that covered even her hoof—not as long as she was with Colonel.

It was going to be a great day in the pasture and in the sunshine. The pasture would get cleared and Grandpa's roof would go back on his house. And at the same time, with the work and the liniment, Colonel's legs would get limber and strong, and all the time Creek's cut in a sack that kept out the flies would be healing like mad—just like Dad in the hospital!

But this was still his birthday! Oh, what a day, and then the day to come with him and Mother talking and telling each other everything over two ice cream sodas, and maybe three. Mark had to blow his nose in his excitement, but that was from the strong liniment, because even in the open pasture Colonel reeked. Creek could hardly stand him. Her nostrils flared, she coughed a little and hobbled away to graze in a clean stretch of grass.

Then came Mark's best birthday surprise from Grandpa. Instead of clearing a lane to Grandpa's roof, he loaded the stoneboat with beams and planks and with two-by-fours that he sorted out from the mess in the pasture. It turned out they were for Creek, for a stall for Creek right next to Colonel's. Last of all they piled slats on the stoneboat, because Creek was going to have a crib for hay and oats that would be a continuation of Colonel's crib, with no partition in between. "That's so they can nuzzle and feed together," Grandpa explained.

A stall for Creek! Mark could hardly believe it—that made it seem so sure that Creek was his and was going to stay. It seemed then that joy and hope could have no bounds, and one body could hardly contain it. Mark had to do all kinds of things at once, all things for Creek.

But Grandpa said, "Look, Grandson, stop going in five directions at one and the same time. I'll lay out the stall and measure things up, but you take Colonel and the stoneboat and get your dad's box of tools. We need tools to build that stall, and it'll be a good test for Colonel's legs before we use him to pull loads to clear the pasture. Take your time and don't hurry the old plug—it's going to be a long day. But if Colonel stumbles and falls, don't you mess around lifting his head to get him up on his feet again. Come back here and tell me."

Mark nodded obediently but scolded himself for having told Grandpa everything. It seemed that only he knew and believed that Colonel wouldn't ever hurt him. Colonel was careful for him.

He and Colonel trudged across the fields. It was an important day, and this an important errand—it was hard to go slow but Mark was careful for Colonel. To his relief, after the long, slow journey the tool box was still under the brush pile along Mason Road, exactly where he'd shoved it.

On the way back it was Colonel that hurried—he wanted to get back to Creek. And Mark wanted to get back to Grandpa and the building of Creek's stall. In spite of the fact that he'd thought he mustn't tell Grandpa everything, he thought of a thousand more things to tell on the long journey back from Mason Road.

When he and Colonel got back, Grandpa wasn't working on the stall. He was up in the hay loft, digging with a pitchfork at the hay-pile-play-pile with its tunnels. But Grandpa was careful of the tunnels, he only scraped hay from the rounded top of the pile. "It's for bedding for Creek. You can bring up a pitchfork and help me with this." When Mark came back up, the first thing he did was to dig right into the entrance of the small tunnel he had made the day of the tornado. Grandpa stopped him. "No, we can get plenty without wrecking your tunnels. I wouldn't mess them up for the world. A kid's got to have tunnels to get away from mothers and fathers fussing and from horses with bad legs and wounds that won't heal fast enough and from dads in hospitals and from grandpas ordering him around."

Mark stopped his digging and looked at the old man in amazement and worship. How did he know the importance of tunnels?

"Did you have tunnels when you were a boy?" he asked hopefully.

"Nope, not being smart like you, I never thought of it. But I wish I had. And I wish last night I'd known you were under here. I'd have crawled in with you and slept here, too. Say!" Grandpa interrupted himself. "And just what is the matter with now—after the short sleep you and I had, and the long, scary, worrisome day, I could sleep right now, couldn't you? Creek's all right out there grazing with Colonel, and after a nap to take yesterday's tiredness out of our bones, we'll fix that stall for her better and faster than ever."

Grandpa threw his fork down and crawled into the wide old tunnel, the first one that Mark had ever made. Then Mark crawled into his small, yesterday's tunnel, stretched out full and sighed his pleasure and his delight—a grandpa in a tunnel. This was a birthday of birthdays. In the other tunnel Grandpa began to snore. Mark giggled but fell asleep in the middle of his giggle.

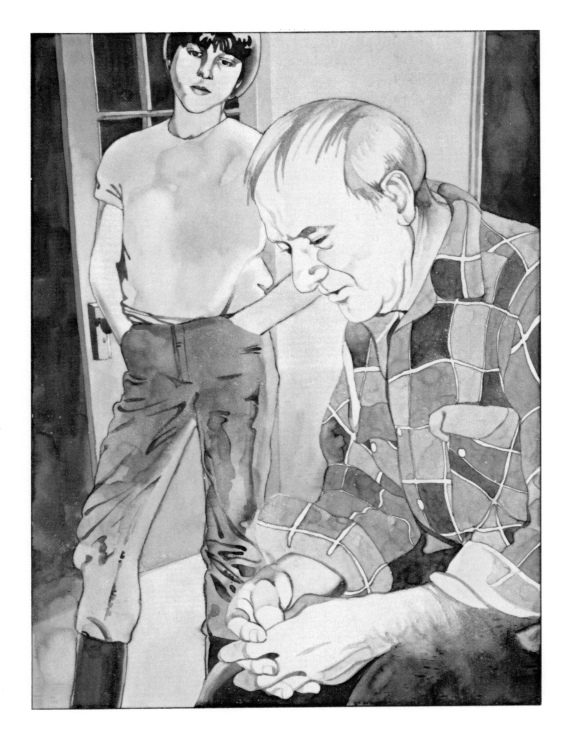

12

It was the beginning of the second day of Grandpa and him alone on the farm. Mark wiped his mouth with the back of his hand. Now he'd eaten his second grandpa-big breakfast, without napkins or orange juice. This time he'd had two cups of coffee. Mark drank it to the last bitter dregs. Awful as it tasted it was wonderful to drink the black brew, just like an adult.

Now they were going out to fix Creek's leg and to sift oats for both horses. But when Mark stepped outside Grandpa wasn't behind him. Mark went back and found the old man going from room to room clicking on the light switches. But even though no light came Grandpa went to listen at the dead telephone and after that he switched on the radio and the television set—the blank screen seemed the deadest and blankest of all.

"What makes a man do silly, childish things like that? And me an old man!" Grandpa said scornfully. "You wouldn't have one here—you wouldn't have a battery radio? The batteries gave out on mine."

Mark shook his head.

They left the silent house that now seemed more dead than ever. "It's awful to know nothing of what's going on—just for the lack of a battery radio. I couldn't sleep for thinking about Mama. You know how it is when you can't sleep—it's got me down."

Mark looked away guiltily—he didn't know how it was; he had slept the whole night. He'd slept until Grandpa had shaken him awake for breakfast. He couldn't help it, after yesterday's big day of work.

"Come on, we've got to tend the horses." Grandpa acted as if he, Mark, had been holding them up.

He held the screen door for the old man; then he let it fall shut. It slammed, banged open, and made a series of small flat slaps.

Grandpa stood on the steps listening, then said sharply, "Stop that blasted door. I can hear something. Listen! Sounds like the grinding of machinery."

Mark listened. "Yeah, it is. They must be clearing the highway."

"The highway? That's pretty far. Maybe they're through with the highway and are coming toward us."

Mark couldn't guess and neither could Grandpa. At last the old man moved away. "Come along, we'll tend to Creek and feed Colonel—by that time we'll know if the sounds are nearer and if they're coming toward us. Let's not get our hopes too high, but if the highway is clear the buses will be running. We could walk to Stanton and get the bus from there into the city." Grandpa was so full of haste that Mark had to trot to keep up with him.

As they got to the barn Colonel neighed hungrily and tossed his hay around in his crib. Colonel didn't want hay. He wanted oats. He even stamped with his stiff old legs. "Look at that!" Grandpa said. "He's stamping. Guess the work and the liniment must be limbering him up—he's a work horse, he feels better with something to do."

Grandpa talked on about Colonel. It must be so he, Mark, wouldn't notice Creek. She lay flat in her stall. She had kicked and worried the feed sack down around her hoof, and though it was early morning the flies buzzed and hovered. It didn't make much difference, for in no time she wore her hoof through the sack as she hobbled around.

"It's still so raw and infected I hate to pour anything in it," Grandpa muttered. "Think I'll wash it out with soapy water. She doesn't look as if she wanted to move around today, so get me another sack and I'll tie it on after I get this washed out."

Mark darted to the corner shelf and came back with two. "This is all we've got left. She wears 'em out so fast, and they're no good once she walks the whole bottom out."

"Two, hunh?" Grandpa said absently. "Well, we'll soon be getting to town and we'll pick up more. If we could find a veterinarian—but even then it'd probably be days before he could come out here. Well, I'll work on her; you run and screen a pail of oats for Colonel."

"Two—one for Creek, too."

"If she'll eat. I doubt she will, but we can try. I think her mouth's too dry with fever. You run along—I'll give her some water if I have to pour it down her from a kettle spout. She's burning up."

"Is she going to die?" Mark blurted.

"Oh, no. A young horse doesn't die that easy. I just wish we had a vet to shoot antibiotic in her. I don't like all the infection, but. . . ." Grandpa suddenly glared up at him. "Haven't you started out for oats yet?"

"Why are you so worried this morning?" Mark stood his ground. "Has something bad happened? If Creek isn't going to die, what is it? Oh, Grandpa, is it Dad who's going to die?"

Grandpa stood up. He was shocked. "Die! Boy, what a question! What put that in your head?"

Mark was startled himself. He said it but he didn't mean it. You couldn't imagine your father could die.

At last Mark answered somberly. "I don't know. But it's Colonel, isn't it? We worked him too hard yesterday."

Grandpa shook his head but he didn't say no. "Didn't you hear him neighing for oats? And there you stand thinking up questions. If the old horse dies, it might be from hunger—and you with that empty pail!"

Grandpa wanted to get rid of him. He started out with the empty pail.

After the long, slow sifting oats job Mark stopped in the kitchen to dig out one of his mother's trays. Grandpa had Creek all doctored up and bandaged—she smelled of the liniment. He must have poured some in her wound. Mark poured some of the oats in the flat tray and shoved it under Creek's head. Grandpa must have gone for water. Creek lay with her head in the tray but she made no effort to eat. Mark rubbed a handful of oats in her mouth but she spluttered them out again.

"I told you," Grandpa suddenly said behind him. "Her mouth and throat are too dry to choke down oats. I poured some water down her but with that fever I guess it's all burned up again. Her mouth is as dry as ever."

Mark stirred his fingers around in the oats but Creek jerked her head away.

Colonel whinnied jealously. He wanted the oats, he was hungry. It seemed hopeful that Colonel wanted to eat. Mark slid the oats out of the tray back into the pail and gave the whole pailful to Colonel, and the last of the vitamins, too. There were only three left. Colonel munched them with his worn old teeth. The way he was crunching oats made it seem a little unbelievable that he'd thought Colonel was going to die.

Grandpa had left the barn forgetting to give the pailful of water to Colonel—Mark couldn't lift it to the crib. He hurried out after Grandpa and found him in the house. Grandpa was going through rooms clicking on switches.

"So you've caught me at it again." Grandpa looked a little guilty. "I hate to admit it, but I'm so lonesome for Mama and so worried about her, I can't stand it any longer without news—it's as if we were on a desert island, not knowing what's going on. And I can't hear the machinery anymore. Could it be they've got our road cleared on the Stanton end?"

"I don't know," said Mark impatiently. "But Grandpa, I couldn't reach the pail of water up to Colonel, and shouldn't Creek have another drink?"

"Don't worry so. I'll give them both water but then you and I are going to start right out for Stanton. Who knows, maybe the buses are running again."

Mark couldn't say what he wanted, but he didn't want to leave Creek and Colonel. But if he had to go maybe he could find out whether Dad had bought Creek for him.

"Potatoes!" Mark suddenly yelled. "We'll feed Creek potatoes the way I fed them to Colonel. Cut potatoes are juicy and easy to swallow."

Grandpa sighed and got up. "Potatoes it is, then. We'll cut her some, but then it's straight to Stanton, or you're going to have to tie me up—at least put my feet in a feed sack, and even then I think I'd hobble all the way to that hospital!"

They cut potatoes until Grandpa refused to do one more. "There's hardly any left anyway. If you're going to feed a horse potatoes, we ought to have a truckload."

"My dad's truck!" Mark was excited. "I'll bet it's still standing by the store he was building. We could go to town in Dad's truck and on the way back stop and get some potatoes."

"If it takes potatoes to get you away from your horses, then let's go look for that truck."

"It's for Creek," Mark pointed out. "If potatoes were good for Colonel, then they're good for Creek, too. Mother thought it up when I was so worried about Colonel, and it worked. It kept him alive when he was lying down so long, and he liked them."

Of course they didn't go until they fed almost the whole pailful to Creek; then Colonel got what was left over. "Maybe we should let them both out," Grandpa said.

"No," Mark said. "They've got to stay in the barn while we're gone." He was so worried about a man coming to claim Creek, that he had no rest until Grandpa agreed to nail the barn door shut.

Grandpa hurried to the house and was already washed when Mark left the horses. That was all Grandpa could do, he couldn't change because all his other clothes were blown away in the tornado. He made Mark change his clothes.

It turned out that the only part of the road to Stanton that was blocked was a long section starting at Grandpa's roofless house. The road lay full of uprooted trees. They had to go around them through the fields; then they walked down the gravel road to town.

Stanton was destroyed—the whole center of it where the stores were, even the brick bank was gone and the church where they'd found the man that was in the ambulance with Mama. Beyond that was the store his father had been building. The front half of the store lay in a tangle of wreckage. "Imagine, your father came out of that mess and is alive."

There among the wreckage, hardly banged up at all, stood Dad's truck. They had to pull away beams and window frames and planks and doors to get to it. Then Grandpa got up in the cab and started the motor. It roared and jolted forward. Then Grandpa stopped it, and Mark climbed up in the cab.

The truck crawled slowly up the main street and then beyond the Stanton road. There was a farmer's market already set up in the destruction. "There's potatoes," Mark screamed. "Stop!"

"Potatoes it is," he said. They bought all the potatoes the man would sell.

Mark wiggled in the seat, glad of the potatoes. "I'm glad we didn't wait until we got back from the hospital. They might have been all gone."

Grandpa didn't answer. The truck just rolled on.

As they were nearing the city, Grandpa said, "Am I glad you thought of the truck. Not a single bus has passed us. Who knows where the tornado took them or in what kind of shape they are now?"

And Mark said, "We'll see Mother now in a minute, and maybe Dad can tell us about Creek."

"Is there ever a moment you haven't your mind on horses?" Grandpa asked.

"Yes, it's sometimes on potatoes." Mark giggled. Then they both laughed and then they were driving into the parking lot of the hospital.

Mark had to run to keep up with Grandpa.

He'd have to stay in the waiting room, Grandpa said. "Kids can't go up where the sick folks are. A kid could give everybody the measles. Though in your case it'd be more likely to be hoof-and-mouth disease."

He rose out of sight in the elevator. Mark watched until it was gone, then dribbled to the waiting room. It was full of people. There wasn't one empty chair. A woman pointed out the windowsill, and he had to sit there. His dangling legs wouldn't be still, they drummed the wall until a man in a chair reached out and stopped them. Then Mark sat motionless and waited and waited.

13

Mark tried to sit quietly, because the man next to him in the waiting room didn't seem to like his feet drumming the wall. It was difficult not to drum, he was so excited. Mark looked down at himself. Here he'd got dressed up because Grandpa had wanted it, but then they'd had to move planks and beams to free the truck, and then still load potatoes. Now in his suit and white shirt he was dirty as any ditch digger. But Mother hadn't seen him for so long that, dirty as he was, he knew she would come in through the door of the waiting room and right away be mushy. Dirty as he was, she'd hug and hold him.

And there she was! She stood in the doorway, staring bewilderedly around at the full room. "Mother!" he yelled, and jumped from the windowsill and ran to her, but with his hand held out. They shook hands solemnly before all the waiting, staring people, then Mother just gathered him to herself and kissed and kissed him. He kissed her back.

"What a lucky time you picked to come," Mother exclaimed so loud that everybody must hear. "What a lucky time! Mark, just before I came down to you, your father spoke to me for the first time. He knew me right away!"

That was a silly thing to say before all the people. Why wouldn't Dad know Mother right off? She was his wife, she lived with him.

But Mother expected something from him, and so did the waiting people, at least the whole room had gone still. "He did? He did?" Mark squealed out. "What did he say? Mother, did he tell you about Creek, and whether he bought her, and Creek is mine?"

Mother looked puzzled—so she hadn't asked Dad. Mark almost wanted to push Mother backward through the door so she could run up again and ask about Creek. It was wonderful about Dad, but it was also important about Creek. Mother hadn't thought about somebody maybe claiming Creek.

Mother wouldn't budge; she still stood holding him tight. "Mother," he asked, muffled against her, "could you run up and quickly ask?"

Mother looked at him in dismay. "Of course not! All they let him do was whisper to me. Know what that dad of yours said the first thing? 'Hello. I love you. How's Mark?' "

Mark stood guilty as she let him go. It was impossible to explain that he was terribly excited about Dad, but that at the same time Creek was his responsibility and worry. He stood dumb and miserable.

Mother understood. She kissed the top of his head, then said: "Here I was told by Grandpa you were going to take me out and buy me an ice cream soda."

"Come on, let's go," Mark yelped. "The first drugstore anywhere."

It turned out they could get their sodas right in the restaurant of the hospital. They sat at a little table across from each other, and Mark ordered them each a double-thick ice cream soda. He hoped Grandpa had given him enough money for double ice cream sodas.

He and Mother could hardly sip them at all for talking. There was so much to tell about Creek and Colonel, and the tornado and the milk wagon, and everything. Then Mark guessed he shouldn't have said so much about Creek's awful cut. Mother listened, but she'd just quietly shoved her soda aside. It ended by Mark not having three sodas at all, just one and a half—his and what was left of Mother's.

Grandpa found them. Mark wanted to buy him a double chocolate soda, too, but Grandpa said, "No, make it coffee. I can stand anybody's coffee after my own. But you have a soda along with me. And it looks as if your mother could stand coffee, too. What did you do to her to make her look so sort of green around the gills?"

"He's been talking about that nasty cut," Mother said. "But I thought you were going to stay up there while I was with Mark," Mother said.

"They kicked me out," Grandpa said. "They had to work on Mama. Just the same," he told Mark, "I got in a few quick words with your dad. He looks wonderful to me for a guy who had a roof caving down on his head. I knew you wouldn't have a minute's rest over Creek. I'm afraid, Mark, he didn't buy Creek."

Grandpa hastily turned to Mother. "That's another reason I came down," he told her. "The doctor said tomorrow both of them can come home—in an ambulance, of course. Mama will be in bed a long time. But he said with the day and night care you've been giving them, they'd actually be better at home, and this place is so overcrowded."

Their coffee came and Mother sipped gratefully at hers.

"So," Grandpa went on, "it looks like you ought to

go home with Mark, and I will stay here. There's no roof on our house, and until there is, we'll have to stay with you, and there'll be lots to do to get ready for them. Can you drive a truck?"

"Well, I never have."

Grandpa laughed, "You're going to, if we're going to get those potatoes home for Creek and Colonel."

"Yes, Mom!" Mark said, letting go of the straw of his new soda. "It's just like with Colonel—Creek can only eat cut potatoes now, but she liked them just as much as old Colonel." It was sad, but his tall glass of soda was just about empty, all but some thick dregs down in the bottom. He had to suck hard.

Grandpa jumped up. "I can't stand that slurping noise. Let's get out of here while he finishes that," he said to Mother. Mark looked up just in time to see him give Mother a significant nod. Grandpa knew he had seen it, because he immediately came back to the table and said, "Say, Mark, when they kicked me out of Mama's room, I went to your dad's. It's all right about flies—the young of flies keep a wound clean. He said he'd learned that in the war. So no sacks or anything, but keep it out in the air and sunshine and all the flies that want to come."

There were no words Mark could say to that amazing thing.

Grandpa abruptly walked to Mother. Mark still had to pay for the coffee and sodas. He went to the cashier, but though he stood quite near them, Mark could only hear a word now and then of what Grandpa was saying to Mother. But that word seemed to be "Colonel"—again and again. Did it mean Colonel was going to die? The chocolate sodas rose up in his throat, and Mark shoved his money at the cashier and turned away without waiting for his change.

Mother and Grandpa turned to him. "It's all arranged,"

Mother said hastily. "Grandpa and I talked it over, and he's right. I should be there on the farm. Grandpa is going to drive the truck to the outskirts of town, and then I'll take over. Grandpa wants to walk back and buy a clean shirt and trousers; otherwise he's afraid they won't let him stay here with Mama—it's such a clean hospital."

"But I thought you couldn't drive a truck." Mark searched their faces.

Grandpa turned away. "I'll go get the truck and meet you at the foot of the steps."

"It looks like I'll have to drive the truck," Mother told Mark as they walked out of the hospital. "You see, I haven't got our car here. It's wherever I left it in Stanton. I got to Stanton just after the tornado had struck, and I abandoned the car to run to the store where Dad was working. I got there as they were putting him into an ambulance, and I sat on the floor with his poor head in my lap all the way to the hospital."

Grandpa roared up with the truck, and it was no use then to ask the dreaded question about Colonel.

Mother sat between Mark and Grandpa in the high cab of the truck and watched everything Grandpa did. Mark sat still and worried.

At last they were near the outskirts of town, and on a quiet street, before getting to the highway, Grandpa got down and made Mother drive while he sat next to her and watched her. "You see, it's no different from a car," he told her. "Only your moves and twists and turns can't be quite as abrupt. But don't worry, you're in a truck, and if anything gets in your way, just lean on your horn. If anybody says anything, just look down from your cab and give him some truck driver talk out of the side of your mouth."

Then Mark had to open the door and let Grandpa

down over him. Grandpa kneaded his shoulder as he stepped down. "Now, Grandson, don't worry so, just remember that no horse has ever been loved like that before. That he's had, and that you've had, so be grateful."

Mark nodded dumbly—words like that always wanted to make the tears come. Then Grandpa slammed the door shut and was gone. The truck roared into motion.

It was miles before Mother stopped wiggle-waggling the big steering wheel. At last she leaned back and sat in the seat, instead of wrestling the steering wheel.

She laughed a little. "It's just like Grandpa said, it's not too much different from a car."

"Another two miles and we'll be home," Mark said somberly. "Mother, Grandpa told you Colonel was going to die, didn't he?"

Mother made believe something was in her way down the road; she leaned toward the windshield. "It's nothing, just a dog, I guess," she muttered. Then, looking straight ahead, she said, "Grandpa doesn't know for sure. He only thinks so; he only guesses. Grandpa doesn't know everything, any more than you or I do. Your father and the old farmer thought that Colonel would have died long ago, and still he's here, and through a tornado. And look at all the potatoes we are bringing him."

Mother's words were just words, but he mustn't worry her now going down the Stanton Road, so narrow with piled ridges of stuff from the tornado. "Hey, linemen!" Mark exclaimed. "They're putting up the lines again."

Mother was steering the truck down the narrow road. Mark told her: "Colonel ate the biggest meal of oats in his life this morning."

They were just words, too. Even he did not believe his brave-sounding voice, and neither did Mother. But they had to leave the road and go between Grandpa's roofless house and the gone barn, and it needed all Mother's attention. Now there was only the single field to get home to Colonel.

"Home!" Mother said. "And it's still there, and we're still here—even Colonel. Oh, Mark, can't we be more thankful?"

Mark nodded his head, but it was false—he couldn't be thankful.

610

14

They parked the truck behind the house. Mark ran in and grabbed the claw hammer. "Help me get the barn door open," he said. "I can't reach the high nails—hurry."

Mother came. Mark ripped out the lower nails, and Mother pulled out the high ones.

"Whatever did you and Grandpa nail up the door for?" Mother asked while they worked.

"So nobody could come and take Creek away," Mark answered shortly.

"But Mark, you must face it. Sooner or later someone is almost bound to claim Creek—unless her owners were killed."

"It isn't Creek now, it's Colonel." As he said that the last nail came away, and he slid the door open.

Colonel wasn't dead, but he didn't neigh out or turn to Mark. He just rested on his threshing-machine straps. He pawed one foot impatiently. "He wants to get out; he wants to get out of the barn," Mark told Mother.

Mark rushed into Colonel's stall and helped let down the straps. By himself Colonel stumbled out of the barn and went through the gateway into the pasture.

They stood looking after him. "I guess he wants to be alone, or maybe just with you," Mother's voice was shaky.

Grandpa had seen it this morning; now Mother must have seen it, too. Colonel was going to die.

Mother would not let him ask the question. "Mark," she said, "Colonel's looking back for you. If you need me I'll be right here on the truck—just yell out and I'll come."

Mark ran to Colonel. Colonel turned his head and looked out of the corner of his eye, but he didn't wait. He started down the length of the pasture.

Mark ran back to the truck. "I'm going to stay with Colonel. I think he wants to go to his creek. I'll go with him because he's going to die. He told me just now when he looked at me."

Mother cleared her throat and put one hand on Mark's shoulder. "Yes, I thought he told me, too, there in the stable. Mark, I don't know, do you want me along or would you rather be alone?"

Mark turned. He wanted to thank her, but his voice wouldn't come. Finally he croaked out, "Alone."

"Mark! Colonel's down. He fell just now," she jumped from the truck, almost fell herself. She grabbed Mark's hand. Together they ran.

Mother and Mark stroked the long white cheek of Colonel as he lay with his head flat to the ground. But Colonel looked only at Mark.

Mother stroked Colonel once more and walked away.

Now Mark and Colonel were alone—a long time they were alone. Mark could see Mother watching from the truck. He told Colonel many important things and then he said them all over again. Colonel listened and slid his head back and forth in the grass until there was no more to say, no more need to listen. Then he warned Mark with his eye. He did it so suddenly, so unexpectedly, that Mark had to jump back and out of the way. Colonel threw himself up, first his head and then his forelegs, and then in one great heave all of him came up. Colonel was on his feet! He staggered away a few steps and looked around to see if Mark was coming. Mark grabbed the end of the halter rope, and immediately Colonel set off down the pasture. He was heading for the creek in the woodlot. Colonel wanted to stand in his cool creek.

It was too far. Mark told Colonel over and over that it was too far, but Colonel kept going. They would never get there, never reach the creek. Colonel was stumbling.

Mark tugged desperately at the rope, and slowly Colonel turned with him toward the spring in the bank of catalpas. "The spring doesn't run and whisper," Mark told Colonel softly, "but it's cool there in the grass."

Colonel listened and they went to the nearby spring that on this sunny afternoon was deep-shadowed by the catalpas growing on the bank. They walked very slowly, for with the spring so close there seemed all the time in the world. All the time in the world in the sadness that lay over the sunshiny land.

They got to the spring. There Colonel lay down in the cool wet grass shaded by the catalpas. He wanted a drink. He couldn't lift his head, but his eye went to the drops of water dripping from the end of the pipe. Mark measured the distance with his eyes. Colonel's head was near the spring. There was a length of old tubing in the barn—if he could slip it over the pipe, he could lead water into Colonel's mouth.

He raced to the barn; everything was all right.

The tubing was long enough. It slid over the end of the pipe and was soft enough to squeeze between Colonel's lips. Colonel drank. He swallowed the trickle-drip that collected around his teeth and flowed into his mouth.

Then Colonel swallowed once more, spit out the tube, looked up at Mark—and died.

Mark dropped the tubing, kneeled down and kissed Colonel. He sat in the wet grass beside his horse. There was no one but the two of them.

At last he got up and walked away, but he didn't go to the truck. He went to the barn to get two shovels. When he came back, Mother was standing beside the truck, searching the pasture with her eyes. He raised the shovels as a sign to her. Mother came.

Mark waited ramrod straight, as if his two shovels were shouldered rifles. He told her, "Colonel died. We have to bury him. We'll bury him because we both loved him."

They talked no more. They walked around Colonel, and Mother studied how he lay. "It'll be easy here under the spring. The ground is soft and I think it's sandy." Her voice was calm and low and steady. "It was wonderful of Colonel to pick this spot."

"He wanted to go to his creek, but I turned him away, and he came."

The hardest digging was the sod. Mother dug, and Mark piled it as she dug. "No, don't pile the sod against the bank," she cautioned. "Pile it above Colonel's head, because as we dig deep, unless the catalpa roots hold it, the whole bottom of the bank may come down to slide over Colonel. And we want the sod to cover the grave, don't we?"

Mark nodded.

After the sod, the moist sand threw out easily, but the moisture made the sand stick together so it stayed in place, and there was no early cave-in. The threat of a cave-in grew as the hole deepened and went into the bank. They both kept a wary eye on the straight side of the grave along Colonel's back—all of Colonel's weight was bearing down on it.

Now the enormous hole was almost deep enough. Mark started digging up into the bank, but Mother kept turned toward Colonel.

The cave-in came with silent swiftness—the way a snake or a weasel comes. There was no time to call out a warning, only time to catch Mother's hand and help pull her up on the bank where he'd been digging. Even then Mother had to wrench one leg out of the silent-flowing sand as Mark tugged her up. Then they were safely on the grass, and Colonel settled on his side down in the hole among the flowing sand. Mark began to cry.

But Mother did not stop digging into the bank. She wanted the sandy bank to slide down over Colonel.

Mark watched her uncertainly, not knowing whether or not to help. That moment the whole bank came streaming, rolling down. It covered Colonel. A small catalpa, low on the bank, slid down in the flowing sand until it stopped upright in the middle of Colonel's grave.

"Mark! Mark!" Mother called. "Look! A little tree came down to Colonel. It's going to be the Colonel Tree."

Mark nodded. Then he had to sit down on one of the sods. He was so drained, so spent. He couldn't even help Mother lay the sod. At last Mother finished. Cautiously she straightened her back, and Mark could hear the weariness creak up out of her stoop.

He did not get up. "Colonel died," he said, "and Dad didn't get Creek for me. Now if they come to claim Creek, I won't have anything." He sat a moment. Suddenly he bawled out at her, "How can I wait and wait—days and days—until they come and get Creek?"

Mother stood spent. At last she said, "I'm too tired to think now. But there must be something we can do. Let's rest for a while. Maybe I can think of something."

Mark nodded wearily and took her hand.

They walked away together—they let the shovels lie.

Mother and Mark walked the whole way home in silence and sadness. Mark had no words, and Mother just plunged straight ahead. She seemed to be thinking deeply. But when they reached the house yard, suddenly she started running—the telephone inside the house was ringing.

"The phone!" Mark yelled. "The lines are up. They finished putting up the lines on the Stanton road."

Mother ran through the kitchen without seeing anything but the telephone. She grabbed the receiver, but when she answered, it was only someone testing the line. She hung up and stood there. Suddenly she grabbed the telephone directory and fluttered the pages. "But I know what to do—now that we have a telephone," she exclaimed. "I'll call the radio station."

She found the number and dialed the phone. Over the phone Mother explained to a loud-voiced man the thing that had happened with Creek running to the farm the night of the tornado, and now the death of Colonel.

"So couldn't I make a radio appeal?" she begged. "Couldn't I make it right over the telephone. You could broadcast it all over, so that if the horse that came running to us is to be claimed, it would be claimed now—instead of our waiting and waiting and never knowing?"

Hanging on to the silent receiver, Mother turned to Mark and hurriedly explained. "It came to me the moment I heard our phone ringing!" She snapped her fingers. "Just like that, I thought I could make an appeal on the radio, the way I did from town the night of the tornado, with your dad unconscious in the hospital, and me not knowing what had happened or what would become of you."

The phone made abrupt loud noises. Mother listened again. At last she turned back to Mark. "The announcer is going to say word for word over the radio exactly what I say to him on the phone, and everywhere people will hear. Maybe Creek's owner will hear, too. Then perhaps he will come, and maybe we can persuade him to sell Creek to us."

Amazement and hope made Mark speechless.

"They're setting things up, and the moment the present broadcast is over, they're going to let me make my appeal," Mother explained so Mark would understand the wait.

At last the telephone crackled and sputtered, and Mother held the receiver so tight to her ear, her ear went dead white. "They're ready for me," she said in a panicky voice. "What will I say—how will I say it?"

Over the telephone the announcer's voice laughed, and Mother had to start talking. Mark couldn't stand there any longer, he raced away to the living room. There—the way Grandpa had done—he clicked on the radio. But now it worked. The electricity was back again; the electric lines were up, too. Mark couldn't yell it to Mother—she was talking. In a slow voice, because his words were going everywhere, the announcer began to repeat Mother's words. Standing between the radio and the kitchen, Mark could hear them both.

"A horse came running to our farm the night of the tornado," Mother said into the phone. "A horse came running," the announcer began.

"A horse came running," Mother repeated, then she stopped confused. "Oh, I already said that." Mother began again. "It's leg had been terribly cut in the tornado, and now it is crippled. My boy found her, and he named her Creek. Colonel is—was—the name of my son's own horse. 'Was,' because Colonel died, and we just now buried him. Now all there is left is Creek, but we don't own her. We want to own her now that Colonel is gone. Even crippled, we'd buy her." Mother hesitated. Then firmly she said, "Yes, we will buy her for a fair price because my boy needs her now."

The announcer broke in. "Lady, describe the horse so the owner will recognize her."

"Oh, how shall I do that?" Mother's voice went wobbly. "She's thin and raggedy now, and run down from her wound, but she was a sleek all-over brown, except for a white blaze, a sort of star running down her forehead. A star—you know, with sort of long rays going down. Creek's star sort of rays down that way toward her nose."

"That's good enough," the announcer interrupted. "Don't try any more, because that is perfect. Now just your address, and anybody that ever owned a horse with a star will know. And all over the countryside, I can tell you, we will hope and wait with you and your boy. Be sure to let us know what develops."

Mark ran to Mother. In a choked, spent voice Mother was giving their address; then slowly she hung up the receiver as if it were leaden and heavy. Together they went to the living room, and Mark shut off the radio. It had to be still now in the house. It had to be still so as to take it all in and run it over in his mind. Mother sat on the couch beside him, and she, too, needed to rest and be still. She took Mark's hand in hers.

They waited and waited until waiting became impossible in the stillness of the telephone, and in the sadness over Colonel, and in the tenseness over Creek. Lumped in a hard ball inside of all that, stood the hard fear of losing Creek.

Mark stirred, wrung his hand out of Mother's nervous hold, and jumped up. "I can't be still like this. I've got to do something. I'm going to exercise Creek. I'll just go with her up and down the lane because from there I can see if anybody comes, and I can hear if you call me when somebody telephones."

"Yes, do," Mother said. "Telephone ring! Anything, anybody, just so we know it still works. The lines may still be up so poorly that nobody can call us now. You can think the worst, if you keep sitting still." Mother jumped up. "Let's get to work."

Mark ran from the house. In the barn, before letting down the straps from under Creek, he pulled the feed sack off her leg. Dad knew that the sack shouldn't be on. Open air was good for the wound.

Creek did not want to back out of the stall. She did not seem to want to move. Mark let her stand and flew to the truck and cut potatoes.

As Mark had hoped, the potatoes tempted Creek. He gave her none, but held some out before him, chest high. And once Creek was turned around, she hobbled after him, head over his shoulder, trying to reach the potatoes. They walked like that the length of the lane, Creek munching potatoes.

When they returned and came past the barn, a car came down the road drawing a horse trailer behind it. It stopped at their driveway. Two men got out of the car. Mark stood there; he couldn't move. He stood frozen with apprehension. Then Mother came out of the house, and he went to her with Creek. Creek tried to reach the last potato.

Mark and Creek got to the house at the same time as the two men. It *was* Creek's owner—Creek's owner with a veterinarian he had brought along with him. He explained it to Mother. "I tried to call, but your telephone isn't right." Abruptly the man turned to Creek. He looked and looked as if he couldn't believe his eyes. "In just three days, that's all that's left of her?" he asked hoarsely. "Can a wound run a horse down that fast?'' he demanded of the veterinarian.

"If it's bad enough and infected enough, like this one looks to be, yes," the veterinarian said.

"But all that's left of her is ribs and hide and a hollow back and a nasty wound!" The owner crouched down to study the deep cut. Abruptly he rose, turned away from Creek, and stayed turned away.

Mark stared at him, unbelieving. He did not want to look at Creek at all. He didn't love her. He was only angry because she had a cut leg. He was not a good man.

The owner turned to the veterinarian. "You look at her."

It didn't take the veterinarian long. Then he, too, straightened up. "The tendon's cut, that's sure," he said. "So unless you want to keep her as a pet, she'll never be good for riding again."

"Pet!" The man spat, his face twisting. "Do you realize I had that horse at my place only a good two days? I'd just bought her. And you wouldn't believe what I paid for her! And now keep her as a crippled pet?" He spat again.

"I hate to tell you this," Mother said, "but they told us that open air was good. We tried to keep the cut bandaged, but they said the wound would heal better in the open air."

The veterinarian told the man, "She's right. Fresh air is good. But, of course, it can't bring back a cut tendon."

The man didn't listen. He walked down the drive without looking back. "Bring the horse," he called over his shoulder, "and load her on the trailer. Then shoot her. I don't want to see her again. I'll get my girl another horse. Three days—and that!"

The veterinarian shrugged and looked at Mother. "I'm

afraid a tornado doesn't first look at the cost of what it's going to wreck."

Mark stood horrified, looking after the man walking to his car. Did he really have a gun in the car? Were they going to shoot Creek right here and now? "Mother!" he croaked.

In big steps Mother went down the driveway, then stopped and called out, "You stop right there. We'll buy Creek as she is, for what in decency you care to ask. She came here; she stays here. If you're going to shoot her, she's not yours anymore. She's my boy's—he loves her."

Mark snatched Creek's halter rope away from the veterinarian. "She's mine!" he yelled. "She's mine—she came to me."

The man at the car turned and looked at him. "Okay, son, she's yours, but not for money. I wouldn't sell anything I don't want myself. Consider her a gift from me to somebody that wants her like that. Keep your Creek—she's yours."

The veterinarian came up beside Mark and hit him teasingly with a soft fist. "Good," he said. "Just keep exercising her. I'll be back to work on your Creek as soon as I can get rid of *him*."

Mark could not say a word. It couldn't be believed; it couldn't be endured—not standing still. "Mother," he whispered, "he said Creek was mine. She's mine, and it's forever."

Then he had to run. He ran to the truck and pulled down more potatoes for Creek. He started up the lane. Creek came hobbling after him, head reaching over his shoulder to get at the potatoes. Then Mother came.

They walked and walked up the lane, down the lane, for walking was the only thing to do in happiness like this. Walking was the only way to wait. Next the veterinarian would come and work on Creek. But the veterinarian knew, as Mother did, that he did not need a perfect horse. He needed Creek.

Then they'd wait still some more, but then Grandpa would come, bringing Dad and Mama Sayers in the ambulance. The great news about Creek would be waiting for them. The moment that they came he'd be in the driveway to yell out the news, so that Dad, Grandpa, and Mama would know even before they opened the ambulance door.

Thinking like that, even walking was not enough for Mark. He had to run. Mother understood. She took the potatoes from him and walked on with Creek down the lane. Mark ran across the pasture and down to the gully of the fallen tree. He touched the tree as he passed it in his running, then ran hard from the gully into the woodlot. He'd run so fast that Mother was only now coming to the end of the lane with Creek. He hugged her, and then he kissed Creek. He took the potatoes from Mother, and Creek walked with her munching head down over his shoulder again. Wait till they heard! Wait till they heard!

"Creek's mine," he had to say to Mother in his wonder. Mother put her arm around his shoulder. Then they walked and walked and walked.

The Runaway

Once when the snow of the year was beginning to fall,
We stopped by a mountain pasture to say, "Whose colt?"
A little Morgan had one forefoot on the wall,
The other curled at his breast. He dipped his head
And snorted at us. And then he had to bolt.
We heard the miniature thunder where he fled,
And we saw him, or thought we saw him, dim and grey
Like a shadow against the curtain of falling flakes.
"I think the little fellow's afraid of the snow.
He isn't winter-broken. It isn't play
With the little fellow at all. He's running away.
I doubt if even his mother could tell him, 'Sakes,
It's only weather!' He'd think she didn't know!
Where is his mother? He can't be out alone."
And now he comes again with clatter of stone,
And mounts the wall again with whited eyes
And all his tail that isn't hair up straight.
He shudders his coat as if to throw off flies.
"Whoever it is that leaves him out so late,
When other creatures have gone to stall and bin,
Ought to be told to come and take him in."

—*Robert Frost*

A HORSE CAME RUNNING

Life brings pleasure as well as pain, happiness as well as grief. Mark experienced all these emotions in a few short days. In "A Horse Came Running," you read of the ways Mark coped with danger and learned to accept the death of something he loved. At the same time, you watched him welcome something new and wonderful into his life. You saw how he developed understanding, respect, and love for another human being as he and Grandpa shared a trying and exhausting experience. Mark is a fictional character, but from reading about his experiences and his feelings, you can gain a deeper understanding of yourself and those around you.

Thinking About "A Horse Came Running"

1. What had happened to the new horse by the time Mark found her in the creek?
2. What did Grandpa mean when he said, "What's least hurt has got to help what's really hurt"?
3. How did Mark and Grandpa demonstrate their trust in each other?
4. What did Mark do that showed how much having a new grandpa meant to him?
5. How do you think Mark would have reacted to Colonel's death if Creek hadn't come along? What makes you think so?
6. What have you learned about people and their reactions to the events around them?
7. If you were the author of "A Horse Came Running," how would you end the story? Write a paragraph describing your ideas.

Glossary

This glossary will help you to pronounce and to understand the meanings of some of the unusual or difficult words in this book.

The pronunciation of each word is printed beside the word in this way: **o·pen** (ō′pən). The letters, signs, and key words in the list below will help you read the pronunciation respelling. When an entry word has more than one syllable, a dark accent mark (′) is placed after the syllable that has the heaviest stress. In some words, a light accent mark (′) is placed after the syllable that receives a less heavy stress.

The pronunciation key, syllable breaks, accent mark placements, and phonetic respellings in this glossary are adapted from the Macmillan *School Dictionary* (1981) and the Macmillan *Dictionary* (1981). Other dictionaries may use other pronunciation symbols.

Pronunciation Key

a	bad	**hw**	white	**ô**	off	**th**	that	**ə**	*stands for*
ā	cake	**i**	it	**oo**	wood	**u**	cup		a *as in* ago
ä	father	**ī**	ice	**ōo**	food	**ur**	turn		e *as in* taken
b	bat	**j**	joke	**oi**	oil	**yōo**	music		i *as in* pencil
ch	chin	**k**	kit	**ou**	out	**v**	very		o *as in* lemon
d	dog	**l**	lid	**p**	pail	**w**	wet		u *as in* helpful
e	pet	**m**	man	**r**	ride	**y**	yes		
ē	me	**n**	not	**s**	sit	**z**	zoo		
f	five	**ng**	sing	**sh**	ship	**zh**	treasure		
g	game	**o**	hot	**t**	tall				
h	hit	**ō**	open	**th**	thin				

A

Aar · on (ar′ən)

Aar · on, Hank (ar′ən, hangk′)

ab · do · men (ab′də mən, ab dō′mən) *n.* the largest of the body cavities of humans and animals with backbones.

ab · dom · i · nal (ab dom′ə nəl) *adj.* of or relating to the abdomen.

ac · a · dem · ic (ak′ə dem′ik) *adj.* **1.** of or relating to an academy, school, or college. **2.** relating to liberal or general education.

ac · cent (ak′sent) *n.* **1.** greater force or emphasis given to a particular syllable or word in speech. **2.** a mark used in writing and printing to indicate a syllable that is spoken with greater force or emphasis. **3.** manner of pronouncing words that is characteristic of a certain part of a country.

ac · cor · di · on (ə kor′dē ən) *n.* a portable musical wind instrument with keys, metal reeds, and a bellows.

accordion

ac · cu · mu · la · tion (ə kyoo′myə lā′shən) *n.* something that is or has been gathered, collected, or piled up.

A · cos · ta, Man · uel (a kos′tə, man′yoo əl)

a · dapt (ə dapt′) *v.* **1.** to change to meet new requirements or to fit new uses; modify; alter. **2.** to adjust (oneself) to new conditions or surroundings.

ad · vance (əd vans′) *v.* **ad · vanced, ad · vanc · ing.** to move forward; proceed.

ad · ven · tur · ous (ad ven′chər əs) *adj.* eager for adventure; willing to encounter danger.

ad · ver · tise (ad′vər tīz′) *v.* **ad · ver · tised, ad · ver · tis · ing. 1.** to make a public announcement describing the good qualities of a product, service, cause, or idea in such a way as to make people want to buy it or support it. **2.** to make known publicly.

a · ga · ve (ə gä′vē) *n.* any of a group of desert plants of the Western Hemisphere, having long flower stalks and thick, fleshy leaves. The most familiar is the century plant.

a · ghast (ə gast′) *adj.* filled with fear, shock, or amazement.

a · larm (ə lärm′) *v.* to cause to feel sudden fear.

al · low · ance (ə lou′əns) *n.* a quantity granted or set apart, especially a sum of money given regularly or for a particular purpose.

Al · pha Cen · tau · ri (al′fə sen tôr′ē) a double star in Centaurus, the brightest in the constellation.

a · lum · nus (ə lum′nəs) *n. pl.,* **a · lum · ni** (ə lum nī) a graduate or former student of a school, college, or university, especially a male graduate.

am · bu · lance (am′byə ləns) *n.* a specially equipped vehicle that is used for carrying persons who are sick, injured, or wounded.

An · des (an′dēz) a 4,000 mile-long mountain system, the longest in the world, extending along the west coast of South America.

an · e · mom · e · ter (an′ə mom′ə tər) *n.* an instrument for measuring the speed of the wind.

an · ti · bi · ot · ic (an′tē bī ot′ik) *n.* any of a group of substances, such as penicillin or streptomycin, used in medicine.

an · vil (an'vəl) *n.* an iron or steel block on which heat-softened metals are hammered into shapes.

ap · pa · rat · us (ap' ə rat'əs, ap' ə rā'təs) *n.* **1.** a device or mechanism used for a particular purpose. **2.** a group of organs working together to perform a particular function.

ap · pe · tite (ap'ə tīt') *n.* a desire for food.

ap · point (ə point') *v.* to name or select for an office or a position.

ap · point · ment (ə point'mənt) *n.* an arrangement to meet or see someone at a certain time and place; engagement.

ap · pre · hen · sion (ap'ri hen'shən) *n.* a fear of what may happen.

arc (ärk) *v.* **arced** or **arcked, arc · ing** or **arck · ing.** to move in a curved line.

ar · chae · ol · o · gist (är'kē ol'ə jist) *n.* a person who studies archaeology.

ar · chae · ol · o · gy (är' kē ol' ə jē) *n.* the scientific study of the remains of past human activities, such as burials, buildings, tools, and pottery.

ar · chi · tect (är'kə tekt') *n.* a person who designs and supervises the construction of buildings.

ar · chi · tec · tur · al (är'kə tek'chər əl) *adj.* relating to architecture.

as·so·ci·ate (ə sō'shē āt', ə sō'sē āt') *v.* **as·so·ci·at·ed, as·so·ci·at·ing.** to keep company as a friend, companion, or partner; be friendly.

as · sort · ment (ə sôrt'mənt) *n.* a collection of various kinds of things.

a · stern (ə sturn') *adv.* **1.** at or toward the rear of a ship. **2.** behind a ship.

as · ton · ish (əs ton'ish) *v.* to surprise greatly.

as · tound (əs tound') *v.* to surprise or amaze greatly; stun.

Au · du · bon Society (ô'də bon') an organization for the preservation and study of wildlife.

au · to · mat · ic (ô'tə mat'ik) *adj.* **1.** acting, moving, or operating by itself. **2.** done without a person's control.

av · a · rice (av'ər is) *n.* an intense desire to acquire money and keep it; greed for wealth or possessions.

a · vi · a · tion (ā'vē ā'shən, av'ē ā'shən) *n.* the science or art of flying in heavier-than-air aircraft.

awe · some (ô'səm) *adj.* inspiring or showing great wonder combined with fear or reverence.

B

bal · der · dash (bôl'dər dash') *n.* nonsense; foolishness.

bal · sa (bôl'sə) *n.* a strong lightweight wood used especially for making airplane or boat models and in rafts and floats.

ban · ish (ban'ish) *v.* **1.** to punish by forcing to leave a country. **2.** to send or drive away.

ban · is · ter (ban'is tər) *n.* a handrail and its upright supports along the edge of a staircase or other raised structure.

ba · sis (bā'sis) *n.* a fundamental part on which a thing rests or depends; foundation; support.

a **b**a**d**, ā c**a**ke, ä f**a**ther; e p**e**t, ē m**e**; i **i**t, ī **i**ce; o h**o**t, ō **o**pen, ô **o**ff; oo w**oo**d, ōō f**oo**d; oi **oi**l, ou **ou**t; th **th**in, th **th**at; u c**u**p, ur t**u**rn, yōō m**u**sic; zh trea**s**ure; ə **a**go, tak**e**n, penc**i**l, lem**o**n, helpf**u**l

batch (bach) *v.* a slang term meaning "to live alone and keep house for oneself."

beam (bēm) *v.* **1.** to shine brightly; radiate. **2.** to smile radiantly or joyfully.

bear · ings (bār′ingz) *n. pl.* knowledge or understanding of one's position or direction.

be · hav · ior (bi hāv′yər) *n.* **1.** a manner of behaving or acting; conduct. **2.** the manner in which something acts under given circumstances.

bel · lows (bel′ōz) *n. pl.* a device for producing a strong air current, used for making a fire burn faster or sounding a musical instrument.

bi · fo · cal (bī fō′kəl) *adj.* (of an eyeglass lens) having two parts, one for seeing close objects and one for seeing distant objects.

bil · i · ru · bin (bil rōō′bin) *n.* a red bile pigment, sometimes found in the urine.

bi · noc · u · lars (bə nok′yə lərz) *n. pl.* an optical instrument for both eyes, used to magnify distant objects. Field glasses and opera glasses are binoculars.

binoculars

bliz · zard (bliz′ərd) *n.* a severe, heavy snowstorm marked by strong winds and intense cold.

bo · a con · stric · tor (bō′ə kən strik′tər) a large, nonpoisonous snake of Mexico and Central and South America, having light brown skin with dark brown marks on its back.

board of dir · ec · tors (bôrd′ ov di rek′tərz) an organized body of administrators.

bo · nan · za (bə nan′zə) *n.* **1.** a rich mine or mass of ore. **2.** any source of great wealth or profit.

bot · a · ny (bot′ən ē) *n.* the science or study of plants. Botany deals with the origin, development, structure, function, and distribution of all forms of plant life.

boul · der (bōl′dər) *n.* a large, rounded rock.

bound · a · ry (boun′dər ē, bound′rē) *n.* a line or thing that limits or marks a separation; border.

boun · ty (boun′tē) *n. pl.*, **boun · ties.** **1.** a reward or premium, especially one given by a government for the killing of certain animals or the raising of certain crops. **2.** generosity in giving, **3.** a gift generously given.

brace (brās) *v.* **braced, brac · ing.** to make strong, firm, or steady; support.

brew (brōō) *n.* a drink prepared by steeping, boiling, mixing, or fermenting.

bri · dle (brīd′əl) *n.* the part of a horse's harness that fits over the head, including the bit and reins, used to guide or control the animal.

brig · and (brig′ənd) *n.* a robber or bandit, especially one who is a member of a band of roving outlaws.

broad · cast (brôd′kast′) *v.* to send out (information or entertainment) by radio or television.

Bronx (brongks) a borough of New York City, northeast of Manhattan.

brush heap (brush′hēp′) a pile of cut or broken twigs or branches.

buck · shot (buk′shot′) *n.* large metal pellets for shotgun shells, used in hunting game.

buil · ding code (bil′ding kōd′) a systematic collection of regulations and rules having to do with the construction of buildings.

bul · ly (bool′ē) *n.* a quarrelsome person who frightens, threatens, or hurts smaller or weaker people.

bun · ga · low (bung′gə lō′) *n.* a small house or cottage, usually of one story.

bu · reau (byoor′ō) *n.* a chest of drawers, especially for clothes.

bush · el (boosh′əl) *n.* a unit of measure equal to four pecks of thirty-two quarts, used for fruit, vegetables, grain and other dry products.

c

cab · i · net (kab′ə nit) *n.* a piece of furniture fitted with shelves or drawers and often having doors, used for storing or displaying objects; cupboard.

ca · lam · i · ty (kə lam′ə tē) *n.* an event that causes great misfortune; disaster.

cap · size (kap′sīz, kap sīz′) *v.* **cap · sized, cap · siz · ing. 1.** to cause to overturn. **2.** to overturn.

cap · sule (kap′səl) *n.* **1.** a small, soluble case enclosing a dose of medicine. **2.** a detachable, sealed compartment of a spacecraft, designed to support life during flight and to be recovered.

car · a · van (kar′ə van′) *n.* **1.** a company of travelers, merchants, or pilgrims traveling together for safety and security, especially through deserts or dangerous regions. **2.** a number of vehicles traveling together.

car · bon 14 (kär′bən) a radioactive isotope of carbon, used in archaeological dating.

car · cass (kär′kəs) *n.* the dead body of an animal.

car · o · tene (kar′ə tēn′) *n.* a red or orange-colored compound found in carrots and certain other vegetables and changed into vitamin A in the body.

car · tridge (kär′trij) *n.* a cylindrical case, usually made of metal or cardboard and containing a percussion cap, a propelling charge of gunpowder, and a bullet.

ca · tal · pa (kə tal′pə) *n.* a tree found in North America and Asia, having large, heartshaped leaves, white, pink or yellow flowers, and pods that resemble beans.

catalpa

cat · a · stro · phe (kə tas′trə fē′) *n.* a great and sudden disaster or misfortune.

cat · e · go · ry (kat′ə gôr′ē) *n. pl.,* **cat · e · go · ries.** a group or division in a system of classification; class.

cau · tion (kô′ shən) *v.* to urge (someone) to be careful; warn—*n.* **1.** care with regard to danger or risk. **2.** a warning. **3.** someone or something that is striking or alarming.

cham · ber (chām′bər) *n.* a room, especially a bedroom.

---

a **b**ad, ā c**a**ke, ä f**a**ther; e p**e**t, ē m**e**; i **i**t, ī **i**ce; o h**o**t, ō **o**pen, ô **o**ff; oo w**oo**d, ōō f**oo**d; oi **oi**l, ou **ou**t; th **th**in, <u>th</u> <u>th</u>at; u c**u**p, ur t**u**rn, yōō m**u**sic; zh trea**s**ure; ə **a**go, tak**e**n, penc**i**l, lem**o**n, helpf**u**l

cha · os (kā′os) *n.* a state of complete confusion and disorder.

charm (chärm) *n.* the power to fascinate, attract, or delight greatly.

char · ter mem · ber (chär′tər mem′bər) any of the founders or original members of an organization, especially of one with a charter.

Cha · vez, Ce · sar (chä′vez, sē′zer)

chee · tah (chē′tə) *n.* an animal of the cat family that resembles a leopard and is found in Africa and southern Asia. It can run at speed up to

cheetah

seventy miles per hour for short distances and is sometimes tamed and trained to hunt.

Cher · o · kee (cher′ə kē) a member of a tribe of North American Indians, formerly the largest tribe that lived in the southeastern United States, now living mostly in Oklahoma.

Chi · hua · hua (chi wä′wä) a city in northern Mexico.

chis · el (chiz′əl) *v.* to cut or shape with a chisel.

cinch (sinch) *n.* a strap for fastening a saddle or pack on a horse. —*v.* to fasten a cinch around; bind firmly.

clam · ber (klam′bər) *v.* to climb by using both the hands and feet.

clam · my (klam′ē) *adj.* cold and damp.

clas · si · fi · ca · tion (klas′ə fi kā′shən) *n.* the act or result of arranging in groups or classes.

claw ham · mer (klô′ ham′ər) a hammer having a head with one end forked for removing nails.

clench (klench) *v.* **1.** to close or press together tightly. **2.** to grasp or grip firmly; clutch.

close-knit (klōs′nit′) *adj.* closely joined or intertwined.

cloud · burst (kloud′burst′) *n.* a sudden, heavy rainfall.

cock · pit (kok′pit′) *n.* the compartment in an airplane where the pilot and copilot sit.

coe · la · canth (sē′lə kanth′) *n.* a large, primitive fish thought to be an important link in the evolution from sea to land animals.

col · lide (kə līd′) *v.* **col · lid · ed, col · lid · ing.** to come together with force; crash.

com · mem · o · rate (kə mem′ə rāt′) *v.* **com · mem · o · rat · ed, com · mem · o · rat · ing. 1.** to serve as a memorial to. **2.** to honor the memory of; celebrate.

com · mun · i · ty (kə myōō′nə tē) *n.* a group of people living in the same area and under the same government; the people of a district or town.

com · ple · tion (kəm plē′shən) *n.* the act or state of being made whole, finished, or brought to an end.

com · pli · cat · ed (kom′plə kā′tid) *adj.* hard to understand or do; complex.

com · pre · hend (kom′pri hend′) *v.* to grasp with the mind; understand.

con · cept (kon′sept) *n.* a general idea.

con · cus · sion (kən kush′ən) *n.* **1.** a violent shaking or jarring; shock. **2.** an injury caused by a fall or blow, especially to the brain or spine.

Con · es · to · ga wag · on (kon′is tō′gə wag′ən) a covered wagon with an arched canvas top and broad wheels, used by pioneers to cross the American praries.

con·fab·u·late (kən fab′yə lāt′) *v.* **con·fab·u·lat·ed, con·fab·u·lat·ing. 1.** to talk informally; chat. **2.** to replace fact with fantasy in memory.

con·fer·ence (kon′fər əns) *n.* **1.** a meeting for the purpose of talking about something of common interest. **2.** an association of schools, churches, athletic teams, or similar groups.

con·fi·dence (kon′fə dəns) *n.* **1.** firm trust or faith; reliance. **2.** faith in oneself; self-assurance.

con·ning tow·er (kon′ing tou′ər) a structure, usually on the deck of a submarine or battleship, used for observation.

con·scious·ness (kon′shəs nis) *n.* the state of being aware.

con·tem·plate (kon′təm plāt′) *v.* **con·tem·plat·ed, con·tem·plat·ing.** to give a great deal of attention to; look at or think about long and carefully.

cor·set (kôr′sit) *n.* a close-fitting undergarment worn chiefly by women to shape and support the waist and hips.

coun·se·lor (koun′sə lər) *n.* **1.** a person who gives counsel or advice; adviser. **2.** a person who supervises children at a summer camp.

Courte·nay-Lat·i·mer (kôrt′nē lat′ə mər)

cow·ard·ly (kou′ərd lē) *adj.* lacking courage; easily made afraid.

cram·pon (kram′pən) *n.* an iron spike attached to the shoe to prevent slipping when climbing or walking on ice.

cre·a·tion (krē ā′shən) *n.* **1.** the act of creating. **2.** anything that has been created.

creed (krēd) *n.* **1.** a formal statement of religious belief. **2.** any formal statement of belief, principles, or opinions.

crib (krib) *n.* **1.** a baby's small bed with high sides, usually barred. **2.** a manger or rack used to hold food for cattle.

crim·son (krim′zən) *n.* the deep red color. —*adj.* having the color crimson.

cri·noid (krī′noid) *n.* any of a group of colorful flower-shaped, saltwater animals, having branched arms around a single mouth opening. Crinoids are usually found in deep tropical waters.

crinoid

cri·sis (krī′sis) *n.* **1.** an important and decisive turning point or event. **2.** a condition or period of difficulty or danger.

crit·i·cal (krit′i kəl) *adj.* **1.** inclined to find fault or judge severely or unfavorably. **2.** of or relating to a crisis.

crook (krook) *v.* to bend into a curved or hooked form.

crouch (krouch) *v.* to stoop or bend low, especially with the knees bent, as an animal does when about to spring or when trying to hide. —*n.* **1.** the act or manner of crouching. **2.** a crouching position.

crow·bar (krō′bär′) *n.* a bar of iron or steel used as a lever or pry.

---

a bad, ā cake, ä father; e pet, ē me; i it, ī ice; o hot, ō open, ô off; oo wood, ōō food; oi oil, ou out; th thin, <u>th</u> that; u cup, ur turn, yōō music; zh treasure; ə ago, taken, pencil, lemon, helpful

cru·el·ty (kr$\overline{oo}$′əl tē) *n.* **1.** the state of being willing or ready to cause suffering or pain to others. **2.** an act or acts causing suffering or pain.

crys·tal (krist′əl) *n.* **1.** a clear, colorless variety of quartz; rock crystal. **2.** a solid body bounded by flat surfaces, whose atoms, molecules, or ions are arranged in an orderly and repeated pattern.

cue (kyo͞o) *n.* a signal, before or during a stage performance, for an actor to speak or to begin or stop some action.

cur·a·tor (kyoo rā′tər) *n.* a person in charge of all or part of the collection or exhibits in a gallery, museum, or zoo.

cur·rent (kur′ənt) *n.* a portion of a body of water or air continuously flowing in approximately the same path.

cut·ter (kut′ər) *n.* **1.** a person who cuts. **2.** a small, fast ship used by the Coast Guard.

D

dam·age (dam′ij) *n.* harm or injury that causes loss.

de·bris (də brē′, dā′brē) *n.* rubbish.

debt (det) *n.* something that is owed to another.

de·cen·cy (dē′sən sē) *n.* proper behavior, as in speech, actions, or dress.

de·cree (di krē′) *n.* **1.** a decision or order issued by a court. **2.** any official decision or order; edict.

de·fect (dē′fekt′, di fekt′) *n.* **1.** an imperfection, flaw, or weakness; fault; blemish. **2.** the lack of something necessary for completeness or perfection.

dense (dens) *adj.* having parts packed closely together; thick; compact.

de·part·ment (di pärt′mənt) *n.* a separate part or division or an organization.

der·by (dur′bē) *n.* **1.** a race for three-year old horses, held annually near London, England. **2.** any similar horse race.

de·sire (di zīr′) *n.* **1.** a longing; wish. **2.** an expressed wish; request.

des·per·ate·ly (des′pər it lē) *adv.* **1.** in a reckless manner because of hopelessness; rashly. **2.** without regard to what happens afterward; irresponsibly. **3.** hopelessly.

des·ti·ny (des′tə nē) *n.* **1.** what happens to a person or thing; lot; fortune. **2.** what is fated to happen; course of events determined beforehand.

de·ter·mi·na·tion (di tur′mi nā′shən) *n.* a fixed and firm purpose.

de·vour (di vour′) *v.* to eat up with great greed or vigor.

Di·en·tje (dē′ən′tī)

dig·ni·ty (dig′nə tē) *n.* nobility of character or manner; stateliness, serenity, or self-respect.

dis·a·bil·i·ty (dis′ə bil′ə tē) *n.* **1.** the loss or lack of ability; disabled condition. **2.** something that disables; handicap.

dis·as·ter (di zas′tər) *n.* any event causing much suffering, distress, or loss; sudden or great misfortune.

dis·ease (di zēz′) *n.* a disturbance in the function of an organ or an organism resulting from a specific cause or causes, such as infection, and characterized by particular symptoms.

dis·gust·ed·ly (dis gus′tid lē) *adv.* in a manner showing strong dislike or distaste.

dis·man·tle (dis man′təl) *v.* **dis·man·tled, dis·man·tling.** to pull down or take apart; disassemble.

dis·mount (dis mount′) *v.* to get off or down, as from a horse; alight.

dor·mant (dôr′mənt) *adj.* **1.** temporarily quiet or inactive. **2.** in a sleeping or inactive condition.

dor·mi·to·ry (dôr′mə tôr′ē) *n.* a building having many bedrooms, as for students at a college to live and sleep in.

dor·sal (dôr′səl) *adj.* of, on, or near the back.

dregs (dregz) *n. pl.* small pieces of matter at the bottom of a liquid.

drei·del (drā′dəl) *n.* a four-sided top used in a game played at Hanukkah.

dumb·struck (dum′struk) *adj.* speechless as with amazement; astonished.

dreidel

E

ea·sel (ē′zəl) *n.* an upright frame used to hold an artist's canvas.

e·col·o·gy (ē kol′ə jē) *n.* a branch of biology that deals with the relationships of living things to their surroundings and to each other.

ed·dy (ed′ē) *n.* a current of air or water moving against the main current.

e·di·tion (i dish′ən) *n.* **1.** the form in which a book is published. **2.** the total number of copies of a publication printed from the same plates or type. **3.** a single copy of such a publication.

e·nam·el (i nam′əl) *n.* **1.** a hard, glossy substance used to decorate or protect a surface. **2.** paint that dries to form a hard, glossy coating.

en·ti·tle (en tit′əl) *v.* **en·ti·tled, en·ti·tl·ing. 1.** to give the title of; call. **2.** to give a claim or right to; qualify.

en·vel·op (en vel′əp) *v.* to wrap up or cover completely.

ep·i·logue (ep′ə lôg′, ep′ə log′) *n.* a passage or section added to the end of a story, poem, or other written work as a conclusion.

e·qua·tor (i kwā′tər) *n.* an imaginary line encircling the earth halfway between the North Pole and South Pole. The equator is the line from which degrees of latitude are measured.

e·ter·ni·ty (i tur′nə tē) *n.* **1.** time without beginning or end; infinite time. **2.** all future time, especially the time after death. **3.** a seemingly endless length of time.

e·volve (i volv′) *v.* **e·volved, e·volv·ing. 1.** to develop gradually; work out. **2.** to undergo evolution.

ex·cur·sion (eks kur′shən) *n.* a short trip made for a special purpose or for pleasure.

ex·pe·di·tion (eks′pə dish′ən) *n.* **1.** a journey made for a specific purpose. **2.** the people, ships, or equipment involved in such a journey.

ex·press (eks pres′) *v.* **1.** to put into words. **2.** to show or reveal outwardly; indicate. **3.** to make known.

ex·pres·sion·ism (eks presh′ən izm) *n* a movement in the fine arts during the latter part of the 19th and early part of the 20th centuries that originated in Europe.

a bad, ā cake, ä father; e pet, ē me; i it, ī ice; o hot, ō open, ô off; oo wood, o̅o̅ food; oi oil, ou out; th thin, th that; u cup, ur turn, yo̅o̅ music; zh treasure; ə ago, taken, pencil, lemon, helpful

ex·pres·sion·is·tic (eks presh'ən is'tik) *adj.* of, having to do with, or related to expressionism.

ex·traor·di·nar·y (eks trôr'də ner'ē, eks'tra ôr'də ner'e) *adj.* beyond or above the usual or ordinary.

ex·ude (eg zōōd', ek sōōd') *v.* **ex·ud·ed, ex·ud·ing. 1.** to discharge (a substance) gradually; ooze forth. **2.** to give forth.

F

Fahr·en·heit (far'ən hīt') *adj.* of, according to, or designating the temperature scale on which the freezing point of water is at 32 degrees and the boiling point is at 212 degrees under standard atmospheric pressure. The name comes from Gabriel D. Fahrenheit, a German physicist.

fal·con (fôl'kən, fal'kən, fô'kən) *n.* **1.** any of various swift-flying birds of prey that resemble hawks, having a short, hooked bill. **2.** a hawk that has been trained to hunt other birds and small game.

falcon

fash·ion·a·ble (fash'ə nə bəl) *adj.* **1.** following current styles or practices; in fashion; stylish. **2.** of, relating to, or used by people who set or follow styles.

fidg·et (fij'it) *v.* to make restless movements; be nervous or jittery.

fil·a·ment (fil'ə mənt) *n.* a very fine thread or a part like a thread; fiber.

flail (flāl) *v.* to wave or swing, especially violently or quickly.

flank (flangk) *v.* to be located at the side of.

flim·sy (flim'zē) *adj.* **1.** lacking strength or substance; thin; frail. **2.** not convincing or adequate; weak.

fon·dle (fon'dəl) *v.* **fon·dled, fon·dling.** to stroke or touch lovingly or tenderly; caress.

fore·ground (fôr'ground') *n.* the part of a picture or view nearest to a person's eye.

fore·man (fôr'mən) *n.* **1.** a person who supervises a group of workers, as in a factory. **2.** a person who is chairman and spokesman of a jury.

forked (fôrkt) *adj.* shaped like a fork; divided into forks.

for·mal (fôr'məl) *adj.* **1.** very stiff, proper, or polite in behavior. **2.** requiring strict form, ceremony, or elaborate dress. **3.** done or made with authority; official.

for·ma·lin (fôr'mə lin) *n.* a forty percent solution of formaldehyde in water, used as an antiseptic.

fos·ter (fôs'tər) *adj.* brought up in or belonging to a family without being adopted or related by blood.

fret (fret) *v.* **fret·ted, fret·ting.** to be upset, unhappy, or worried.

fringe (frinj) *v.* **fringed, fring·ing.** to decorate with an edging of threads, cords, or strips.

fun·nel-shaped (fun'əl shāpt') *adj.* having the form or shape of a funnel. A funnel is a utensil with a tube at one end and a wide, cone-shaped mouth at the other.

fu·ri·ous·ly (fyoor'ē əs lē) *adv.* in an extremely violent or intense manner; angrily.

fur·ri·er (fur'ē ər) *n.* a person who deals in or works with furs.

G

gab (gab) *v.* **gabbed, gab·bing.** to talk idly or too much; chatter.

gal·lump (gə lump′) *v.* to walk heavily and clumsily.

gav·el (gav′əl) *n.* a small mallet used by the person in charge of a trial, meeting, or other gathering to call for attention or order.

gavel

Gem·i·ni (jem′ə nī′)

gi·gan·tic (jī gan′tik) *adj.* like or resembling a giant, especially in size.

glimpse (glimps) *n.* a brief view; passing glance.

grad·u·ate (graj′ōō āt′) *v.* **grad·u·at·ed, grad·u·at·ing.** to receive a diploma or degree after the completion of a course of study.

gran·ite (gran′it) *n.* a hard, durable igneous rock that is composed of feldspar and quartz with specks of darker minerals.

grate·ful·ly (grāt′fə lē) *adv.* in a thankful and appreciative manner.

graze (grāz) *v.* **grazed, graz·ing.** to feed on growing grass.

Great Je·ho·sha·phat (jə hō′shə fat′)

gris·tle·like (gris′əl līk′) *adj.* resembling a tough tissue found in meat; cartilaginous.

groats (grōts) *n. pl.* hulled, usually crushed grain, especially oats.

grudg·ing·ly (gruj′ing lē) *adv.* in an unwilling manner; with ill will or resentment.

gruff·ness (gruf′nis) *n.* state or quality of being abrupt or stern.

Guer·ni·ca (gwär′nē kä, ger nē′kä) a town in north-central Spain, northeast of Bilboa. It was destroyed during the Spanish Civil War by German and Italian aircraft in 1937.

gul·den (goold′ən) *n. pl.,* **gul·den** or **gul·dens.** another word for *guilder,* any of several coins formerly used in the Netherlands, Germany, and Ausria, and now the basic unit of money used in the Netherlands.

gull·er·y (gul′ər ē) *n.* a breeding place or colony of gulls.

H

hack·les (hak′əlz) *n. pl.* the hairs along the neck and back of a dog or other animal that stand up when the animal is angry or frightened.

hai·ku (hī′kōō) *n. pl.,* **hai·ku.** a form of Japanese poetry containing seventeen syllables, usually on a subject from nature.

ha·lo (hā′lō) *n.* **1.** in art, a ring or disk of light surrounding the head of a saint, angel, or other sacred figure. **2.** a circle of light that appears to surround the sun, moon, or another heavenly body, caused by the reflection and refraction of light by ice crystals in the earth's upper atmosphere.

a bad, ā cake, ä father; e pet, ē me; i it, ī ice; o hot, ō open, ô off; oo wood, ōō food; oi oil, ou out; th thin, th that; u cup, ur turn, yōō music; zh treasure; ə ago, taken, pencil, lemon, helpful

hal · ter (hôl′tər) *n.*   a rope or strap used for leading or tying an animal, usually designed to fit around the animal's nose and over or behind its ears.

Ha · nuk · kah (hä′nə kə) *also,*
Cha · nu · kah.   a Jewish holiday commemorating the restoration of the Temple of Jerusalem after the victory of the Maccabees over the king of ancient Syria. It is celebrated by lighting candles on eight successive nights.

haunch (hônch) *n. pl.,*   **haunch · es.**   a part of the body including the hip, buttock, and upper thigh in man and four-footed animals.

hay · mow (hā′mou′) *n.*   another word for *hayloft.* A hayloft is the upper section in a barn, used for storing hay.

hearth (härth) *n.*   **1.** the floor of a fireplace, often extending out into the room. **2.** home; fireside.

hel · ter-skel · ter (hel′tər skel′tər) *adv.*   in a hurried, confused, or disorderly way.

hem · a · chrom · a · to · sis
(hē′mə krō′mə tō′səs) *n.*   general coloration by the red pigment of the blood.

her · pe · tol · o · gy (hur′pə tol′ə jē) *n.*   a branch of zoology that deals with reptiles and amphibians.

Hey · er · dahl, Thor (hā′ər däl′, toor′)

hid · e · ous (hid′ē əs) *adj.*   very ugly; horrible; detestable.

Him · a · la · yas (him′ə lā′əz)   the highest mountain system in the world, extending across Asia from the north-eastern border of Afghanistan through northern India and Tibet to the north-western border of Burma.

hoarse (hôrs) *adj.*   **1.** having a harsh or grating voice. **2.** sounding deep and harsh or grating.

hoist (hoist) *n.*   an apparatus used for lifting or pulling.

hon · or · ar · y (on′ə rer′ē) *adj.*   **1.** given an honor. **2.** holding a title or position as an honor without the usual duties or salary.

host · ess (hōs′tis) *n.*   **1.** a woman who receives or entertains others. **2.** a woman who interviews on television or radio.

hos · tile (hos′təl) *adj.*   feeling or showing hatred or dislike.

house-hold (hous′hōld′) *n.*   all the people who live in a house.

hum · bug (hum′bug′) *n.*   **1.** foolish or empty talk; nonsense. **2.** something intended to deceive or trick; hoax. **3.** a person who tries to deceive; fraud.

hun · ker (hung′kər) *v.*   to crouch; squat.

hur · ri · cane (hur′ə kān′) *n.*   a storm with violent winds of more than seventy-five miles per hour that spin around a calm center and are accompanied by heavy rain, high tides, and flooding.

hy · dran · gea (hī drān′jə) *n.*   a large, showy flower that grows in clusters of usually white, blue, or pink blossoms.

hydrangea

hy · po · der · mic
(hī′pə dur′mik) *adj.*   **1.** lying under the skin. **2.** made to be injected under the skin.

I

ich · thy · ol · o · gy (ik′thē ol′ə jē) *n.*   the branch of zoology that deals with fish.

il · le · gal (i lē′gəl) *adj.*   not legal; unlawful.

636

il · lit · er · a · cy (i lit′ər ə sē) *n.*   a lack of the ability to read or write.

im · age (im′ij) *n.*   **1.** a picture, statue, or other likeness of a person, animal, or thing. **2.** a picture or idea held in the mind.

i · mag · i · na · tion (i maj′ə nā′shən) *n.* **1.** the power or process of forming images in the mind of things that are not actually present. **2.** the mental power or ability to create new images or ideas of things never experienced or to use or combine past images and ideas to form new ones.

im · pris · on · ment (im priz′ən mənt) *n.*   confinement, especially in a prison.

in · dig · nant (in dig′nənt) *adj.*   filled with anger; aroused by something unfair, cruel, or evil.

in · dus · try (in′dəs trē) *n.*   **1.** manufacturing plants and other businesses considered as a whole. **2.** a branch of business, trade or manufacturing.

in · fest (in fest′) *v.*   to grow or exist in large numbers so as to cause harm.

in · flu · ence (in′ flo͞o əns) *n.*   the power or ability of a person or thing to produce an effect on others.

in · jus · tice (in jus′tis) *n.*   the lack of justice; unfairness.

ink · ling (ingk′ling) *n.*   **1.** a vague idea or notion. **2.** a slight suggestion; hint.

in · no · cent (in′ə sənt) *adj.*   **1.** free from guilt or wrongdoing. **2.** free from or knowing nothing of sin or evil; pure.

in · tel · li · gence (in tel′ə jəns) *n.*   **1.** the ability to learn, understand, and reason. **2.** secret information, especially about an enemy. **3.** the agency engaged in collecting such information.

in · tent (in tent′) *adj.*   having the mind firmly fixed on something. —*n.*   intention; aim.

in · tern (in′ turn′) *n.*   a recently graduated doctor serving in a hospital or clinic under the supervision of experienced doctors.

in · ter · pret (in tur′prit) *v.*   **1.** to make clear or understandable; reveal the meaning of. **2.** to translate. **3.** to understand or regard.

in · ter · val (in′tər vəl) *n.*   time or space between.

in · ter · view (in′tər vyo͞o′) *n.*   **1.** a meeting between a writer or reporter and a person from whom information is wanted. **2.** a broadcast or published report resulting from such a meeting. —*v.*   to talk with someone for the purpose of obtaining or exchanging information.

in · volve (in   volv′) *v.*   **in · volved, in · volv · ing. 1.** to include as a necessary part, condition, or result. **2.** to draw or bring into a situation.

in · ward · ly (in′wərd lē) *adv.*   **1.** in, on, or toward the inside; within. **2.** in the mind or thought.

Ith · a · ca (ith′ə kə)   a city and manufacturing center of south-central New York state.

---

a **ba**d, ā **ca**ke, ä **fa**ther; e **pe**t, ē **me**; i **i**t, ī **i**ce; o **ho**t, ō **o**pen, ô **o**ff; oo **woo**d, o͞o **foo**d; oi **oi**l, ou **ou**t; th **thin**, <u>th</u> <u>th</u>at; u **cu**p, ur **tu**rn, yo͞o **mu**sic; zh trea**s**ure; ə **a**go, tak**e**n, penc**i**l, lem**o**n, helpf**u**l

J

jour·nal·ism (jurn'əl iz'əm) *n.*   the writing or publishing of facts and opinions in newspapers or magazines.

juic·y (jo͞o'sē) *adj.*   having much juice.

ju·ni·per (jo͞o'nə pər) *n.*   any of a group of ornamental evergreen shrubs or trees related to the cypress. Junipers bear purple fruits that look like berries.

juniper

jury (joor'ē) *n.* a group of persons selected according to law to hear evidence on a matter submitted to them in a court of law and to make a decision according to the law and the evidence.

K

Kan·din·sky (kan din'skē)

Ken·ne·dy, John Fitz·ger·ald (ken'ə dē, jon fits jer'əld)

khak·i (kak'ē, kä'kē) *adj.* a dull, yellowish-brown or tan color. *—n.* a sturdy cotton cloth of this color that is often used for military uniforms.

ki·lom·e·ter (ki lom'ə tər, kil'ə mē'tər) *n.* a unit of length in the metric system equal to 1,000 meters, or 3280.8 feet.

King, Mar·tin Lu·ther (king, mär'tin lo͞o'thər)

knead (nēd) *v.* **1.** to mix or work (a substance, such as dough or clay) into a uniform mass, especially by pressing and squeezing with the hands. **2.** to press and squeeze with the hands.

knick·ers (nik'ərz) *n. pl.* loose-fitting trousers ending just below the knee.

Ko·kosch··ka, Os·kar (kə kosh'kə, os'kər)

L

la·goon (lə go͞on') *n.* **1.** a shallow body of water partly or completely surrounded by a coral island or islands. **2.** a shallow body of sea water partly cut off from the sea by a narrow strip of land.

Las Cru·ces (läs kro͞o'səs, kro͞o'sis) a city in New Mexico.

lash (lash) *v.* to tie or fasten with a rope or cord.

Lat·i·mer·i·a (lat i mer'ē ə) *n.* the generic name of the living coelacanth found in the Indian Ocean off the east coast of Africa.

launch (lônch) *v.* to put a boat or ship into the water.

lav·a·liere (lav'ə lēr') *n.* a pendant worn on a chain around the neck; a kind of necklace.

Le·ah (lē'ə)

lean (lēn) *adj.* with little or no fat.

lest (lest) *conj.* **1.** for fear that. **2.** that.

lev·er (lev'ər, lē'vər) *n.* **1.** a device made of a rigid rod or bar that transmits force or motion from one point to another as it rotates about a fixed point, or fulcrum. A lever is used to lift weights and pry things loose. **2.** anything that operates in this way, such as a crowbar.

lim·ber (lim'bər) *adj.* bending or moving easily; flexible. *—v.* to make or become limber.

line·man (līn'mən) *n.* a person who installs or repairs telegraph, telephone, or electric wires.

Lin · gu · la (ling′gyo͞o lə) *n.* the generic name of a living shellfish that is somewhat like a clam.

lin · i · ment (lin′ə mənt) *n.* a liquid rubbed on the skin to relieve pain or stiffness, as from a bruise, sore muscle, or sprain.

lo · cust (lō′kəst) *n.* any of several grass-hoppers having short feelers. Locusts travel in huge swarms, destroying the crops in their path.

lop · sid · ed (lop′sī′did) *adj.* larger or heavier on one side than on the other; leaning or slanting to one side.

lung · fish (lung′fish′) *n. pl.,* **lung · fish** or **lung · fish · es.**
any of several fish that have lungs as well as gills, enabl-ing them to breathe in or out of water. Lungfish live in freshwater swamps

lungfish

and marshes in Africa, South America, and Australia.

lurch (lurch) *n.* a sudden rolling or sway-ing to one side or from side to side.—*v.* **1.** to move jerkily and unsteadily; stagger. **2.** to roll or sway suddenly to one side or from side to side.

M

mag · got (mag′ət) *n.* the worm-like larval stage in the life of a fly, in which the insect has a thick body and no legs.

mag · ne · sium (mag nē′zē əm, mag nē′zhəm) *n.* a tough, very light, silver-white, metallic element used espe-cially in the making of lightweight alloys.

ma · neu · ver (mə no͞o′vər) *v.* **1.** to per-form or cause troops or ships to perform a planned and strategic movement or movements. **2.** to move or manage skill-fully or cleverly.

ma · re (mä′rā) *n. pl.,* **ma · ri · a** (mä′rē ə). any of the large dark areas on the moon or Mars.

mar · shal (mär′shəl) *n.* in some states, a law officer of a city or borough, having powers similar to those of a sheriff.

mar · vel (mär′vəl) *v.* to be or become filled with wonder or astonishment.

Mas · sa · soit (mas′ə soit′, mas′ə soit′) a Wampanoag Indian chief who aided the Pilgrims and signed a peace treaty with them.

mat · i · née i · dol (mat′ən ā′īd′əl) a per-former whose looks and manner make him or her popular with theatergoers.

Ma · tisse, Hen · ri (mä tēs′, än rē′)

maw (mô) *n.* the jaws, mouth, throat, gul-let, or stomach of an animal.

me · an · der (mē an′dər) *v.* **1.** to follow a winding course. **2.** to wander aimlessly or idly.

Meir, Gol · da (mā ēr′, gōl′də)

mem · brane (mem′brān) *n.* a thin lay-er of tissue that lines a cavity or pas-sage in the body or covers a body sur-face.

a **ba**d, ā **ca**ke, ä **fa**ther; e **pe**t, ē **me**; i **i**t, ī **i**ce; o **ho**t, ō **o**pen, ô **o**ff; oo **woo**d, o͞o **foo**d; oi **oi**l, ou **ou**t; th **thi**n, th **tha**t; u **cu**p, ur **tur**n, yo͞o **mu**sic; zh trea**s**ure; ə **a**go, tak**e**n, penc**i**l, lem**o**n, helpf**u**l

mem·o·ry (mem′ ər ē) *n. pl.,*
mem·o·ries. 1. the mental power or
ability to recall past experiences. **2.** all
that one can or does recall. **3.** someone or something remembered.

Mem·phis (mem′fis) the largest city in
Tennessee, in the southwestern part of
the state.

men·ace (men′is) *v.* **men·aced,
men·ac·ing.** to put in danger;
threaten; endanger.

mer·cy (mur′sē) *n.* **1.** kindness, forgive-
ness or compassion toward another or
other where harshness is expected or
deserved. **2.** the disposition or power
to be kind or forgiving.

me·trop·o·lis (mə trop′ə lis) *n.* a large
city, especially one that is an important
center of commerce or culture.

mi·cro·scop·ic (mī′krə skop′ik) *adj.* **1.**
too small to be seen with the naked
eye. **2.** extremely small; minute.

midst (midst) *n.* **1.** the condition or position of being surrounded by or involved in something. **2.** a gathering or
association of people; company.

mi·gra·tion (mī grā′shən) *n.* **1.** the act
or instance of moving from one
country or region to another in order
to settle there. **2.** a seasonal or peri-
odic movement from one region or
climate to another.

mi·gra·to·ry (mī′grə tôr′ē) *adj.* characterized by or given to migration; mi-
grating.

mi·li·tia·man (mi lish′ə mən) *n. pl.,*
mi·li·tia·men. a member of the militia. The militia is a military force that is
not professional and is called into service in time of emergency.

min·is·ter (min′is tər) *n.* **1.** a person
who is the head of an important gov-
ernmental department. **2.** a person
who is ordained for religious service in
a church; pastor.

mi·nor·i·ty (mə nôr′ə tē, mə nor′ə tē)
n. **1.** the smaller part of a group or
whole. **2.** a racial, religious, political, or
other group that is different from the
larger group of which it is a part.

mis·ap·pre·hen·sion
(mis′ap ri hen′shən) *n.* a misunder-
standing.

mis·chief (mis′chif) *n.* **1.** an act or conduct that is often playful but causes
annoyance or harm. **2.** an inclination to
tease or play pranks; teasing play-
fulness. **3.** harm or damage.

mis·er·a·ble (miz′ər ə bəl) *adj.* **1.** very
unhappy; wretched. **2.** causing or
marked by great discomfort.

mis·sion·ar·y (mish′ə ner′ē) *n.* **1.** a person who is sent by his or her church to
spread his or her religion among non-
believers, especially in a foreign
country. **2.** a person who goes or is
sent to do humanitarian or educational
work, especially in a foreign country.

moc·ca·sin (mok′ə sin) *n.* a shoe having a soft sole
and no heel,
usually made
from one piece
of leather.

moccasin

moist (moist) *adj.*
1. slightly wet;
damp. **2.** containing moisture; humid.

mois·ture (mois′chər) *n.* **1.** water or
other liquid in the air or on a surface. **2.**
dampness; slight wetness.

mo·ment (mō′mənt) *n.* **1.** a short period
of time. **2.** a particular point in time.

mor · al (môr′əl, mor′əl) *n.* the lesson taught by a fable, story, or event.

Morse code (môrs) a code used in telegraphy in which combinations of short and long signals, or dots and dashes, are used to represent the letters of the alphabet, numerals and punctuation marks. It was invented by Samuel F. B. Morse.

Mo · ti · va · tor (mō′tə vāt′ər)

mount (mount) *v.* **1.** to go up; climb. **2.** to set in place, as for display.

moun · tain · eer (mount′ən ēr′) *n.* **1.** a person who lives in a mountainous region. **2.** a person who is skilled at mountain climbing.

Mount Fu · ji (fōō′jē) the highest mountain in Japan, in the south-central part of the island of Honshu.

mourn (môrn) *v.* **1.** to feel or express sorrow or grief. **2.** to lament the death of someone.

Mt. O · lym · pus (ō lim′pəs) a mountain in northeastern Greece that, in Greek mythology, was the home of the twelve major gods.

murk · y (mur′kē) *adj.* dark, gloomy, or cloudy.

mus · ter (mus′tər) *v.* **1.** to call forth from within oneself; collect; summon. **2.** to gather or call together; assemble.

mut · ton (mut′ən) *n.* the flesh from a sheep, especially one between one and two years old, used as food.

N

Nan · tuck · et (nan tuk′it) an island of Massachusetts, about 46 square miles in area, in the Atlantic Ocean 25 miles south of Cape Cod.

Nar · ra · gan · sett Bay (nar′ə gan′sit) an inlet of the Atlantic Ocean, extending into Rhode Island.

nav · i · gate (nav′i gāt′) *v.* **nav · i · gat · ed, nav · i · gat · ing. 1.** to direct the course of (a boat, ship, or aircraft); pilot. **2.** to plan or direct the course of (a voyage, flight, or the like).

nav · i · ga · tion (nav′i gā′ shən) *n.* **1.** the act or practice of navigating a boat, ship, or aircraft. **2.** the art or science of determining the position and directing the course of boats, ships, and aircraft.

nav · i · ga · tor (nav′i gā′tər) *n.* **1.** a person who navigates. **2.** a person who has skill in or practices navigation.

Na · zi (nä′tsē, nat′sē) *n.* a member or follower of the fascist political party that controlled Germany under the leadership of Adolf Hitler from 1933 to 1945.

nec · es · sar · ies (nes′ə ser′ēz) *n. pl.* necessary things; things essential to life; things that cannot be done without.

nev · er · the · less (nev′ər thə les′) *adv.* anyway, in any case.

New Guin · ea (gin′ē) the second largest island in the world, north of Australia, divided into West Irian and the Territory of New Guinea.

---

a b**a**d, **ā** c**a**ke, **ä** f**a**ther; e p**e**t, **ē** m**e**; i **i**t, **ī** **i**ce; o h**o**t, **ō** **o**pen, **ô** **o**ff; oo w**oo**d, **ōō** f**oo**d; oi **oi**l, ou **ou**t; th **th**in, th th**a**t; u c**u**p, ur t**u**rn, yōō m**u**sic; zh trea**s**ure; ə **a**go, tak**e**n, penci**l**, lem**o**n, helpfu**l**

Nic·o·de·mus (nik'ə dē'məs)

noz·zle (noz'əl) *n.* a spout at the end of a hose, pipe, or the like that serves as an outlet for a liquid or gas.

nug·get (nug'it) *n.* a lump, especially a lump of gold as it is found in nature.

numb (num) *adj.* lacking or having lost feeling or movement.

nuz·zle (nuz'əl) *v.* **nuz·zled, nuz·zling. 1.** to touch or rub with the nose. **2.** to press or lie close; nestle; cuddle.

ob·ser·va·to·ry (əb zur'və tôr ē) *n. pl.,* **ob·serv·a·to·ries. 1.** a place or building furnished with telescopes and other equipment for observing, studying, and collecting information about the moon, planets, or stars. **2.** a building or place equipped for observing the weather.

oc·ca·sion·al (ə kā'zhən əl) *adj.* happening or appearing now and then.

oc·cur (ə kur') *v.* **oc·curred, oc·cur·ring. 1.** to take place; come to pass. **2.** to appear or be found. **3.** to come to mind; suggest itself.

oc·cur·rence (ə kur'əns) *n.* something that takes place; incident.

o·dor (ō'dər) *n.* the quality of a thing or substance that affects the sense of smell; scent.

On·tar·i·o (on tār'ē ō) a province of Canada, in the southeastern part of the country, north of the Great Lakes.

Oosterveld, Johann (ō'stər felt, yō'hän)

op·por·tu·ni·ty (op'ər tōō'nə tē, op'ər tyōō'nə tē) *n.* **1.** a time or circumstance that is favorable or suitable for a particular purpose. **2.** a good chance.

o·rang·u·tan (ô rang'oo tan') *n.* a large tree-dwelling ape of the forests of Borneo and Sumatra, having very long powerful arms, short legs, and a shaggy coat of reddish-brown hair.

or·bit (ôr'bit) *n.* **1.** the path of a heavenly body as it revolves in a closed curve about another body. **2.** one complete trip of a spacecraft or artificial satellite along such a path. —*v.* **1.** to move in an orbit around. **2.** to put (a spacecraft or satellite) into orbit.

o·rig·i·nate (ə rij'ə nāt') *v.* **o·rig·i·nat·ed, o·rig·i·nat·ing. 1.** to start or bring into existence. **2.** to come into existence; begin.

or·ni·thol·o·gist (ôr'nə thol'ə jist) *n.* a student of or an expert in the branch of zoology that deals with the study of birds.

oust (oust) *v.* to force or drive out; expel; dispossess.

out·law (out'lô') *n.* **1.** a person who habitually breaks or defies the law; criminal. **2.** formerly, a person who was excluded from the benefits and protection of the law; fugitive or exile.

out·skirts (out'skurts') *n. pl.* the regions or sections surrounding or at the edge of a specified area, as a city.

out·ward·ly (out'wərd lē) *adv.* **1.** on or toward the outside. **2.** in appearance.

ox (oks) *n. pl.,* **ox·en.** the adult castrated male of domestic cattle, used as a work animal or for beef.

OX

ox·y·gen (ok'sə jən) *n.* a colorless, odorless, gaseous element that makes up about one-fifth of the air. Oxygen is essential to life.

P

pag·eant (paj′ənt) *n.* **1.** a theatrical presentation that is based on or dramatizes events in history or legend. **2.** an elaborate spectacle or parade.

pa·le·on·tol·o·gy (pā′ lē ən tol′ ə jē) *n.* the science that deals with fossils and extinct forms of life.

pan·ic (pan′ik) *n.* a terrible, often uncontrollable fear that can spread suddenly through a crowd. — *v.* **pan·icked, pan·ick·ing.** to affect or become affected with panic.

par · ings (pār′ingz) *n. pl.* the cutoff outer layer or part (of fruits or vegetables); peelings.

par·ka (pär′kə) *n.* **1.** a hooded, fur outer garment worn by Eskimos. **2.** any hooded jacket for outdoor wear.

par·lor (pär′lər) *n.* a room in a house in which visitors are received and entertained.

par·ti·tion (pär tish′ən) *n.* **1.** a division into shares or distinct parts. **2.** something that divides, especially a movable structure that separates parts of a room.

pas·ture (pas′chər) *n.* a field or other tract of land used for the grazing of cattle, sheep, or other animals.

pa·thet·i·cal·ly (pə thet′ik lē) *adv.* **1.** in a manner arousing pity, sadness, or sympathy. **2.** in a pitifully unsuccessful or inadequate way.

pa·tient (pā′shənt) *n.* a person who is under the care or treatment of a doctor.

pa·trol (pə trōl′) *n.* one or more persons who go through or around an area or place for the purpose of guarding or inspecting.

pause (pôz) *v.,* **paused, paus·ing.** to stop for a short time.

peas·ant (pez′ənt) *n.* a member of a class of small farmers or farm laborers.

Pe·cos Bill (pā′kōs) a cowboy of American legend whose feats included digging the Rio Grande.

pe·cul·iar (pi kyōōl′yər) *adj.* strange or unusual; odd.

pen·e·trate (pen′ə trāt′) *v.* **pen·e·trat·ed, pen·e·trat·ing.** **1.** to pass into or through, especially by force or with difficulty. **2.** to seep or spread through.

pen·nant (pen′ənt) *n.* **1.** a long, usually triangular, flag, used especially as a school or team emblem or, on a ship, for signaling or identification. **2.** such a flag

pennant

symbolizing a victory or championship, especially in professional baseball.

per·i·car·di·um (per′ə kär′dē əm) *n.* the thin membranous sac that surrounds and protects the heart.

per·se·cute (pur′sə kyōōt′) *v.* **per·se·cut·ed, per·se·cut·ing.** to subject continually to cruel, harmful, or unjust treatment.

---

a **b**ad, ā **c**ake, ä **f**ather; e **p**et, ē **m**e; i **i**t, ī **i**ce; o **h**ot, ō **o**pen, ô **o**ff; oo w**oo**d, ōō **f**ood; oi **oi**l, ou **ou**t; th **th**in, th **th**at; u **c**up, ur **t**urn, yōō **m**usic; zh trea**s**ure; ə **a**go, tak**e**n, penc**i**l, lem**o**n, helpf**u**l

per · son · al · i · ty (pur′sə nal′ə tē) *n.*
pl., **per · son · al · i · ties.** **1.** the sum of
the traits, habits, attitudes, and behavior
of a person that makes him or her different
from all others. **2.** attractive personal
qualities.

phase (fāz) *n.* a stage of development of a
person or thing.

phe · nom · e · non (fə nom′ən non′) *n.*
1. a fact, event or condition that can be
observed or perceived. **2.** a person or
thing that is extraordinary.

pho · tog · ra · phy (fə tog′rə fē) *n.* **1.** the
technique of recording the image of a
given area or object by the action of light
on a light-sensitive surface. **2.** the art or
practice of taking photographs.

pig · ment (pig′mənt) *n.* **1.** a substance
used for coloring, especially a powdered
substance that is mixed with a liquid to
produce a paint or dye. **2.** a substance,
such as chlorophyll, that gives color to
plant or animal tissues.

pi · lot (pī′lət) *n.* **1.** a person who operates
the controls of an aircraft or spacecraft. **2.**
a person who steers a ship, especially into
or out of a harbor.

pine pitch (pīn′ pich′) a translucent yellow or brown sticky substance that comes
from pine trees.

pi · ñon (pin′yon, pin′yōn) *n.* a small pine
tree found in the southwestern United
States.

pis · ton (pis′tən) *n.* a disk or cylinder that fits
closely inside a
sleeve or hollow
cylinder, where it
moves back and
forth.

piston

pith hel · met (pith hel′met) a light sun hat
made from dried pith; topi.

plank · ton (plangk′tən) *n.* very small
plants and animals that drift or float in the
sea or other body of water. Plankton is the
basic source of food for all animals that
live in the sea.

plumb · er (plum′ər) *n.* a person who installs and repairs plumbing. Plumbing is
the pipes and fixtures for bringing water
into or taking water and wastes out of a
building or other structure.

plun · der (plun′dər) *v.* **1.** to loot or rob, as
during a war. **2.** to steal.

pneu · mo · nia (noo mōn′yə, nyoo mōn′yə)
n. any of several diseases that cause an
inflammation of the lungs, usually caused
by a bacterial or viral infection.

poise (poiz) *v.* **poised, pois · ing.** **1.** to
balance or be balanced. **2.** to remain in
one spot as if suspended.

po · lite (pə līt′) *adj.* having or showing
good manners, consideration for others,
and a regard for correct behavior.

Pol · y · ne · sia (pol′i nē′zhə) one of the
main divisions of the Pacific islands, in the
central and southern Pacific.

port · fo · li · o (pôrt fō′lē ō′) *n.* a portable
case for holding or carrying loose papers,
drawings, documents, and similar
materials.

por · tray (pôr trā′) *v.* **1.** to give a picture of
in words; tell or write about; describe. **2.** to
make a picture or other likeness of. **3.** to
play the part of.

po · si · tion (pə zish′ən) *n.* **1.** the place
where a person or thing is. **2.** an arrangement of the body or of its parts.

pov · er · ty (pov′ər tē) *n.* the state or
condition of being poor.

pre·cau·tion (pri kô′shən) *n.* **1.** a measure taken beforehand to avoid danger, failure, loss, or harm. **2.** caution or care taken beforehand; foresight.

pre·cau·tion·ar·y (pri kô′shə ner′ē) *adj.* relating to, advising, or using precaution.

pre·cede (pri sēd′) *v.* **pre·ced·ed, pre·ced·ing.** to be, go, or come before or ahead of, as in time, order, or rank.

prej·u·dice (prej′ə dis) *n.* **1.** an opinion or judgment, especially an unfavorable one, formed beforehand or without knowing all the facts. **2.** hatred or intolerance of a particular group, such as members of a race or religion.

pre·scribe (pri skrīb′) *v.,* **pre·scribed, pre·scrib·ing. 1.** to set down or give as a rule or direction to be followed. **2.** to order or recommend for use as a remedy or treatment.

pre·sume (pri zōōm′) *v.* **pre·sumed, pre·sum·ing.** to accept as true until proven to be untrue; take for granted; suppose.

pre·vi·ous (prē′vē əs) *adj.* coming or made before, earlier.

priv·i·leged (priv′ə lijd) *adj.* **1.** having or enjoying a privilege or privileges. **2.** confidential; private; restricted.

pro·ce·dure (prə sē′jər) *n.* **1.** a particular course of action, especially one that follows a definite order of steps. **2.** the customary or established way of conducting legal, parliamentary, or similar business.

pro·ceed (prə sēd′) *v.* **1.** to continue, especially after a stop or interruption. **2.** to begin or undertake. **3.** to move on or forward.

pro·ceed·ings (prə sē′dingz) *n. pl.* a record of business transacted at a meeting of a society.

proc·ess (pros′es, prō′ses) *n.* the series of acts or operations performed in making or doing something.

pro·duce (prod′ōōs, prod′yōōs, prō′dōōs, prō′dyōōs) *n.* **1.** something that is produced. **2.** farm products, especially fresh fruit and vegetables.

pro·duc·er (prə dōō′sər, prə dyōō′sər) *n.* a person in charge of producing a play, motion picture, or other form of entertainment.

pro·file (prō′fīl) *n.* **1.** a side view, especially of a human face or head. **2.** an outline drawing or other representation of this. **3.** a brief biographical sketch.

profile

pro·nounce·ment (prə nouns′mənt) *n.* **1.** a formal or official declaration or statement. **2.** an opinion, judgment, or decision.

prop·er (prop′ər) *adj.* suitable, appropriate, or correct for a given purpose.

prowl (proul) *v.* **1.** to move about quietly and secretly, as in search of prey. **2.** to move or roam over or through.

pry (prī) *v.* **pried, pry·ing.** to raise or move with or as with a lever.

---

a **b**ad, ā **c**ake, ä **f**ather; e **p**et, ē **m**e; i **i**t, ī **i**ce; o **h**ot, ō **o**pen, ô **o**ff; oo **woo**d, ōō **f**ood; oi **oi**l; ou **ou**t; th **th**in, <u>th</u> **th**at; u **c**up, ur **t**urn, yōō **m**usic; zh trea**s**ure; ə **a**go, tak**e**n, penc**i**l, lem**o**n, helpf**u**l

puff ad·der (puf′ad′ər)　a poisonous African snake having crescent-shaped yellowish markings.

pun (pun) *n.*　a play on words in which a double meaning is applied to one word or to two words having the same sound.

pu·ri·ty (pyoor′ə tē) *n.*　**1.** the state or quality of being free of impurities or foreign elements. **2.** the quality or state of containing nothing inappropriate or extraneous.

Q

qual·i·fied (kwol′ə fīd′) *adj.*　having the necessary abilities, accomplishments, or requirements.

qual·i·ty (kwol′ə tē) *n. pl.,* **qual·i·ties.**　**1.** something that makes a person or thing what it is. **2.** basic character; nature. **3.** excellence; fineness; superiority.

quar·ry (kwôr′ē, kwor′ē) *n.*　a place where stone is cut or blasted out for use in building, road construction, or the like.

quea·si·ly (kwē′zə lē) *adv.*　**1.** characterized by sickness or nausea. **2.** uneasily.

quill (kwil) *n.*　**1.** a large, stiff feather. **2.** the hard, hollow stem of a feather. **3.** a pen made from the hollow stem of a feather.

quill

quilt · ed (kwil′tid) *adj.*　made like a quilt, with an inner layer of padding.

quirk (kwurk) *n.*　**1.** a strange mannerism or way of acting. **2.** a sudden or unexpected twist or turn.

quiv·er (kwiv′ər) *v.*　to shake slightly; shiver; tremble.

R

rap (rap) *v.* **rapped, rap·ping.**　to knock or tap sharply.

rasp (rasp) *v.*　**1.** to scrape or grate with a rough tool, such as a file. **2.** to say in a rough, grating voice.

rav·en·ous (rav′ə nəs) *adj.*　extremely hungry; famished.

re·ac·tion (rē ak′shən) *n.*　an action in response to something.

re·ceipt (ri sēt′) *n.*　a written statement that something, such as money, goods, or mail, has been received.

re·cit·al (ri sīt′əl) *n.*　a performance or concert of music or dance, often given by a single performer.

reck·on (rek′ən) *v.*　**1.** to count or figure; calculate. **2.** to think; suppose; guess.

rec·og·ni·tion (rek′əg nish′ən) *n.*　the act of recognizing or the state of being recognized.

rec·om·mend (rek′ə mend′) *v.*　**1.** to speak of or present favorably. **2.** to advise; suggest.

reek (rēk) *v.*　to give off or be filled with a strong, bad odor; smell strongly and unpleasantly.

ref·er·ee (ref′ə rē′) *n.*　**1.** an official in certain sports and games, often the chief official, who interprets and enforces the rules. **2.** a person who settles a matter or question in dispute.

reg·is·trar (rej′is trär′) *n.*　an official, especially at a college or university, in charge of keeping records.

re·hears·al (ri hur′səl) *n.*　a period of practice in preparation for a public or official performance.

re · la · tions (ri lā′shənz) *n. pl.* matters or conditions that bring one person or thing in contact with another; affairs; dealings.

re · lax · a · tion (rē′lak sā′shən) *n.* the act of relaxing or the state of being relaxed; release from tension or pain.

re · lent · less · ly (ri lent′ lis lē) *adv.* harshly; severely; pitilessly; unyielding.

re · luc · tance (ri luk′təns) *n.* the state of being reluctant; lack of eagerness; hesitation or unwillingness.

re · mem · brance (ri mem′brəns) *n.* **1.** something that is remembered; recollection. **2.** the state of being remembered.

re · mote (ri mōt′) *adj.* **1.** located at a distance; not near. **2.** located out of the way; secluded. **3.** far removed from the present; distant in time.

res · er · va · tion (rez′ ər vā′shən) *n.* **1.** an arrangement by which something, such as a theater seat or hotel room, is set aside for a particular person or purpose. **2.** land set aside by the U.S. government for a special purpose, as for an Indian tribe to live on or for a wildlife preserve.

res · er · voir (rez′ər vwär′) *n.* a place used for the storage of water.

res · ig · na · tion (rez′ig nā′shən) *n.* **1.** the act of voluntarily giving up a job, position, or office. **2.** the acceptance of something without protest or complaint; submission.

res · o · lute · ly (rez′ ə lo͞ot′lē) *adv.* in a strongly determined manner.

re · solve (ri zolv′) *v.* **re · solved, re · solv · ing.** to decide (to do something); determine.

rest · less · ness (rest′lis nis) *n.* a nervous or agitated state of the mind or body; inability to rest.

Reuven (ro͞o′vən)

re · ver · ber · ate (ri vur′bə rāt′) *v.* **re · ver · ber · at · ed, re · ver · ber · at · ing.** to be echoed; resound.

re · vive (ri vīv′) *v.* **re · vived, re · viv · ing. 1.** to bring or come back to consciousness. **2.** to give or show new strength, vitality, or freshness.

rheu · ma · tism (ro͞o′mə tiz′əm) *n.* any of several diseases characterized by inflammation, swelling, and stiffness of the muscles and joints.

ridge (rij) *n.* the long and narrow upper part of something.

Ri · o Grande (rē′ō grand′, rē′ō gran′dē) a river flowing from southwestern Colorado into the Gulf of Mexico and forming the border between Texas and Mexico.

rit · u · al (rich′o͞o əl) *n.* **1.** a set form or procedure for the performance of a religious or solemn rite. **2.** a system or body of rites. **3.** a routine faithfully followed.

rook · er · y (rook′ər ē) *n.* a breeding place or colony of rooks or other birds or of animals such as penguins and seals.

---

a bad, ā cake, ä father; e pet, ē me; i it, ī ice; o hot, ō open, ô off; oo wood, o͞o food; oi oil, ou out; th thin, <u>th</u> that; u cup, ur turn, yo͞o music; zh treasure; ə ago, taken, pencil, lemon, helpful

rou·tine (roō tēn′) *adj.* according to or using a routine; regular; habitual.

rove (rōv) *v.* **roved, rov·ing.** to wander aimlessly from place to place; roam about.

ruck (ruk) *n.* a large number mixed together; jumble.

ru·ta·ba·ga (roō′tə bā′gə) *n.* a turnip having a thick yellow root that is used as a food.

rutabaga

S

sac (sak) *n.* a part in a plant or animal that is shaped like a pouch or bag and that often contains a liquid.

salm·on (sam′ən) *n. pl.,* **salm·on** or **salm·ons.** a popular food fish that usually has a large, silver body with a dark back. Some salmon live and spawn in fresh water, but most live in salt water and migrate to fresh water to spawn.

sand·bar (sand′bär′) *n.* a ridge of sand in a river or bay or along the shore, built up by the action of waves and currents.

San·ta Fe Trail (san′tə fā′) an overland trade route between Independence, Missouri, and Santa Fe, New Mexico. It was used from 1821 to 1880.

sap·ling (sap′ling) *n.* a young tree.

Sar·a·to·ga trunk (sar′ə tō′gə) a large traveling trunk, once popular in Saratoga Springs, a resort center in eastern New York state.

scoff (skof, skôf) *v.* to express ridicule or contempt; mock; jeer.

sculpt (skulpt) *v.* to carve or otherwise form (a figure or design); sculpture.

sculp·ture (skulp′chər) *n.* **1.** the act or process of making figures or designs, as by carving or chiseling stone or marble, modeling in clay or wax, or casting in bronze or a similar metal. **2.** a figure or design so made. **3.** such figures or designs as a group.

scur·ry (skur′ē) *v.* **scur·ried, scur·ry·ing.** to go or move hurriedly.

se·clu·sion (si kloō′zhən) *n.* the act of keeping apart or isolated; the state of being apart or isolated.

se·cre·cy (sē′krə sē) *n.* the state of being secret or being kept secret.

self-ev·i·dent (self′ev′ə dənt) *adj.* needing no proof or explanation; evident in itself.

self-ex·pres·sion (self′iks presh′ən) *n.* the expression of one's own thoughts, feelings, and true personality.

sen·sa·tion (sen sā′shən) *n.* **1.** the process of feeling or being aware of things by means of the senses. **2.** a feeling or impression arising from some particular condition or set of circumstances.

sen·ti·men·tal (sen′tə ment′əl) *adj.* **1.** characterized by or showing emotion or feeling. **2.** influenced by or inclined to be moved by feeling rather than by reason. **3.** appealing to the emotions.

ser·geant (sär′jənt) *n.* in the U.S. Army and Marine Corps, a noncomissioned officer ranking above a corporal.

ser·pent·like (sur′pənt lik′) *adj.* like a snake.

Shaw, Sep·ti·mus (sep′tə məs)

sheep·ish·ly (shē′pish lē) *adv.* **1.** in an awkwardly bashful or embarrassed manner. **2.** in a sheep-like way; timid or meek.

shep·herd (shep′ərd) *n.* a person who takes care of a flock of sheep.

Sher·pa (shur′pə) a member of a Tibetan people living in the Himalaya Mountains of northern Nepal.

shield (shēld) *n.* a piece of armor carried on the arm for defense in battle.

shot·gun (shot′gun′) *n.* a gun designed to fire cartridges that release a quantity of shot when discharged.

shrewd (shro͞od) *adj.* clever or keen in practical matters; astute.

sick·le (sik′əl) *n.* a hand tool made up of a sharp, curved blade attached to a short handle, used for cutting grass, grain, or weeds.

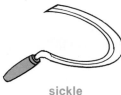

sickle

Si·er·ra Ne·vad·as (sē er′ə nə vad′ez, sē er′ə nə vä′dəz) a mountain range in eastern California.

sig·nif·i·cant (sig nif′i kənt) *adj.* **1.** having special value or importance. **2.** having or expressing a special or hidden meaning; suggestive.

sin·is·ter (sin′is tər) *adj.* **1.** threatening or suggesting evil; ominous. **2.** malicious or evil.

sky·scrap·er (skī′skrā′pər) *n.* a very tall building.

snarl (snärl) *n.* a tangled or knotted mass.

sod (sod) *n.* **1.** the surface of the ground, especially when covered with grass. **2.** a piece of this grassy surface, usually cut in a square or strip and held together by roots.

sod·den (sod′ən) *adj.* **1.** filled with water or moisture; soaked through. **2.** damp and heavy.

sol·emn (sol′əm) *adj.* **1.** serious and earnest; grave; sober. **2.** having much dignity or majesty.

sol·i·dar·i·ty (sol′ə dar′ə tē) *n.* agreement among the members of a group, as in opinion, objectives, interests, or the like.

so·lo (sō′lō) *adj.* made or done by one person alone.

so·lu·tion (sə lo͞o′shən) *n.* **1.** the act, process, or method of solving a problem. **2.** a mixture of two or more substances. Solutions are usually formed by solids, liquids, or gases dissolved in liquids.

soot (soot, so͞ot) *n.* a black, powdery material composed mostly of carbon. It is formed during the burning of such fuels as wood, coal, or oil.

SOS **1.** a radio signal of distress, used especially by ships and airplanes. **2.** any call or signal for help.

soul (sōl) *n.* **1.** the nonphysical part of human beings that is thought to control thinking, feelings, and actions. **2.** the emotional part of people; seat of deep feeling.

---

a bad, ā cake, ä father; e pet, ē me; i it, ī ice; o hot, ō open, ô off; oo wood, o͞o food; oi oil, ou out; th thin, th that; u cup, ur turn, yo͞o music; zh treasure; ə ago, taken, pencil, lemon, helpful

spe · cies (spē′shēz) *n. pl.,* **spe · cies.** a subdivision of a genus in plant and animal classification. Members of a species have certain permanent characteristics in common.

spec · i · men (spes′ə mən) *n.* **1.** a single person or thing considered to be typical of its class or group; example. **2.** a sample, as of blood, taken for medical analysis.

spec · tac · u · lar (spek tak′yə lər) *adj.* of relating to, or resembling an unusual or impressive sight.

spent (spent) *adj.* worn out; exhausted.

Sphen · o · don (sfēn′ə don) *n.* the generic name of a lizard-like creature that lives on the islands off New Zealand.

sphere (sfēr) *n.* **1.** a round, three-dimensional figure having all the points of its surface at an equal distance from the center. **2.** a body having this shape; ball; globe.

spike (spīk) *n.* **1.** a large, heavy nail. **2.** one of several sharp-pointed metal projections attached to the sole and heel of a shoe to prevent slipping—*v.* **spiked, spik · ing.** to secure, fasten, or provide with a spike or spikes.

splen · dor (splen′dər) *n.* **1.** a great display, as of riches or beautiful objects; magnificence; pomp. **2.** great brightness; brilliance.

spout (spout) *n.* a tube or lip projecting from a vessel that channels liquid when it is poured.

sprad · dle (sprad′əl) *v.* **sprad · dled, sprad · dling.** to sit with one leg on each side of (as on a horse) or to spread the legs wide apart in an awkward and careless manner.

sprint (sprint) *v.* to run at full speed, especially for a short distance.

sprout (sprout) *v.* to put forth young growth or buds; begin to grow.

sput · ter (sput′ər) *v.* **1.** to make popping, spitting, or hissing noises. **2.** to utter words or sounds in a confused or hasty manner. **3.** to throw out or spit small bits of food or saliva, as when speaking excitedly.

stage fright (stāj frīt) fear or nervousness felt when appearing before an audience, as by an inexperienced performer.

stair · well (stār′wel′) *n.* the vertical shaft (in a building) containing a staircase.

stall (stôl) *n.* **1.** a compartment in a barn or stable for a horse, cow, or other animal. **2.** a booth or counter for setting up wares for sale.

stand-off · ish (stand′ôf′ish) *adj.* lacking warmth or friendliness; reserved; aloof.

stark (stärk) *adj.* **1.** absolute or unqualified; complete. **2.** harsh, grim, or severe.

star · va · tion (stär vā′shən) *n.* the state of suffering from or dying of hunger.

stat · ic (stat′ik) *n.* random noise produced in a receiver, such as hissing or crackling in a radio, or specks on a television screen.

stat · ue (stach′ōō) *n.* a representation, often life-size or larger, of a human or animal figure, carved, cast, or modeled in stone, bronze, clay, or a similar material.

stench (stench) *n.* a very strong and bad odor.

sten·cil (sten′səl) *n.* **1.** a thin sheet, as of metal or paper, in which a pattern is cut. The sheet is put on top of something that is to be decorated, and only the areas that show through the cut out parts are painted or inked. **2.** a printing or design produced by using a stencil.

ster·i·lize (ster′ə līz′) *v.* **ster·i·lized, ster·i·liz·ing.** to make sterile; make free from dirt and bacteria.

ster·ling (stur′ling) *n.* **1.** a silver alloy containing 92.5 percent pure silver; sterling silver. **2.** British money.

stern·ly (sturn′lē) *adv.* **1.** strictly or severely. **2.** in a harsh, grim, or forbidding manner; gloomily.

stone·boat (stōn′bōt′) *n.* a flat sledge or drag for transporting stones or other heavy articles, or when weighted, for smoothing tilled soil or breaking clods.

straight·a·way (strāt′ə wā′) *adv.* at once; immediately.

strew (strōō) *v.* **strewed, strewed** or **strewn, strew·ing. 1.** to spread or throw about at random; scatter. **2.** to cover with something spread or thrown about in this way.

stroke (strōk) *n.* **1.** the act of striking; blow. **2.** a single unbroken or complete movement, as of the hand, an instrument, or something held in the hand.

stut·ter (stut′ər) *v.* to speak haltingly with frequent, repeated sounds or syllables; stammer.

sub·mar·ine (sub′mə rēn′) *adj.* below the surface of the sea.

sub·merge (səb murj′) *v.* **sub·merged, sub·merg·ing.** to place under or cover with some liquid, especially water.

suc·tion (suk′shən) *n.* a force created by a complete or partial vacuum that draws a gas or liquid into a space from which all or part of the air or liquid has been removed.

suit·case (sōōt′kās′) *n.* a flat, usually rectangular bag used for carrying clothes and other articles when traveling; valise.

suitcase

sum·mit (sum′it) *n.* the highest part or point; acme.

su·per·nat·u·ral (sōō′pər nach′ər əl) *adj.* **1.** of or relating to a realm or existence beyond or exceeding the power of the natural world. **2.** of or relating to ghosts or spirits.

sur·geon (sur′jən) *n.* a doctor of medicine who specializes in surgery.

sur·ger·y (sur′jər ē) *n.* **1.** the branch of medicine that deals with the removal or repair of injured or diseased parts of the body. **2.** the removal or repair of injured or diseased parts of the body.

sur·viv·al (sər vī′vəl) *n.* the act of living through and after; the state of having lived through or after.

---

a bad, ā cake, ä father; e pet, ē me; i it, ī ice; o hot, ō open, ô off; oo wood, ōō food; oi oil, ou out; th thin, <u>th</u> that; u cup, ur turn, yōō music; zh treasure; ə ago, taken, pencil, lemon, helpful

sur·vive (sər vīv′) *v.* **sur·vived, sur·viv·ing.** to continue to live or remain active; endure.

su·sur·ruse (sōō′sə rōōs′) *v.* **su·sur·rused, su·sur·rus·ing.** to whisper, rustle, or murmur.

T

tac·tics (tak′tiks) *n. pl.* **1.** the art or science of using and maneuvering military forces and equipment in combat. **2.** any methods or devices used to achieve a goal.

tail·gate (tāl′gāt′) *n.* a board at the rear of a truck, wagon, station wagon, or other vehicle that can be let down or removed for loading or unloading.

tall tale (tôl′ tāl′) a fanciful or boastful recital of events or happenings.

tal·on (tal′ən) *n.* the claw of a bird or other animal.

tas·sel (tas′əl) *n.* a hanging ornament made up of a group of threads, cords, or similar materials bound together at one end.

tax·i·der·mist (tak′si dur′mist) *n.* a person whose work is preparing and stuffing the skins of dead animals and mounting them in lifelike positions.

tech·ni·cian (tek nish′ən) *n.* a person who is skilled in some science, art, or profession, especially a person trained to deal with specialized equipment or processes.

tech·nique (tek nēk′) *n.* a method of bringing about a desired result in a science, art, sport, or profession.

tel·e·graph (tel′ə graf′) *n.* the system, process, and equipment used for sending messages over a distance with coded electrical impulses.

tem·per (tem′pər) *n.* **1.** a tendency to become angry or irritated. **2.** an angry state of mind; rage.

tempt·ing (temp′ting) *adj.* that tempts or allures; attractive.

ten·don (ten′dən) *n.* a strong cord or band of tissue that attaches a muscle to a bone or other part of the body.

ten·ta·cled (ten′tə kəld) *adj.* having long, slender, flexible growths protruding from the head or about the mouth.

thatch (thach) *v.* to cover with straw, reeds, or similar material, as for a roof.

the·o·ry (thē′ə rē) *n.* an idea or ideas that explain a group of facts or an event; assumption that has been proved to be true.

thresh·ing ma·chine (thresh′ing mə shēn′) a machine that separates the grain (of a cereal grass) from the straw or chaff.

tin·ny (tin′ē) *adj.* **1.** of, relating to, or containing tin. **2.** having a metallic flavor, sound, or quality.

to·bog·gan (tə bog′ən) *n.* a long, flat-bottomed sled without runners, having a curled-up front end. Toboggans are used for coasting on snow or transporting goods.

toboggan

ton·ic (ton′ik) *n.* **1.** anything that refreshes, invigorates, or strengthens. **2.** a medicine or drug that invigorates or strengthens.

top·ic (top′ik) *n.* the subject of a speech, discussion, written composition, or the like.

tor·na·do (tôr nā′dō) *n. pl.*, **tor·na·does** or **tor·na·dos.** a dark column of air shaped like a funnel; extending down from a mass of dark, black clouds and rotating at speeds of up to 500 miles per hour. Tornadoes travel rapidly and suck up and destroy almost everything in their paths.

tornado

tor·rent (tôr′ənt, tor′ənt) *n.* a violent, swiftly flowing stream, especially of water.

To·ry (tôr′ē) *n. pl.*, **To·ries.** **1.** a member of a political party in Great Britain that favored rule by the king and the preservation of the established Anglican Church. **2.** any colonial American who remained loyal to England at the time of the American Revolution.

trag·e·dy (traj′ə dē) *n.* **1.** a drama in which life is viewed or treated seriously. **2.** a sad, dreadful, or disastrous event.

trans·fer (trans fur′, trans′fər) *v.* **trans·ferred, trans·fer·ring. 1.** to move or remove from one person, place, or the like to another. **2.** to move or remove oneself from one place to another.

trans·fu·sion (trans fyōō′zhən) *n.* the act of transfusing, especially the transfer of blood from one individual to another.

trawl·er (trô′lər) *n.* a fishing boat used for fishing with a strong net towed over the ocean bottom.

trem·or (trem′ər) *n.* **1.** a rapid shaking or vibrating movement. **2.** a shaking or trembling, especially of the body or a limb. **3.** a nervous thrill caused by emotion or excitement.

tribes·man (trībz′mən) *n.* a member of a tribe.

tro·phy (trō′fē) *n. pl.*, **tro·phies. 1.** a cup, bowl, or statuette on a pedestal, or similar object, usually awarded for some achievement, such as winning a sports contest or other competition. **2.** something taken and kept as a reminder or proof of victory.

truce (trōōs) *n.* a temporary halt to fighting by mutual agreement, often in order to reach a final settlement.

tweed (twēd) *n.* a rough fabric, usually made of wool, woven with yarns of two or more colors.

U

Uck·wars (uk wärz′)

ud·der (ud′ər) *n.* a large sac hanging from the underside of certain female animals, such as cows, containing the milk-producing glands and teats through which milk can be drawn by milking or nursing.

UFO unidentified flying object.

un·con·scious (un kon′shəs) *adj.* **1.** temporarily without consciousness. **2.** not knowing; unaware.

---

a bad, ā cake, ä father; e pet, ē me; i it, ī ice; o hot, ō open, ô off; oo wood, ōō food; oi oil, ou out; th thin, th that; u cup, ur turn, yōō music; zh treasure; ə ago, taken, pencil, lemon, helpful

un·du·ly (un do͞o′lē, un dyo͞o′lē) *adv.* unnecessarily or excessively.

un·furl (un furl′) *v.* to open or spread out; unroll.

un·in·formed (un′in fôrmd′) *adj.* not informed; without knowledge (of something).

u·nique (yo͞o nēk′) *adj.* **1.** not having an equal; being unsurpassed. **2.** being the only one of its kind; single; sole. **3.** highly unusual, rare, or noteworthy.

un·lim·ber (un lim′bər) *v.* to make ready for or prepare for action.

un·ru·ly (un ro͞o′lē) *adj.* difficult to control or manage.

ur·gent (ur′jənt) *adj.* **1.** calling for immediate action or attention; compelling; pressing. **2.** insistent or earnest, as in pleading.

ut·ter (ut′ər) *adj.* complete or perfect; total.

V

vac·u·um (vak′yo͞o əm, vak′yo͞om) *v.* to clean with a vacuum cleaner. A vaccuum cleaner is an apparatus for cleaning carpets, floors, upholstery, or the like, that operates by means of suction.

vag·a·bond (vag′ə bond′) *n.* a person who wanders from place to place, having no regular home.

val·u·a·ble (val′yo͞o ə bəl, val′yə bəl) *adj.* **1.** having great value, worth much money. **2.** of great use, worth, or importance.

val·ue (val′yo͞o) *n.* **1.** relative or considered worth, usefulness, importance, or merit. **2.** monetary worth.

var·i·ance (vâr′ē əns) *n.* difference; disagreement.

var·i·ous (vâr′ē əs) *adj.* **1.** different from one another; of different kinds. **2.** more than one; several; many.

vast·ness (vast′nis) *n.* greatness of size, extent, or amount.

ve·hi·cle (vē′ə kəl) *n.* a device designed or used for transporting persons or goods. An automobile, sled, or carriage is a vehicle.

vein (vān) *n.* one of the vessels that carry blood from all parts of the body to the heart.

ven·dor (ven′dər) *n.* a person who sells goods.

ver·i·fy (ver′ ə fī′). *v.* **ver·i·fied, ver·i· fy·ing. 1.** to prove (something) to be true; confirm. **2.** to check or test the accuracy or truth of.

ver·mil·lion (vər mil′yən) *n.* a bright red color. *—adj.* having the color vermillion; bright red.

ves·sel (ves′əl) *n.* a ship or large boat.

vet·er·i·nar·i·an (vet′ər ə när′ē ən) *n.* a person trained and licensed to give medical treatment to animals.

vic·tim (vik′təm) *n.* **1.** a person who is injured, killed, or ruined. **2.** a person who is cheated or tricked.

vi·o·lent (vī′ə lənt) *adj.* **1.** acting with, characterized by, or resulting from strong physical force or roughness. **2.** caused by or showing intense feeling or emotion; passionate. **3.** characterized by great intensity or force; severe.

vir·tu·al·ly (vur′cho͞o ə lē) *adv.* in almost every way; practically.

vis·i·bil·i·ty (viz′ə bil′ə tē) *n.* **1.** the state, condition or quality of being visible. **2.** the distance that the eye can see when affected by physical conditions, such as light or weather.

vol · can · ic (vol kan′ik) *adj.*   **1.** of, relating to, or characteristic of a volcano or volcanoes. **2.** produced by or discharged from a volcano.

vol · ume (vol′yo͞om) *n.*   a collection of written or printed pages bound together; book.

W

wad (wod) *n.*   a small, tightly packed mass or lump of soft material.—*v.*   **wad · ded, wad · ding.** to stuff, pad, or pack with wadding.

wake (wāk) *n.*   the track left by a boat, ship, or other object moving through water.

walk · ie-talk · ie (wô′kē tô′kē) *n.*   a small, portable, two-way radio.

war bon · net (wôr′ bon′it) a ceremonial headdress worn by certain North American Indians, especially the Plains Indians. It is usually made up of eagle feathers, and each feather represents an act of bravery or other honor earned by the warrior.

ward (wôrd) *n.*   a division of a hospital containing a number of patients.

warn (worn) *v.*   **1.** to put on guard by giving notice beforehand, as of approaching danger; caution. **2.** to give notice to; make aware of; signal.

warp (wôrp) *v.*   **1.** to bend, curve, or twist out of shape. **2.** to be or become bent, curved, or twisted.

war · y (wār′ē) *adj.*   **1.** always on the alert; watchful. **2.** characterized by caution; guarded.

Wau · ke · wa (wä kē′wə)

wea · sel (wē′zəl) *n.*   any of various small meat-eating animals, having a slender body, short legs, a long neck, and a soft, thick, brownish coat.

wedge (wej) *v.*   **wedged, wedg · ing. 1.** to separate or split by driving a wedge into. **2.** to drive, push, or crowd.

weep (wēp) *v.*   **wept, weep · ing. 1.** to show grief, joy, or other strong emotion by shedding tears. **2.** to feel sorrow or grief; mourn.

wel · ter (wel′tər) *n.*   **1.** a rolling and tossing motion. **2.** confusion; turmoil.

wept (wept) *v.*   see *weep.*

whim · si · cal (hwim′si kəl) *adj.*   **1.** full of or characterized by odd or fanciful notions. **2.** fanciful or odd.

whine (hwīn) *v.*   **whined, whin · ing.** to make a low, plaintive cry or sound, as from pain or peevishness.

whop · per (hwop′ər) *n.*   **1.** something very large. **2.** a big lie.

wolf · hound (woolf′ hound′) *n.*   any of various large dogs originally bred for hunting wolves, such as the Irish wolfhound.

wolfhound

wor · ship (wur′ship) *v.*   **wor · shiped** or **wor · shipped, wor · ship · ing** or **wor · ship · ping. 1.** to pay respect, honor, or reverence to. **2.** to have a great or intense devotion to or regard for; adore.

---

a b**a**d, ā c**a**ke, ä f**a**ther; e p**e**t, ē m**e**; i **i**t, ī **i**ce; o h**o**t, ō **o**pen, ô **o**ff; oo w**oo**d, o͞o f**oo**d; oi **oi**l, ou **ou**t; th **th**in, th **th**at; u c**u**p, ur t**u**rn, yo͞o m**u**sic; zh trea**s**ure; ə **a**go, tak**e**n, penc**i**l, lem**o**n, helpf**u**l

wrath (rath) *n.* extreme or violent anger; rage.

wreck·age (rek′ij) *n.* the remains of anything that has been wrecked; debris.

wrench (rench) *n.* **1.** a sharp or violent twist, turn, or pull. **2.** any of various tools having fixed or movable jaws, used especially for gripping and turning a nut, bolt, or pipe. — *v.* **1.** to twist, turn, or pull with a sudden sharp or violent motion. **2.** to injure or strain by twisting or turning suddenly or violently.

wretch·ed·ness (rech′id nis) *n.* the state of being very unhappy or deeply distressed.

Y

Yang·tse (yäng′tsē′, yang′sē) the longest river in China. The Yangtse flows northeastward from Tibet through central China and into the China Sea near Shanghai.

yield (yēld) *v.* **1.** to give up; surrender; submit. **2.** to give in; consent.

yon·der (yon′dər) *adv.* in that place; over there. — *adj.* at a distance, but within sight.

Z

zig·zag (zig′zag′) *v.* **zig·zagged, zig·zag·ging.** to form or move in a series of short, sharp turns or angles in alternating directions.

Zla·teh (zlä′tə)

zone (zōn) *v.* **zoned, zon·ing.** to divide into areas, regions, or sections distinguished from each other by some quality, condition, or use.